TOXIC
BEAUTY

TOXIC BEAUTY

How hidden chemicals in
cosmetics harm you

Dawn Mellowship

GAIA
THINKING

An Hachette UK Company
www.hachette.co.uk

First published in Great Britain in 2009 by
Gaia, a division of Octopus Publishing Group Ltd
2–4 Heron Quays, London E14 4JP
www.octopusbooks.co.uk

ISBN 978-1-85675-306-7

A CIP catalogue record for this book is available from the British Library

Printed and bound in Italy

Printed on Cyclus Offset, a 100 per cent recycled paper

1 3 5 7 9 10 8 6 4 2

This b<!--partially obscured-->ook is not intended as a substitute for medical advice. The reader
should c<!--obscured-->onsult a physician on all matters relating to health, <!--obscured--> the advice
and inf<!--obscured-->e of going
to press<!--obscured-->ponsibility
or <!--obscured-->nade.

Contents

Introduction   7

Part 1: Beauty products in context   12

Chapter 1: Why are personal care products in question?   14

Chapter 2: Help, I'm allergic! – Skin problems, asthma
            and allergies   36

Chapter 3: The C word – Cancer   64

Chapter 4: Feeling hormonal – Endocrine disruption   92

Chapter 5: Nanotechnology – Technological breakthrough
            or nightmare?   117

Chapter 6: What *is* a natural beauty product?   130

Chapter 7: Organic labelling initiatives   145

Part 2: Resources   166

Alternative beauty brands   168

A–Z Common chemical ingredients   176

Glossary of chemical and cosmetic terms   252

Recommended reading   258

Recommended resources   259

References   262

Index   291

Acknowledgements   304

Introduction

For 81 per cent of women in Europe and America, lipstick and lip gloss are make-up bag must haves. Over a lifetime you will potentially swallow a kilogram (2 lb) of lipstick, that is, if you manage to work your way through five each year between the ages of 16 and 60. Did you know that lipstick may contain a variety of chemicals that have demonstrated some evidence of causing cancer in studies on experimental animals? These include: artificial colours, butylated hydroxyanisole (BHA), fragrance, plasticizers, talc, Teflon (yes the substance used to coat non-stick pans) and formaldehyde. Suddenly a slick of lipstick seems a lot less innocuous – and it's not the only cosmetic item containing noxious substances.

On a daily basis millions of us smother our bodies with a concoction of creams, lotions and potions, many of which are manufactured by household brand names that routinely make bold and extravagant claims about the nature of their heavily marketed products. In fact, a 2007 report by the campaign group Chemical Safe Skincare revealed that the average woman uses approximately 12 personal care products a day. We are told that merely by topically applying a particular product we will attain physical perfection by 'delaying time', 'sculpting and reshaping the body', and 'lifting away the look of deep wrinkles faster than ever before'. These are just a few examples of the slogans used by some of the most renowned mainstream brands and they are a tall order by anyone's standards.

Ironically, in the light of such claims, the ingredients used in many mainstream beauty products have come into question as more of us have grown concerned about what we consume, what we wear and what we rub into our skin. It may come as a shock to learn that up to 70 per cent of what we apply to our skin finds its way into our bodies.[1] In 1988 Congress issued a request to the US National Institute of Occupational Safety and Health (NIOSH) to match a list of 3,000 chemicals that were claimed to be cosmetic ingredients against a database of toxicity information held by NIOSH. Around 900 of these chemicals had toxicity data in the database, some of which have been linked with skin irritation, tumours, cell mutation, allergies, reproductive complications and endocrine disruption, among other health concerns.

Perhaps even more alarmingly, the majority of ingredients used in beauty products have not been thoroughly evaluated for safety. The European Union is more vigilant in this area than the United States, having banned around 1,000 chemicals in the last 30 years. In contrast, the US Food and Drug Administration (FDA) have reviewed the safety of just 11 per cent of the 10,500 ingredients used in beauty products; banning only nine chemicals outright since 1976.

I'm the first to admit that in days gone by I was a toiletry and cosmetic addict, if there is such a thing. I used to rush out and purchase the latest newfangled beauty fad in the hope that it would live up to the advertising spiel.

This changed when I developed a chronic illness, which caused me to re-evaluate my life and rethink my priorities. Mainstream medicine didn't offer a solution to my ill health and the complementary health route was largely unsuccessful, bar one healing therapy called Reiki. I undertook a course in Reiki so that I could practise it myself and began to look at my lifestyle, endeavouring to pinpoint the causes of my illness. Through research to this end I developed insights into nutrition and skin care. I was shocked at some of the discoveries I unearthed about pesticides on food crops, the dairy and animal farming industry and processed and packaged food. As a result I switched to an organic, vegan diet.

When I read about the lack of government regulation and safety assessments in terms of the thousands of chemicals routinely used in beauty products and the link between certain health problems and chemicals in toiletries, I also replaced my old conventional beauty regime with a new organic one.

My attitudes have certainly changed and as well as teaching and practising Reiki, I am a journalist and frequently write about ethical, green and health-related issues.

The Cosmetic, Toiletry and Perfumery Association are quick to defend the self-regulation of the cosmetics industry and the safety of chemicals used in beauty products. Some also point out that natural plant-based products are not necessarily intrinsically inert, which is an issue that needs to be addressed.

Before you run for the hills screaming blue murder, remember that millions of people use cosmetic products every day and we are not all dropping like flies as a result. However, there are a growing number of people who are developing illnesses and health issues that cannot be fully explained by other lifestyle factors. Some experts are concerned that our increased exposure to chemicals in a wide range of household products may have a role to play in increasing incidences of allergies, asthma and other health problems seen over the past few decades. One of the experts I interviewed for this book, Dr Philippa Darbre, senior lecturer in oncology at the University of Reading, pointed out to me, 'We all know, whether we are industrialists or scientists, that if someone uses enough of anything it can become toxic. At what point does the industry start to worry about the level of usage of these products?'

Cosmetics are regulated in the European Union by the EU Cosmetics Directive. It states that 'a cosmetic product put on the market within the Community must not cause damage to human health when applied under normal or reasonably foreseeable conditions of use'.[2] But precisely what are 'normal and reasonably foreseeable conditions of use'? Some individuals use a whole can of deodorant in one week, apply lipstick 15 times a day and brush their teeth ten times a day. Some mothers have been known to use deodorant on their babies. Is this normal and foreseeable? Where does it specify on your hairspray the number of times it should be applied before adverse effects can be expected to occur?

'Our bodies are designed to deal with things that they haven't come across before', says Dr Darbre, 'we have ways of detoxifying. The problem is overload and it is all about excess use. Usage of cosmetic products is spiralling out of control.' She adds, 'Synthetic chemicals that don't exist in the body normally ... are able to bioaccumulate in biological tissue, which means that the body doesn't deal with them very efficiently and over years of exposure they accumulate.' Bioaccumulation refers to the accumulation of substances in an organism or part of an organism, with the concentration of the substances increasing over time compared with levels in the organism's surrounding environment.

Mounting scientific evidence about the dubious nature of chemicals we are regularly exposed to in toiletries is encouraging a consumer shift in attitude towards the multi-billion-pound beauty industry and organic and natural beauty brands are becoming more popular. Sadly it is important to be aware that in many cases these products are masquerading as 'organic' and 'natural', when lurking inside is a synthetic chemical soup and perhaps the odd organic ingredient as a final token gesture; or a watery herbal infusion that manufacturers sneakily include in their percentage of organic ingredients labelled on the product. Still, don't let this put you off. If consumers boycott conventional and pseudo-natural brands and opt for organic alternatives, the cosmetics industry as a whole will have to sit up and listen.

How to use this book

I have broken the book down into two parts. Part 1: Beauty Products in Context – sets the scene, explaining in depth why toiletries are an area for concern, in terms of our health, the environment and the relatively lacklustre regulation that is currently in place.

Once you have the above knowledge firmly under your belt, another tool for your natural beauty toolkit is grasping what bona fide organic beauty products amount to. This part also addresses the terms 'organic' and 'natural', along with various organic certification initiatives.

There are very few brands offering genuinely organic beauty products. In Part 2: Resources – the main ones are listed in a directory of alternative beauty brands, along with brands that use a mixture of organic and synthetic ingredients, keeping the latter to a minimum. Here you will also find an A–Z of some common chemical ingredients used in personal care products. This list is by no means exhaustive. There are hundreds of thousands of untested chemicals in circulation and I have featured a small collection of some of the most relevant ones to be aware of when shopping for cosmetics and toiletries.

Various experts have contributed quotes and interviews for this book, including but not limited to:

- **Dr Andrew Maynard** – chief science advisor of the Project on Emerging Nanotechnologies at the Woodrow Wilson International Center for Scholars.
- **Dr Christopher Flower** – director-general, the Cosmetic, Toiletry and Perfumery Association (CTPA).
- **Dr Kris G. McGrath** – associate professor of clinical medicine at the Feinberg School of Medicine, Northwestern University.
- **Dr Philippa Darbre** – senior lecturer in oncology, Biomolecular Sciences Section, School of Biological Sciences, the University of Reading.
- **Dr Shanna Swan** – professor in the Department of Obstetrics and Gynaecology and director of the Centre for Reproductive Epidemiology at the University of Rochester School of Medicine and Dentistry.

- **Elizabeth Salter-Green** – former director of WWF-UK's Toxics Programme and current director of CHEM Trust.

For the purposes of this book I predominantly discuss the dangers of synthetic chemicals and therefore frequently use the terms 'toxic substance(s)' and 'toxicant(s)' in reference to chemical compounds (typically introduced into the environment by human activity) that are potentially harmful to living organisms. The term 'toxin' is often misused as a synonym for toxicant but technically speaking a toxin is a poison produced by living cells or organisms and usually capable of inducing the production of antibodies. Toxins can be by-products of ordinary metabolism, such as lactic acid.

Switching to organic beauty products might seem a tad daunting at the outset, but with this book it becomes a whole lot simpler. Throughout you will notice boxed-in areas featuring snippets of information, such as facts about the beauty products and the industry itself, quotes from leading experts in the field and straightforward, stress-free natural beauty tips and recipes. Read this book at your leisure and discover a brand new understanding of the multi-billion-pound beauty industry.

PART 1

Beauty products in context

Chapter 1

Why are personal care products in question?

Did you know?

- The average woman spends 450 days applying her make-up in a lifetime.[1]

- The cosmetic, toiletry and perfumery industry in the UK is worth over £6.5 billion annually and provides employment for tens of thousands of individuals.[2]

- According to market analysts Mintel, between 2001 and 2006 the cosmetics market in the UK witnessed a huge growth of nearly 40 per cent, exceeding the value of this market in Spain, Germany and even France, where many of the world's leading cosmetic houses reside.[3]

With a whopping 89.7 per cent of British women using fragrances and 80.4 per cent using lipsticks,[4] it's evident that today we see beauty products as integral everyday items. But it's not just women; men, too, are also subject to the beauty industry's campaign to coax them into a lifetime of cosmetic consumerism. Rexam, a leading global consumer packaging company, state that men are driving market growth. In 2006 the men's toiletries market grew by 5.2 per cent to £881 million.[5] It is no surprise then than that globally the cosmetics market is worth hundreds of billions of dollars. Within the European Union (EU) alone the cosmetics industry directly employs in excess of 150,000 people.[6] Make-up is a winning money-spinner in any language and not one that's about to go out of fashion, as long as physical perfection is a mainstay of our society.

If you are an average consumer, your make-up bag and bathroom cabinet is probably brimming with an assortment of creams, shower gels, shampoos, conditioners, perfumes, cosmetics and other beauty products that promise to enhance your appearance by zapping your wrinkles, revitalizing your hair, masking 'unpleasant' body odours and attracting the opposite sex, among many other pledges. Messages to this effect are transmitted into our homes every day via television, radio and the worldwide web. Advertisers would have us believe that cosmetics are an absolute necessity, without which we become social pariahs. Many cosmetic houses spend more than or as much money on marketing as they do on new product development.[7]

Looks can be deceiving

Looking at all those neatly packaged items lining your shelves you wouldn't necessarily suspect that anything dubious was afoot. To invite the right kind of consumer attention the cosmetic houses strive to make the packaging as eye-catching, appealing and convenient to use as possible, employing packaging manufacturers to implement strategic design concepts and nifty devices, such as lockable dispensing systems and pump mechanisms. Perfume bottles have become almost objects of art, with alluring aesthetics that entice the consumer before they have even caught a whiff of the heady scent within.

Rather worryingly though, inside those visually appealing bottles and tubes lurks a cocktail of synthetic chemicals. There are over 100,000 chemicals registered on the European Inventory of Existing Commercial Substances (EINECS). Around 30,000 of these are believed to be in use and many of them have never been tested or barely tested for safety on humans, or their impact on the environment. In the USA there are around 75,000 chemicals registered for use and the top ten cosmetic companies alone use more than 10,000 of these.[8]

Did you know?

Volatile organic compounds (VOCs) contribute
to ground level ozone formation, which at the
abnormally high concentrations occurring as a result
of human activity can cause a myriad of respiratory
problems in healthy humans. Ground level ozone is
a constituent of smog. VOCs are emitted from
numerous sources including petroleum storage tanks,
oil refineries, paints, varnishes, petroleum, cleaning
chemicals, cosmetics and vehicle exhausts. These
chemicals readily evaporate at room temperature and
are referred to as organic because they contain carbon
in their molecular structures. According to the US
Environmental Protection Agency, concentrations of
VOCs are consistently up to ten times higher indoors
than outdoors.[9]

Hazardous to our health

It is ironic that cosmetics manufacturers continue to claim that their
products will make us look and feel better when increasingly experts
are concerned that the long-term effects on our health could actually
be harmful. Contact dermatitis, asthma, skin, eye and respiratory tract
irritation, skin sensitization, photosensitivity, immune and nervous system
disruption, birth defects and cancer are just a handful of the potential
negative effects of many of the chemicals we regularly apply to
our bodies.

It has become increasingly apparent that toxic chemicals accumulate
over time and they are transferred to the womb and through the food
chain to our children. We can absorb chemicals through a number of
routes including: inhalation, ingestion, through the skin, placenta and
breast milk and via absorption through the mucous membranes in the
eyes, mouth and nose. The total amount of chemicals in someone's body
at any given moment is known as the toxic body burden. While some
chemicals and their breakdown products only remain in our bodies for a
short period of time before being excreted, others are not readily excreted
and can be stored in our adipose (fat), blood, muscle, bone, brain tissue and

other organs. If we are continually exposed to an easily metabolized substance it can still contribute to our overall toxic body burden over a period of time.

Certain chemicals can attack the body, for example, by damaging or killing cells or tissues or even altering DNA, the genetic material in the cell nucleus, which can lead to inheritable defects. Changed or mutated genes can instigate a process that can lead to cancer, birth defects, developmental and reproductive disorders. These types of chemicals are known as:

- **carcinogens** – causing cancer;
- **teratogens** – causing birth defects;
- **developmental/reproductive toxicants** – affecting the normal development of the fetus and subsequent child or damaging the reproductive tissues;
- **endocrine disruptors** – causing damage by interfering with normal hormone functioning.

Toxic chemicals can, through the above routes, lead to a myriad of health problems. For example, phthalates are chemicals routinely used in personal care products and studies have shown that some of them are endocrine disruptors, with oestrogenic effects (mimicking the sex hormone oestrogen), feminizing male fetuses and highlighting an association between early puberty and premature breast development in young females.[10] Some research has shown that mothers with high levels of phthalates in their bodies are giving birth to boys with a reduced anogenital distance (the distance between the genitals and the anus), which is a sign of feminization.

It is important to remember that our circumstances, degree of exposure and environment play a part in our sensitivity to chemicals. Factors contributing to an individual's risk of illness include environmental exposures, genetic factors, diet and lifestyle, social and economic status, age and gender.[11] This can make it difficult to accurately identify the risks posed by certain chemicals to humans. Our susceptibility to a particular disease can be affected by inherited mutations in genes leading to a genetic predisposition for developing a particular illness. Those who are exposed occupationally to high levels of chemicals are more likely to develop certain conditions. Also, although some people will feel healthy while using chemical-infused products, the effects of constant usage may not become apparent until later on in life and may appear unrelated to the products used. If you developed an illness would you instantly put it down to your use of cosmetic products?

Poisoning baby

'I have had two mothers on the phone to me, one of them in tears, because they used underarm anti-perspirants on their babies and they were concerned about whether this was safe or not. The thing is there is nothing to say you shouldn't because cosmetics companies do not tell you whether they are safe over the age of three or five or ten. Some women just assume they are safe and use them on their babies.'

Dr Philippa Darbre, senior lecturer in oncology, Biomolecular Sciences Section, School of Biological Sciences, the University of Reading.

Babies and young children are especially vulnerable to damage from toxic chemicals, which can often cause more harm than the same level of exposure would to an adult. There are various reasons for this. For instance, children take in more oxygen per kilogram of body weight than an adult and therefore more air pollutants. The skin of newborn babies is more absorbent because the skin's outer layer (horny layer or stratum corneum) is not yet fully developed (therefore without one of the skin's main protective barriers) until several days after birth. The higher skin-to-weight ratio of babies compared to adults puts them at a greater risk of toxicity through the absorption of topically applied substances. Various organs such as the lungs and brain, along with the respiratory and immune systems are still developing in infants.

Chemicals that disrupt the process of development can cause severe birth defects, learning or behavioural difficulties and possibly cancer or degenerative brain diseases in later life. The timing of exposure to a substance is as relevant as the amount a child is exposed to because the nature of the damage caused may depend on the stage of development of different organ systems when exposure took place.[12] A 1989 report by the Natural Resources Defense Council (an environmental action group) surmised that 'More than 50 per cent of a person's lifetime cancer risk from exposure to carcinogenic pesticides is typically incurred in the first six years of life.'[13]

It may be hard to believe that babies can absorb environmental chemicals so readily. However, a 2004 study released by the US Environmental Working Group (EWG) in collaboration with Commonweal, the Californian health and environmental institute, identified an average of 200 different chemicals and pollutants in umbilical cord blood from ten babies, including flame retardants, pesticides, stain- and grease-resistant coatings used for food packaging, carpets and furniture, polycyclic aromatic hydrocarbons (PAHs) from car emissions and electrical insulators.[14]

Take home message

Try to minimize your exposure to synthetic chemicals when you are pregnant and avoid using these products on babies and young children, who are especially sensitive to any chemicals present.

Who's looking at cosmetics?

Traditionally, cosmetics have not come under a great deal of scrutiny because it was thought that they did not cause any ill health effects. The belief that our skin was an impervious barrier to externally applied substances was virtually omnipresent for many years until evidence showed that either through sweat glands, hair follicles or the skin itself chemicals could infiltrate the skin to varying degrees, depending on their molecular size and shape.[15] Products that are intended to be left on the skin rather than washed away, such as moisturizer and foundation, can penetrate the skin in quite considerable amounts.

Certain chemical constituents in beauty products are known as penetration enhancers (e.g. sodium lauryl sulphate and propylene glycol). These modify the structure of the skin, enhancing its absorption of other chemicals and allowing them to enter the bloodstream more rapidly. Penetration enhancers can trigger immune system reactions such as irritation, allergy or inflammation,[16] as well as allowing other more toxic chemicals to be absorbed. Do you really want your moisturizer to aid your skin's absorption of toxic substances found in other cosmetic and household products?

At the moment, however, cosmetic manufacturers don't appear to be particularly concerned about this issue. Instead they are enthusiastically employing nanotechnology, in the form of adding tiny particles or 'nanoparticles' into cosmetic products to transport active ingredients deeper into the skin and increase the production of new cells to 'fight' the visible signs of ageing. Health concerns about such technology have been prompted because of the potential ability of these miniscule nanoparticles to enter cells or the bloodsteam and cause harmful reactions. This has occurred in animal experiments, where nanoparticles have damaged vital organs and DNA, as well as causing lung tumours when inhaled. You can read more about nanotechnology in Chapter 5.

What's in your shampoo?

Shampoo contains detergents (the same ones used in laundry powder and washing-up liquid) that can strip away the natural oils from your scalp and hair. When the skin's natural protective sebum is removed, greater water loss occurs from the surface, which can lead to skin dryness and increase permeability, allowing the chemicals in hair dyes and other chemical solutions to be more readily absorbed.

- **Sodium laureth sulphate** – can cause contact allergies and skin and eye irritation.

- **Sodium lauryl sulphate** – can cause contact allergies, skin irritation and potentially damage the cornea if it comes into contact with the eyes. It also dissolves the protective oily layer of the skin, which can cause skin dryness. Sodium lauryl sulphate readily enters the heart, lungs, liver and brain via skin contact, where residual levels are stored.[17] A penetration enhancer.

- **Laureth-16** – can cause skin irritation.

- **Malic acid** – an alpha hydroxy acid (AHA), which can cause skin irritation. AHAs can increase sensitivity to sunlight because of their ability to remove the protective outer layer of the skin.

- **PEG-12 dimethicone** – PEG (polyethylene glycol) compounds can become accidentally contaminated with 1,4-dioxane, a substance 'reasonably anticipated to be a carcinogen', by the US Department of Health and Human Services. The adverse effects of PEG-12 dimethicone have not been widely investigated.

- **Cocamide MEA** – can cause skin irritation and sensitization and become contaminated, forming carcinogenic nitrosamines.

- **PPG-9** – can cause skin irritation.

- **Benzyl alcohol** – a skin and eye irritant, classified as a well-recognized consumer allergen by the Scientific Committee on Cosmetic Products and Non-food Products Intended for Consumers (SCCNFP).

- **Glycine** – in animal studies reactions to this substance (depending on how it is administered) have included endocrine disruption and alterations in motor activity.

- **Cocamide MIPA** – can cause allergies and skin irritation.

- **Propylene glycol** – can cause irritation of the skin, eyes and respiratory tract. It can also provoke allergic reactions in some individuals.

- **Iodopropynyl butylcarbamate** – can cause skin irritation and contact allergies.

- **Disodium EDTA** – can cause skin and eye irritation.

- **Diazolidinyl urea** – in its safety assessment this substance was a mild skin irritant in humans at concentrations of up to 0.4 per cent. It can cause contact dermatitis in some individuals and is a formaldehyde releaser. Formaldehyde is classified as a probable human carcinogen by the International Agency for Research on Cancer (IARC).

• **Parfum** – a concoction of synthetic fragrance chemicals that often exceed 100 in number. Many of these may be potential skin irritants, allergens and sensitizers, as well as being linked with other health concerns.

Cocktails and low doses

Although cosmetics manufacturers have asserted that the chemicals used in their products are added in very low concentrations, chemicals in combination can cause undesirable additive effects and this is an area that has not been fully investigated. The cocktail effect is used to describe a phenomenon where more than one chemical is combined either in a product or in the body, producing a total toxic effect far greater than would be the case for the sum of the individual chemicals.

It is not enough to simply say that low levels of exposure to certain chemicals are safe; as the European Environment Agency (EEA) has noted, 'it is very difficult to know, or predict, what the harmful level of exposure to chemicals may be, and then to ensure that actual exposures in the environment are kept below those levels'.[18]

Another potential flaw in the 'low concentrations are safe' argument has come to light courtesy of the low-dose phenomenon, first reported in the 1990s, which is contrary to one of the intrinsic tenets of toxicology, that 'the dose makes the poison'. It has been shown that in certain circumstances low doses of compounds can cause more damaging health effects than higher doses, including the disturbance of normal hormonal functions. Some individuals will react more severely to low doses of substances than others, and again, babies and children are more likely to experience adverse effects.

Critics of this theory have argued that its findings are based on a few small-scale studies conducted on experimental animals that have demonstrated reproductive or development effects. The US Environmental Protection Agency (EPA) asked the National Toxicology Program (NTP) to carry out a scientific peer review of studies relevant to the low-dose theory and the peer review panel concluded that although there were 'credible studies supporting a low dose effect, the effects were dependent on the compounds studied and the endpoint measured'. In 2002 the EPA stated that routine testing of substances for the low-dose effect in the Endocrine Disruptor Screening Program would be 'premature'.[19]

By December 2004, however, there were 115 published in vivo studies (i.e. conducted on the living tissue of living organisms) pertaining to the low-dose effects of bisphenol A (widely used in plastic packaging for food and cosmetic containers) alone and nearly 82 per cent of these reported significant effects.[20] Other animal and cell-based studies have also demonstrated the low-dose effect of bisphenol A. Given that there are other examples of substances shown to cause adverse effects at low doses it is quite clear that 'the dose makes the poison' is a gross over-simplification of the complex world of chemical reactions and interactions. Chapters 2, 3 and 4 look in more detail at the effects of cosmetics on our health.

Did you know?

Oil-free moisturizers are based on humectants, which are used in moisturizing creams to ensure that the product does not dry out and to attract moisture from the atmosphere to the stratum corneum. The skin remains moist providing there is adequate moisture in the air. However, humectants draw moisture from anywhere, so in a dry environment a cosmetic product containing humectants will absorb moisture from the nearest source, in other words the lower epidermal layers of the skin. If the humectants draw too much water from the skin they can actually dry it out.

Chemicals lingering in the environment

It is not just our health that may be affected by the increasing amounts of chemicals we use on a daily basis. Our environment suffers as well. Many of the chemicals in our beauty products are also present in a myriad of other household or other products that we eat, drink, apply or otherwise encounter on a daily basis, and scores of these can persist and accumulate in our bodies and the surrounding environment.

In 1998 the European Environment Agency (EEA) commented that,

> 'Manufactured chemicals are widespread in the air, soil, water sediments and biota of Europe's environment following the marketing of up to 100,000 chemicals in the EU, their use and disposal and degradation. There is a serious lack of monitoring and information on these chemicals ... and related exposures and effects on people and ecosystems .... Current toxicity risk assessments are based mainly on single substances, but people and ecosystems are generally exposed to complex mixtures ... widespread exposures to low doses of chemicals may be causing harm, possibly irreversibly, particularly to sensitive groups such as children and pregnant women and to parts of the environment.'[18]

Fish, birds and a variety of other animals have been shown to suffer embryo defects, cancers, and injury to nervous, reproductive and immune systems as a result of environmental chemical exposures. Declining populations of certain bird species have been linked with the indirect effects of pesticides.[21] In the 1970s dichlorodiphenyltrichloroethane (DDT) was associated with reproductive malfunction in eagles and other birds. Since then other studies have highlighted the damaging effects of this pesticide on wildlife.

Unfortunately the harmful long-term effects of many toxic chemicals do not become apparent until years after their release into the environment. Once we reach the stage where there is clear evidence of the negative consequences for our health, significant damage has already taken place. Daily we flush away and wash down the drain millions of gallons of chemicals, which enter the sewer systems and pollute the waterways. If toxic chemicals are not sufficiently removed before being released and entering the aquatic environment they can be absorbed by wildlife, thereby entering the food chain.

Persistent chemicals are not easily broken down in the environment and can travel long distances and survive for many years. When they fail to degrade and are constantly being released into the environment, their concentration increases. Lipophilic (fat-loving) molecules are not water soluble and tend to become concentrated in the fatty tissues of living organisms, including humans. Substances that are lipophilic *and* persistent can easily be taken in by organisms from polluted environments, where they can bioaccumulate in the food chain. Under the process known as biomagnification the concentration of a substance is multiplied every time it is consumed by something higher up in the food chain. This results in concentrations millions of times higher than they were in the original physical environment. Fairly high levels of contaminants have been found in top predator species in the Arctic, such as polar bears, beluga whales and seals.

The industry fights back

Question Are certain synthetic chemicals in cosmetics not just adding to the undesirable bioaccumulation of such chemicals in the environment, food chain and in humans?

Answer 'No, that's not the case. The cosmetics industry is well aware of issues such as bioaccumulation and also of how the term can tend to be misused. Bioaccumulation is where there is evidence of a substance remaining present and building up over time. The presence of a substance, whether it be in a human or in the environment, is not evidence of bioaccumulation, though the ability to detect such small levels does demonstrate the advances made in chemical analysis in recent years. Levels of substances may be falling over time (and therefore cannot be described as bioaccumulating), may be static or may be increasing. The key indicators are the rate of change, the anticipated steady-state level and the safe level. Only if any substance is accumulating to a point where it may exceed safe levels is there any need to take action, and this goes for all of the substances used in commerce. In fact, levels of cosmetic ingredients sometimes claimed to be bioaccumulating have actually been shown to have fallen.'

Dr Christopher Flower, director-general, the Cosmetic, Toiletry and Perfumery Association (CTPA).

Beauty at the expense of the environment

Cosmetics and toiletries, like other consumer products, contain ingredients that can persist in the environment and bioaccumulate in our bodies and other living organisms. Let's take a closer look at some of the chemicals found in our cosmetics that are now present in the environment to an alarming degree.

Triclosan

Triclosan is found in many common household products including washing-up liquid, toothpastes, hand washes, soaps and other cosmetic products. An estimated 60–90 tonnes of this substance are released into the UK environment each year, the majority of it heading straight for the sewers. Most of it is removed prior to the effluent being discharged back into the environment, but some still remains. Triclosan can degrade into the persistent metabolite methyl triclosan, which bioaccumulates in fish.[22] As mentioned in Chapter 4 on endocrine disruptors (see page 108), triclosan can also degrade under sunlight to produce a form of dioxin.

Synthetic musks

Synthetic musks, man-made chemicals commonly used in a range of fragranced consumer products, including laundry detergents, air fresheners, household cleaners, perfumes, aftershaves, cosmetics and personal care products, are persistent environmental contaminants that have been detected in rivers, lakes, sediment, soil, sewage sludge and effluent from wastewater treatment plants in the UK, Canada, the US and Europe.[23,24]

Although produced to replace natural musks derived from musk deer and musk ox, synthetic musks are not structurally similar and behave more like polychlorinated biphenyls (PCBs) and organochlorine pesticides, increasing in concentration as they move higher up the food chain.[23] Due to the prolific use of synthetic musks in consumer items they have also been identified in the atmosphere, both indoors and outdoors. As discussed in Chapter 4 on endocrine disruption (see page 113), synthetic musks have been shown to possess oestrogenic and anti-oestrogenic properties. Many retailers are discontinuing their use.

Phthalates

Commonly used in cosmetic products as plasticizers and solvents, phthalates are the most abundant synthetic chemicals in the environment.[25] They are ubiquitous environmental contaminants that are deemed to be hazardous waste and regulated as pollutants when released into the environment by industry.[26] Phthalates have been detected in rainwater, water, soil, sediments, indoor air and dust, fish/marine food webs, meat, dairy products, human blood and breast milk. Phthalate metabolites have also been identified in the urine of adults and children.[27]

Analyses of wastewater from residential, commercial and industrial sites in the San Francisco Bay area by the Environmental Working Group (EWG) and East Bay Municipal Utility District (EBMUD) detected, in 18 out of 19 wastewater samples evaluated, at least one of three unregulated and commonly used hormone disruptors – phthalates, bisphenol A and triclosan.[24] Phthalates have even been detected in Arctic air and seawater samples, although the concentrations detected were low.[28]

Perfluorinated chemicals (PFCs

Perfluorinated chemicals (PFCs), a group of fluorine-containing chemicals used for their heat-stable properties and ability to resist degradation and repel water and oil, can be found in a host of applications, including non-stick coatings for kitchenware, stain- and water-repellent treatment for carpets, paper coatings, surfactants, furniture and clothing, floor polishes, cleaning products, shampoo and food packaging materials. PFCs are persistent and bioaccumulative contaminants. Perfluorooctane surfactants have been detected in living organisms, water and air samples worldwide.[29] A study of archived polar bear liver tissue samples from two geographic locations in the North American Arctic, collected between 1972 and 2002, detected levels of perfluorooctane sulfonate (PFOS) and perfluorocarboxylic acids (PFCAs).[30]

One of the most commonly used PFCs is the chemical known as perfluorooctanoic acid (PFOA), also known as C8 (because it has eight carbons). PFOA is used in the manufacture of Teflon and is persistent and bioaccumulative in the environment, wildlife and humans. The US Environmental Protection Agency (EPA) has found an association between PFOA and various cancers in laboratory animals, as well as birth defects, suggesting a potential risk for humans of developmental and other undesirable effects. A 2005 survey by the Environmental Working Group (EWG) found that the chemical is present in the blood in more than 95 per cent of Americans.[31] PFOA and similar chemicals were reviewed by the EPA following its investigation of perfluorooctyl sulfonates (PFOS) in 1999, due to their persistence, bioaccumulation and toxicity.

You can reduce your exposure by avoiding packaged greasy and oily fast foods, stain-resistant furniture, clothing and other goods, Teflon or non-stick cookware and cosmetics containing Teflon or related compounds. Check cosmetic labels for ingredients including the words 'fluoro' or 'perfluoro'.

Alkylphenols (APs)

Alkylphenols (APs) are the breakdown products of alkylphenol ethoxylates (APEs) and are toxic to aquatic organisms and potent endocrine disruptors.[32] Although APEs were phased out of dosmetic detergents in the 1970s, they are still used in various other consumer products, including shampoos and shaving foams, and they break down into ecologically hazardous APs such as nonylphenol (NP) and octylphenol (OP) after being discharged into sewage treatment plants or undergoing environmental processes. Once discharged from treatment plants they are disseminated into the environment via effluent discharge into surface waters and sludge disposal on lands.[33]

The breakdown products of APEs are approximately ten times more toxic than the original compounds. In one study on sea urchin embryos, NP and OP were shown to cause malformations in the skeletal system at low concentrations, while high concentrations hindered the growth of the embryos.[34]

Dr Christian Daughton and Dr Thomas Ternes of the US Environmental Protection Agency explain in a special report published in the scientific journal *Environmental Health Perspectives* that personal care products are constantly entering the environment through sewage treatment facilities and where untreated sewage is discharged directly in rivers, streams and the ocean. They suggest that exposure to personal care products and pharmaceuticals may be more chronic than exposure to pesticides because they are constantly introduced into the environment in places where humans reside or visit.[35]

Take home message

We are powerful as consumers. The products we use, even in small amounts, have a measurable effect on the environment. Choose all your household products – personal care and cleaning – according to their kindness to the environment. And, reduce packaging as much as you can. Choose glass containers where possible and seek out manufacturers who encourage refills of containers.

But aren't these chemicals tested?

You could be forgiven for expecting that regulatory authorities would do their utmost to ensure rigorous safety testing of all ingredients in personal care products. Sadly this seems to be a utopian vision, rather than a reality.

Why is this the case? According to Elizabeth Salter-Green, former director of WWF-UK's Toxics Programme and current director of CHEM Trust:

> 'The research always seems to come out a long time in advance of the policy that is subsequently developed. That is why organizations like WWF, Greenpeace and CHEM Trust are working to try and reduce that lag between finding out that a chemical is toxic and getting it properly controlled and, if necessary, legislated off the market.
>
> We have always been running to catch up. A chemical goes on the market, we find it's horrid and then we produce some legislation to deal with that. What we have not done until recently is reverse the onus of proof, making companies take the responsibility for their chemicals and products prior to putting them on the market. This has to be a more intelligent modus operandi.'

In the European Union (EU) and its member states the manufacture and marketing of cosmetics comes under the regulatory framework of the European Cosmetics Directive (no. 76/768/EEC) and its subsequent amendments. This directive is a patchwork of the original legislation and 55 amendments, often with conflicting provisions and inconsistent terminology.[36]

The Scientific Committee on Consumer Products (SCCP) produces opinions on the safety of cosmetic and non-food products intended for consumers, and issues guidelines for safety evaluations to be taken into consideration by cosmetics manufacturers, which are, according to the European Commission, largely ignored.[36] Cosmetic manufacturers are required to maintain good manufacturing practices, but the regulations provide no definition of what this entails. Ultimately the burden of proof for assessing the safety of products rests with the industry itself, who often seem to be more concerned with profit than consumer health, frequently perceiving attempts at government regulation or intervention as an obstacle to product innovation and free trade.

It is also the case that adverse effects from cosmetics are not as widely reported as reactions to food and drugs. Individuals tend to just stop using the suspected products and any negative effects are not usually so instantaneously life-threatening, therefore they receive less government attention. Pilot studies conducted by the Council of Europe (CoE) in Austria, Denmark, France and Norway revealed that only around 25 per cent of consumers suffering from unpleasant reactions to cosmetic products consulted a physician.[37]

Europe is endeavouring to get its act together to better regulate the industry. The Seventh Amendment to the Cosmetics Directive introduced an animal testing ban, prohibited the continued use of three classes of toxic substances – carcinogens, mutagens and reproductive toxicants (CMR) – and required the labelling of 26 fragrance ingredients that may instigate allergic reactions. And, in 2007, legislation was introduced intended to test a large number of chemicals. This is called REACH (Registration, Evaluation, Authorisation and Restriction of Chemicals) and is described below.

The European Commission are also proposing a single EU law on cosmetic products with the intention of cutting costs and strengthening manufacturer responsibility.

The revelation of REACH

REACH (not for the stars but the Registration, Evaluation, Authorisation and Restriction of Chemicals) legislation is a major new system established to evaluate numerous chemicals for their effects on human health and the environment and to encourage the replacement of hazardous chemicals with safer alternatives. It came into force in June 2007, in the EU and its member states, and replaces about 40 different pieces of chemicals legislation. Over the next 11 years approximately 30,000 chemicals currently in use will have to be registered according to a set timetable. As far as consumer products go, REACH takes into account the human and environmental impact of chemicals used in the products and packaging.

The onus for demonstrating the safety of a substance falls on the industry itself and the 'no data, no market' rule applies, so if companies fail to submit safety data on a substance, they should not manufacture nor place it on the market, meaning that producers and users will have to prove the safety of thousands of products.

REACH in a nutshell

- **Registration** – each manufacturer or importer of a substance in excess of 1 tonne per year will have to provide safety information on that substance to the new European Chemicals Agency in Helsinki.

- **Evaluation** – the European Chemicals Agency and member states will evaluate information submitted on a substance to identify any risks.

- **Authorisation** – substances of very high concern will be subject to use-specific authorization and may have to be replaced by safer alternatives.

- **Restriction** – certain chemicals of concern may be restricted in terms of manufacturing, placing on the market or use.

Some loopholes

REACH has been welcomed by environmental groups, but criticisms have also been levelled due a reported loophole in the authorization stage, which means that the use of high concern chemicals can continue, even if safer alternatives exist, as long as they are 'adequately controlled'. A clause mandating safer substitutes of the most toxic chemicals was abandoned. REACH does mandate the replacement of persistent and bioaccumulative chemicals and all non-threshold substances (that is, chemicals for which there is no safe level of exposure), wherever safer alternatives are available. The controversy will be over carcinogens, where companies may try to claim adequate control instead of substituting them. The idea of adequate control rests on the premise that substances are safe below a certain threshold. However, persistent and bioaccumulative chemicals are not readily controlled. They cannot easily be broken down in the environment and lipophilic chemicals remain in the fatty tissues of organisms.

The World Wide Fund for Nature (WWF) have noted that the registration will only apply to 30,000 of the 100,000+ chemicals on the market, due to a caveat that stipulates that only substances imported in volumes exceeding 1 tonne, per year, per producer or importer will have to undergo REACH registration. Only rudimentary information will be required for substances within the 1–10 tonnage band.

In addition, the decision on whether to mandate industry to replace endocrine disruptors with safer alternatives in every instance has been delayed.[38,39]

It is also important to note that chemicals in cosmetics are only covered by REACH in terms of their environmental impact, not with regard to their effect on human health (which will remain under the remit of the Cosmetics Directive). Cosmetic products are also exempt from the requirement to provide a safety data sheet on the ingredients in them.

Dr Ninja Reineke of WWF's Toxics Programme also points out that 'REACH will make a difference only in the long term, because it will take three years until we get more information on the higher volume chemicals and some of them may be used in cosmetics. So, for the consumer REACH will not change things overnight.'

Take home message

In a perfect world all governments would protect us from harmful products by ensuring that the ingredients used are always reliably tested and then enforcing strict regulations on product manufacturers so that anything potentially harmful is totally banned from inclusion and replaced with a safer alternative. Maybe one day this will be the case, but until then, you can become savvy about shopping safely for beauty products. Your body will thank you for it.

What's happening in the United States

If you live in America, you'll be disappointed to know that cosmetics are the least regulated products under the Federal Food, Drug and Cosmetic Act (FD&C Act).[40] As the Breast Cancer Fund note in their 2008 report, *State of the Evidence: The Connection Between Breast Cancer and the Environment*, 'Major loopholes in federal law allow the $50 billion cosmetics industry to put unlimited amounts of chemicals into personal care products with no required testing, no monitoring of health effects and woefully inadequate labelling requirements.' The US Food and Drug Administration (FDA) is responsible for enforcing cosmetic and pharmaceutical regulations and within the FDA, the Office of Cosmetics and Colors regulates cosmetic products.

In contrast to products classified as drugs or cosmetics *and* drugs, under the FD&C Act introduced in 1938, cosmetics and their ingredients do not legally have to be approved, tested for safety or reviewed before being marketed to consumers, with the exception of colour additives. Any testing undertaken is the responsibility of the manufacturer. This regulatory chasm means that potentially harmful substances can readily be introduced into cosmetic products.

The FD&C Act prohibits the marketing of adulterated or misbranded products that are in some way contaminated or improperly labelled, but the FDA can usually only intervene to restrict or ban an adulterated or misbranded product once it has been released to the marketplace and if it can prove that its use may cause injury to users, it has been labelled incorrectly, or contravenes the law in some other way. This is difficult for the FDA because the agency lacks the authority to obtain the necessary information. There is a system under which manufacturers can voluntarily report information to the FDA, but only around 35 per cent do so and sometimes companies file incomplete data.

Since 1976, if the safety of a product has not been substantiated prior to marketing it is considered as misbranded if the label does not bear the statement, 'Warning: The safety of this product has not been determined.' However, a huge number of cosmetic ingredients have not been adequately assessed for safety and most of the beauty products containing them are not labelled with this warning. Even if the FDA considers them to be misbranded or adulterated, with a shortage of safety data available and the agency's lack of oversight to access records relating to safety and proof of effect, this is difficult to prove. Plus, how many manufacturers are going to willingly convey on their products that their safety has not been substantiated?

It is also worth knowing that some cosmetic companies practise double standards, producing formulations for the European market minus ingredients prohibited in the EU (such as certain phthalates) and concocting separate formulations for the US market that contain substances banned in the EU.

The Cosmetic Ingredient Review

In 1976 the Cosmetic Ingredient Review (CIR) was set up to review and test the safety of cosmetic ingredients. Its safety assessment monographs are submitted for publication in the peer-reviewed *International Journal of Toxicology*, but the CIR is funded by the cosmetics industry body in the USA known as the Personal Care Products Council and the FDA is not legally obliged to enforce regulations based on its conclusions.

The CIR does not safety test all cosmetic ingredients. As of 2005, 1,285[41] of the 10,500 ingredients used in cosmetic products had been assessed for safety and only nine of those reviewed since 1976 have been deemed to be unsafe.[42] Only the nine considered as unsafe are banned outright in cosmetic formulations. The CIR panel of dermatologists have been accused by some of directing their attention towards testing substances for skin sensitization, irritation and contact allergies, rather than more long-term adverse effects such as cancer, neurotoxicity (damage to brain cells and other parts of the nervous system caused by toxic substances) and endocrine disruption. According to Stacy Malkan, co-founder of the Campaign for Safe Cosmetics and author of the book, *Not Just a Pretty Face: The Ugly Side of the Beauty Industry,*

> *'The beauty industry has a different definition of safe than we do. They consider products to be safe if they don't cause a rash or allergic reaction; we're concerned about long-term health effects caused by repeated and prolonged exposure to toxic chemicals in personal care products. These products should be safe for pregnant women, developing babies, children and for everyone else.'*

The largely self-regulated cosmetics industry often flouts the advice of the CIR. An investigation by the Environmental Working Group (EWG) of the ingredients in over 23,000 products discovered that nearly one in every 30 products sold in the US does not meet one or more industry or governmental cosmetics safety standards. They also found close to 400 products containing chemical ingredients that cosmetic industry safety panels, including the CIR and the International Fragrance Association (IFRA), have identified as unsafe.[43]

The bottom line

So where does all this leave the average cosmetics user? Over the past few decades we've seen a phenomenal worldwide increase in the use of synthetic chemicals in virtually every household item. Every year around 1,000 new chemicals come on to the market. Currently we rely on cosmetic manufacturers to assure us that all the chemicals in these products have been fully tested and are safe to use over the short and long term. However, there is growing evidence from scientists that this may not be the case. It makes sense for us all to become better informed about what's in the personal care products we use and what the health implications may be. The following chapters will help you to do just that.

Chapter 2
Help, I'm allergic! – Skin problems, asthma and allergies

Did you know?

Emollients (also referred to as occlusives) are used in face and body creams to soften the skin and form a protective waterproof layer of oil or wax on the skin, thereby preventing the evaporation of water from the skin's surface. This causes the stratum corneum to swell as it draws moisture from the lower layers of skin, leading the cells to swell and press against each other, which temporarily reduces the cracks in the skin's surface. Emollients don't provide additional moisture they merely prevent it from escaping. What is more, synthetic emollients can clog pores and cause

skin irritation, contact allergies, blocked hair follicles,
inflammation of the hair follicles (folliculitis) or
boils and rashes. If the pores and hair follicles are
blocked dirt and bacteria build up, causing blackheads
and acne.[1]

Is the concern about the chemicals commonly found in beauty products
just hype? You've probably been using personal care products for years
with no obvious ill effects, so what's all the fuss about? In the following
chapters we look a bit more closely at the chemicals we're exposed to and
what the evidence is for their harmful effects. I'm starting with the most
common health problems arising from personal care products – allergies,
irritation and sensitivity.

Cosmetic chemical constituents can provoke a variety of different
health problems, including skin, eye and respiratory irritation, allergic
reactions, sensitization and cancer. While there are statistics charting the
number of people who have experienced certain negative effects, there
are millions of individuals who will not report their reaction to a cosmetic
product. Instead they will either stop using the product and switch to an
alternative, or grin and bear the skin, eye and respiratory irritation, or the
multitude of other symptoms that chemical-infused products can activate
or exacerbate. Others will not necessarily realize that it is their use of
cosmetics that is triggering these reactions. Those who have an existing
skin condition or asthma may have an increased risk of reacting adversely
to cosmetic ingredients.

Specific chemicals used in cosmetics are often referred to as being
allergens, irritants or sensitizers. It is important to distinguish between
these three terms, because they are often incorrectly used interchangeably.

An **allergy** refers to an exaggerated immune system response when
the body comes into contact with a foreign substance (or antigen) that
does not usually cause a reaction in most individuals. In allergic individuals specific antibodies (special blood proteins produced by the body) are
activated to attack the antigens, perceiving them as a threat. In classical
allergic reaction (e.g. urticaria), after initial exposure to an antigen there
is a sensitization period, during which the body develops an abnormal
response and overproduces immunoglobulin E (IgE) antibodies, making
the antigen an allergen. The next time the individual is exposed to the
allergen, the immune system continues to overproduce these IgE
antibodies, which then attach to specialized cells in the immune system

called mast cells. When the allergens attach to the IgE antibodies, the mast cells try to fight them off by releasing numerous chemicals, including serotonin and histamine, which produces allergic symptoms in the form of a runny nose, itchy skin, wheezing, swelling, anaphylactic shock, and in some cases death.

Did you know?

In 1994 the US Food and Drug Administration (FDA) conducted a survey into the cosmetic usage of 1,687 consumers aged 14 and above. Almost 25 per cent of those questioned said they had suffered an allergic reaction as a consequence of using personal care products, including moisturizers, foundations and eyeshadows.[1]

Irritants cause a direct inflammatory response at the point of contact. Irritation is different to an allergy because it is not mediated by the acquired immune system response. The concentration of the substance used can dictate the severity of symptoms experienced and the effects subside once the product is no longer used. Irritation caused by exposure to cosmetic ingredients is very common; in fact, according to the British Association of Dermatologists all members of the population will experience an irritant contact reaction at some point in their lives.[2]

Did you know?

Skin irritation is the most common problem associated with shaving. In addition to the hair being removed, the stratum corneum is stripped away, leaving the skin more permeable to the chemical constituents in applied shaving products and aftershave. Potentially exacerbating the problem, aftershave products contain between 40 and 50 per cent denatured alcohol (ethanol mixed with small amounts of foul-tasting chemicals to make the mixture unfit for consumption), which is a penetration enhancer.[1]

Sensitizers are substances that cause hypersensitivity to an antigen on initial contact. With prolonged and ongoing use of the offending substance or related chemicals, this results in an allergic inflammatory reaction. The inflammation may appear anywhere on the skin, as opposed to being confined to the contact site and can persist for days or weeks. The first few encounters with the substances may cause a milder reaction, which then worsens with subsequent exposures, leading to strong reactions even after brief exposure to low concentrations of the substances. Respiratory sensitizers cause hypersensitivity of the airways after inhalation of the substance.[3]

The chemical culprits

Fragrances and preservatives are two of the most common causes of allergy, irritation and sensitization.

Fragrances

Aromatic oils have been used for thousands of years, traditionally to mask body odours. In the 19th century the use of natural oils was replaced by cheaper and more readily available synthetic copies that demonstrated undesirable side-effects and lacked the therapeutic properties of the natural versions. Today around 95 per cent of chemicals used in fragrances are synthetic, petroleum-derived compounds.[4] Ladd Smith, president of the Research Institute for Fragrance Materials (RIFM), the scientific arm of industry body the International Fragrance Association (IFRA), states, 'Now a fragrance, or what is called a fragrance compound, probably consists of anywhere from 50–200 ingredients.'[5]

Perfumes are added to cosmetics, toiletries, laundry products and a whole range of other consumer items. Their volatile nature means that fragrance material emissions are present in the air everywhere – at home and at work. The complex mixture of fragrance chemicals in a product means that the molecules can react with each other and other ambient pollutants and break down in the air to produce compounds more irritating than those originally used.[6] Fragrance chemicals often end up in our environment and have been detected in US stream samples,[7] rivers and lakes.

While the allure of perfume rarely fails to captivate us, there are a growing number of people who report adverse health effects resulting from exposure to fragrances and scented products, including headaches, nausea, dizziness, fatigue, difficulty breathing, diminished ability to concentrate and allergy-type symptoms. Some researchers believe that exposure to certain chemicals in perfumes and fragranced products contributes to, and exacerbates, 'sick building syndrome', a condition purportedly caused by indoor air pollution.[8]

Perfume allergies

Fragrance ingredients are the second biggest group of skin allergens and the most common cause of cosmetic allergies.[9] Perfume is the most common contact allergen in men, possibly caused by shaving, which scrapes the outer layer, allowing the scented ingredients of soaps, after-shave lotions and shaving foams to penetrate the skin.[10] Women often shave their legs and underarms so applying the same logic a similar reaction might occur.

Cinnamal and isoeugenol are two of the commonest causes of fragrance contact allergies.[11] However, of around 2,500 fragrance ingredients in use, at least 100 are known contact allergens.[12]

Other adverse effects

Some fragrance chemicals are carcinogens and many fragrance materials have also been found to exacerbate asthma, enhance the penetration of other chemicals in a product and instigate adverse brain and nervous system responses. *Poucher's Perfumes, Cosmetics and Soaps*, a reference book in the cosmetics field, notes that small quantities of volatile chemicals rapidly instigate sensory responses in the brain, 'transfer through the skin is an obvious possibility and penetration across the blood–brain barrier might give access to vulnerable regions of the central nervous system'.[13] Chemicals can enter the brain through inhalation via the nasal passage. When a chemical substance is inhaled, the molecules pass through the nose and into the brain. This was demonstrated in studies on rodents, and it is believed by researchers to be the case for humans too.

Research published in 1998 found that chemical

emissions from fragrance products caused acute toxic reactions in mice, including 'sensory irritation, pulmonary irritation, decreases in expiratory airflow velocity, as well as alterations of the functional observational battery indicative of neurotoxicity'.[14] Repeat exposures to the fragrance products exacerbated the neurotoxic effect.

A number of fragrance chemicals are also designated by the US Environmental Protection Agency (EPA) as hazardous waste, yet they are routinely added to a myriad of consumer products, including those that are easily inhaled and applied directly to the skin.

One of the major problems in identifying fragrance allergens has been the lack of a legal requirement for fragrance ingredients to be listed on consumer products. The current regulations do not require a list of fragrance ingredients to be labelled on beauty products, due to 'trade secret' status given to manufacturers. The term 'parfum' or 'aroma' is used in Europe and 'fragrance' in the USA to denote anything up to and exceeding 100 ingredients.

The fragrance industry established the Research Institute of Fragrance Materials (RIFM) in 1966 to undertake safety testing of fragrance ingredients, after questions arose about the safety of fragrance ingredients. Around 1,500 out of over 5,000 substances have been evaluated by the RIFM, with only 150 restricted or prohibited. If an ingredient is used by only one company, the RIFM will not undertake a safety assessment, leaving that to the individual company, and patented chemicals are only tested after the patent has expired. In addition, an ingredient may be in use for a number of years prior to evaluation by the RIFM.[15] Results of tests are submitted to the International Fragrance Association (IFRA) which was founded in 1973 to represent the collective interests of the fragrance industry worldwide.[16] After reviewing the information the IFRA develops safety guidelines for the raw materials. Those that are shown to have adverse effects are subject to restriction. The adherence to guidelines is voluntary on the part of fragrance companies. It is not known how many of the chemicals have been tested for carcinogenicity and the RIFM assess raw materials rather than final formulations, so there is little data on how these ingredients interact in combination.

People who suffer adverse reactions to fragrances may understandably opt for products labelled as 'fragrance free', but these often contain masking fragrances to conceal any unpleasant odours originating from the raw materials in a product or plant extracts that are potential sensitizers, such as rose oil.[17]

Natural but not always nice

It is important to note that natural as well as synthetic fragrance materials can also cause adverse effects. For instance, bergamot oil can cause berloque dermatitis (see page 60). A variety of essential oils are phototoxic, including almond, angelica, anise, cedarwood, linalool, orange, neroli, petitgrain, rosemary, yarrow and ylang ylang (see Chapter 6). In studies of in vitro human lymphocytes, dill pine and peppermint essential oils caused chromosome abnormalities. There have been case studies in which sage and other essential oils were found to induce epileptic seizures in normal individuals.[18]

Adverse effects of 20 common fragrance materials

- **Acetaldehyde** – linked to asthma, mild irritation of the skin, eyes and respiratory tract in humans and gene mutation, developmental and reproductive abnormalities in animal-based studies and a possible human carcinogen.

- **Acetone** – central nervous system depressant. Has caused endocrine disrupting effects in animal studies. Designated as hazardous waste by the US Environmental Protection Agency (EPA). At high concentrations its vapours can cause central nervous system depression, cardiorespiratory failure and death. Can cause contact allergies and skin irritation. It is known to be neurotoxic in humans.

- **Alpha-pinene** – an eye, skin and respiratory irritant that may be absorbed through the skin. Inhalation can cause palpitations, dizziness, nervous disturbances, stupor, chest pain, bronchitis, convulsions and nephritis (inflammation of the kidneys). Chronic skin exposure can cause benign tumours.

- **Alpha-terpineol** – can adversely affect the central nervous system and cause skin, respiratory and mucous membrane irritation, and gastroenteritis (when ingested). Has been known to cause coma, lip lesions, vomiting, bradycardia (abnormally slow heart rate) and low blood pressure when ingested in large amounts. Occupational asthma has been reported.

- **Benzaldehyde** – can cause contact dermatitis, sensitization and central nervous system depression. Can irritate the eyes and respiratory tract. The National Toxicology Program (NTP) found benzaldehyde to be carcinogenic in some studies on mice.

- **Benzyl alcohol*** – a skin and eye irritant, linked with contact dermatitis and contact urticaria. Its vapours can irritate the nose and throat. In animal studies it caused lethargy, respiratory and gastrointestinal problems, haemorrhaging, liver, kidney and endocrine disruption, reproductive abnormalities and DNA damage, depending on the method of administration and dosage.

- **Camphor** – central nervous system stimulant. Symptoms from ingestion and skin absorption can include headache, confusion, vertigo, delirium, hallucinations, convulsions and coma. It may cause skin irritation. Camphor crosses the placenta and has been implicated in fetal and neonatal death.[19]

- **Cinnamal*** – a common allergen, which can cause skin sensitization and irritate the skin and mucous membranes. In animal studies cinnamal has caused liver, respiratory, gastrointestinal, reproductive and brain and nervous system effects.

- **Coumarin*** – a skin irritant that can cause contact allergies and photosensitivity. In animal studies reactions to this substance have included lung tumours, blood, liver, brain, nervous, endocrine and respiratory system effects and reproductive abnormalities. It may affect the central nervous system.

- **Ethanol** – can affect the central nervous system, cause moderate eye irritation and drying and cracking of the skin. Designated as hazardous waste by the EPA. Exposure to ethanol via inhalation can result in difficulty breathing, respiratory irritation, headache, drowsiness and fatigue.

- **Ethyl acetate** – can cause irritation of the skin, eyes, nose and throat. Acute intoxication can cause impaired motor coordination, slurred speech, drowsiness, rapid pulse, sweating and coma.

- **Eugenol*** – can cause contact dermatitis, skin irritation, inhibition of peripheral sensory nerve activity at low doses and result in neurotoxicity at high doses.[20] There is limited evidence of the carcinogenicity of eugenol.

- **Furfural (2-furaldehyde)** – can cause central nervous system depression, skin, eye and respiratory tract irritation, irritant dermatitis and skin sensitization. It is phototoxic, toxic by inhalation and ingestion and a confirmed animal carcinogen. Occupational exposures have been associated with chronic bronchitis.

- **Geraniol*** – can cause contact allergies and skin irritation. On exposure to the air it has the potential to autoxidize (oxidation in the presence of oxygen) and form incredibly allergenic compounds.[21]

- **Limonene*** – toxic to the immune system and can cause skin and respiratory irritation, sensitization and contact dermatitis. Limonene is very toxic to aquatic organisms and dangerous for the environment, according to its EC classification.

- **Methylene chloride** – was banned from hairsprays in 1989 by the FDA but is still found in perfumes. It is considered as hazardous waste by the EPA and listed as a toxic substance under Section 313 of the Emergency Planning and Community Right to Know Act. Direct contact with methylene chloride causes burning and reddening of the skin and corneal burns. Occupational overexposure has caused worker deaths. Acute exposure has caused organ damage and cancer in experimental animals. It can adversely affect the central nervous system and cardiovascular system.

- **Resorcinol** – immune system and potential skin toxicant, with limited evidence of carcinogenicity and endocrine disruption. Can cause contact dermatitis and is irritating to the mucous membranes. It is classified by the EC as harmful if swallowed, irritating to the eyes and skin, very toxic to aquatic organisms and dangerous for the environment. Absorption can cause convulsions and death.

- **Styrene oxide** – harmful if swallowed or inhaled and can cause skin irritation and corrosion and eye irritation. It is reasonably anticipated to be a human carcinogen by the National Toxicology Program (NTP), based on evidence of carcinogenicity in experimental animals. It is reported to be a central nervous system depressant.

- **Toluene** – can cause central nervous system depression, respiratory irritation and cardiac affects. Designated as hazardous waste by the EPA. High levels can potentially damage the kidneys. It is listed on California's Proposition 65 as a reproductive toxicant. It can be contaminated with the carcinogen benzene.

- **Vanillin** – has irritation and sensitization potential. It is an eye and respiratory tract irritant. Ingestion of high concentrations in animals caused acute toxaemia and death. Long-term inhalation caused toxic effects.

*Labelled in the EU on cosmetic products.

Preservatives

Along with fragrances, preservatives are one of the primary cosmetic causes of contact dermatitis. Preservatives are used in cosmetic products containing water to protect the product from becoming contaminated with microbes that might otherwise cause infections. Parabens are the most commonly used preservatives, followed by Kathon CG, which consists primarily of methylchloroisothiazolinone and methylisothiazolinone. Kathon CG and many other preservatives have been identified as contact allergens and sensitizers. Research has suggested that most instances of contact allergy are caused by applying moisturizing creams to slightly damaged skin.[22]

Chemical nasty: Kathon CG

Isothiazolinone-derived biocides, such as Kathon CG (primarily consisting of methylisothiazolinone and methychloroisothiazolinone) are commonly used as anti-microbials in cosmetics and industrial settings. In occupational situations isothiazolinone-derived agents have caused chemical burns, contact dermatitis and skin sensitization.[23]

Kathon CG, often used in cosmetic formulations such as moisturizers, body and sun tanning lotions and some shampoos, surfactants and conditioners, is a potent skin sensitizer[24] and frequent cause of contact dermatitis in Europe, mainly occurring through the use of moisturizers containing the substance on slightly damaged rather than healthy skin.[22] A study addressing the sensitization to preservatives in 811 Italian children with atopic dermatitis or other eczema found that 4.9 per cent demonstrated a reaction to Kathon CG.[25]

A 1992 Cosmetic Ingredient Review (CIR) safety assessment of methylisothiazolinone and methychloroisothiazolinone found them to be highly toxic to rats when administered orally and moderately toxic when applied to the skin. Pregnant rabbits were force fed the compound, which was shown to be embryotoxic (adversely affecting the growth or development of the embryo) and fetotoxic (toxic to the fetus in the womb). It also caused dose-dependent skin irritation in human volunteers.[26]

It is not just skin irritation that is a problem with Kathon CG; it may also have a harmful effect on brain cells; this is called neurotoxicity. Methylisothiazolinone was linked to neuron cell death in a study on rat brain cells conducted in 2002 by the Department of Neurobiology, University of Pittsburgh School of Medicine. The study's authors concluded that 'There is no question that in addition to the many known cases of occupational exposure to these compounds [i.e. isothiazolinones], a significant portion of the general population is being constantly exposed to low levels of these compounds, which are potent neurotoxins.'[23]

Some cosmetics may contain formaldehyde as a preservative in small concentrations, or release formaldehyde as a degradation product. Formaldehyde is a carcinogen and a common contact allergen, sensitizer and respiratory irritant. Almost 20 per cent of the population may have a strong reaction to low concentrations of formaldehyde (0.25 ppm).[27] Preservatives that are formaldehyde releasers include diazolidinyl urea, DMDM hydantoin, imidazolidinyl urea, quaternium-15, 2-bromo-2-nitropropane-1,3-diol (bronopol), sodium hydroxymethylglycinate and benzylhemiformal.

Is your bath giving you the itch?

Soaking in the bath leaves the skin, urogenital and anal areas exposed to the harsh agents (such as SLS) used in shampoos, bubble baths, soaps and other such products. This can trigger urinary tract infections in sensitive individuals (particularly babies and children) by stripping away the delicate protective mucus that lines the genitourinary tract. The FDA has received numerous complaints from consumers about itches, rashes and urinary tract problems following the use of bubble baths and soaps. In the USA children's foaming bath products must bear the following warning: 'Caution: Use only as directed. Excessive or prolonged exposure may cause irritation to skin and urinary tract. Discontinue if rash, redness or itching occurs. Consult your physician if irritation persists. Keep out of reach of children.'[28]

Chemical nasty: Sodium lauryl sulphate

Sodium lauryl sulphate (SLS) is reported to be the most frequent cause of eye irritation by commercial shampoos.[29] It is used in a range of personal care and household products as a cleansing agent and is also used as an industrial degreasant and floor cleaner. Sodium lauryl sulphate can damage the protective outer layer of the skin (stratum corneum) and is 'known to penetrate the skin and cause cutaneous irritation'.[30] Researchers at the Department of Dermatology, School of Medicine, University of California, found that sodium lauryl sulphate penetrated the skin directly to a depth of 5–6 mm (¼ inch) and deeper transference occurred via systemic redistribution (redistribution throughout the bodily systems). It was suggested that underlying tissues, including the dermis, subcutaneous layers and muscle 'may be exposed to high levels of SLS'.[30] Seven days after a single application of SLS to a hairless rat, traces of the agent were identified in tissues.

Sodium lauryl sulphate and other surfactants (short for surface active agent) are commonly used in laboratory testing on humans and animals to induce skin irritation as a point of reference to measure the healing or modifying properties of other substances or to increase the penetration of other substances. As the *Handbook of Detergents* notes, 'surfactants may allow other toxicants to penetrate the skin'.[31] One study showed that 4 per cent SLS applied to the skin increased its permeability, with exposure to SLS at a concentration as low as 0.25 per cent for two hours enabling nickel to penetrate the skin.[31] Repeated exposure to SLS can cause contact dermatitis in some individuals.

Toothpastes often contain SLS, even though it has been reported to irritate the mucous membranes in the mouth, 'especially in individuals predisposed to recurrent mouth ulcers'.[32]

When SLS undergoes ethoxylation to form the less abrasive detergent sodium laureth sulphate, the probable carcinogen 1,4-dioxane can be formed. Sodium laureth sulphate is milder than sodium lauryl sulphate but can still cause skin irritation, especially in those who have pre-existing skin conditions.

A hair-raising experience

Numerous hair dye ingredients are also potent irritants, allergens and sensitizers, with some consumers reporting hair loss, burning, redness and irritation from hair dye use.[33] Hair dyes sold in the EU containing phenylenediamines, resorcinol and 1-naphthol must carry the cautionary statement, 'Can cause allergic reaction. Do not use to colour eyelashes or eyebrows.' In a memorandum published in March 2007 the Scientific Committee on Consumer Products (SCCP) – a scientific advisory body to the European Commission – assessed and ranked the skin-sensitizing potential of 46 hair dye substances, and noted that a high proportion were found to be skin sensitizers. The European Commission has also acknowledged that further epidemiological studies are needed to examine the extent of skin allergies to hair dyes in the EU population.[34] Aside from the synthetic chemicals briefly outlined here there are a plethora of other substances used in cosmetic products that can potentially cause allergic reactions. The following table names a few of them.

Substances that can potentially cause allergic reactions	
Chemical ingredient	**Commonly found in**
Alpha hydroxy acids (AHAs)	Moisturizers, cleansers, eye cream, sunscreen, foundations
Ammonium thioglycolate	Hair relaxer, perm and straightener, depilatories
Azo dyes	Hair dyes and cosmetics
Benzalkonium chloride	Eye drops, cleansers, moisturizers, acne treatment, sunscreen, baby lotion, hair conditioner
Benzophenone-3 (oxybenzone)	Sunscreen and other products with spf (sun protection factor)

Butylated hydroxyanisole (BHA)	Lipstick and lip liner, moisturizers, eyeshadow and eye liner, skin lightener, anti-ageing products, concealer
Butylated hydroxytoluene (BHT)	Lipstick, moisturizers, concealer, foundation, anti-ageing products, antiperspirant/deodorant, fragrance
Cetrimonium bromide	Cleansers, conditioner, moisturizers, exfoliants, styling gel, acne treatment, aftershave
Cetrimonium chloride	Hair dyes and bleaching products, conditioner, styling gel, shampoo, hair relaxer, hairspray, scalp treatment
Cinnamates	Sunscreen and other products with spf such as moisturizers and lip balm; lipstick, foundation, styling gel
Cocamide DEA	Shampoo, body wash, cleansers, dandruff treatment, bubble bath, liquid hand soap, bath oil, hair relaxer, exfoliants, hair dyes and bleaches
Cocamidopropyl betaine	Body wash, shampoo, cleansers, hair dyes and bleaching products, bubble bath, exfoliants, liquid hand soap, acne treatment, toothpaste, conditioner
Colourants (e.g. 2,5-toluenediamine, 3,4-toluenediamine, acid blue 9, acid orange 3, acid yellow 6, FD&C Red 2, FD&C Blue 2, paraphenylenediamine, resorcinol)	Make-up (lipstick, eyeshadow, face powder etc.) and hair dyes
Coumarin	Acne treatments, deodorants, cleansers, skin fresheners, moisturizers, hand cream, body firming lotion, hair dyes, fragrance, sunscreens, soaps, tanning products, shampoos
Diazolidinyl urea	Moisturizers, cleansers, sunscreen, styling gel, conditioner, acne treatment, shampoo, eye cream
Dihydroxyacetone	Tanning products, sunscreen, moisturizers, bronzer, skin lightener
Disodium cocoamphodipropionate	Hair dyes and bleaching products, shampoo, hair relaxer, cleansers, hair conditioner, styling gel, exfoliants, body wash, foundation
DMDM hydantoin	Shampoo, hair conditioner, body wash, moisturizers, styling gel, cleansers, anti-ageing products, sunscreen

Formaldehyde	Nail treatment, hair colour and bleaching products
Iodopropynyl butylcarbamate	Moisturizers, sunscreen, shampoo, cleansers, styling gel, anti-ageing products, body wash, baby wipes
Lanolin	Lipstick, lip balm, lip gloss, foundation, moisturizers, hair conditioner, styling gel, foundation
Para-aminobenzoic acid (PABA)	Shampoo, conditioner, hair-loss treatment, body wash, exfoliants, moisturizers, cleansers, some sunscreens
Parabens	Moisturizers, anti-ageing products, cleansers, lipstick, sunscreen, foundation, eyeshadow, lip gloss
Phthalates (dibutyl phthalate, benzyl butyl phthalate and diethyl phthalate banned in EU)	Nail polish, nail treatment and cuticle treatment; fragrance
Polyethylene glycol (PEG) compounds	Numerous skincare products; hair dyes and bleaching products; shampoo and conditioner; make-up
Propylene glycol	Moisturizers, hair dyes and bleaching products, anti-ageing products, hair conditioner, shampoo, body wash, sunscreen
Salicylates	Sunscreen, fragrance, hair dyes and bleaches, moisturizers, styling gel, body wash
Thimerosal	Mascara and other eye make-up (not commonly used)
Turpentine	Fragrance

Contact dermatitis

Contact dermatitis refers to a form of skin inflammation related to eczema that is caused by external substances coming into contact with the skin. It is reported to affect 5–9 per cent of men and 13–15 per cent of women.[35] When substances directly act on the skin causing irritation and inflammation it is known as **irritant contact dermatitis**, which is the most common type. Irritant contact dermatitis is particularly common among hairdressers, due to the surfactants, preservatives, fragrances and colours used in shampoos and conditioners.[36] Where an immune hyper-sensitivity reaction takes place (i.e. the immune system provokes a skin reaction), it is referred to as **allergic contact dermatitis**.

Contact urticaria is an instant reaction to a substance that causes severely itchy welts (swellings on the skin surrounded by redness). This can be either an irritant or an allergic reaction and it is believed that the irritant form can promote the onset of the allergic form.[37]

Irritant contact dermatitis commonly causes itching, swelling, oozing, dryness and crusting. Allergic contact dermatitis normally only takes place in the area of the skin that is exposed to the allergen and occurs as a result of repeated exposure to a substance, which instigates an immune system reaction that causes the skin to become inflamed. The reaction may not take place until one or two days after exposure. Fragrances and preservatives such as formaldehyde are known causes of irritant contact dermatitis. It usually subsides once the offending products are no longer used.

There are different types of reaction within the two broad definitions of irritant and allergic contact dermatitis I have provided. Looking at irritant contact dermatitis, for example, subjective irritancy refers to stinging and burning responses that take place within a short space of time (usually minutes) and is often precipitated by cosmetics or chemicals used in sunscreens. Acute irritant contact dermatitis is frequently initiated by extreme exposure to corrosive and highly concentrated substances, such as occupational work chemicals. Chronic cumulative irritancy usually occurs through repeated exposure to milder cleansing irritants such as detergents, soaps and skin cleansers (wet agents).[38]

Research carried out between 1977 and 1983, found that skin and hair care products and facial make-up were responsible for the majority of cosmetic dermatitis reactions in participants studied. The most common allergic sensitizers in the correct order were: fragrance, the preservatives quaternium-15, formaldehyde, imidazolidinyl urea and parabens, plus p-phenylenediamine and glyceryl monothioglycolate.[39]

Some chemicals associated with contact dermatitis

Acetic acid
Acrylates
Alkylphenols
Aluminium compounds
Aminophenols

Ammonium thioglycolate
Benzaldehyde
Benzoyl peroxide
Benzyl alcohol
Bronopol
Butane
Butylated hydroxyanisole
Butylated hydroxytoluene
Butylene glycol
Chlorhexidine
Chloroxylenol
Cinnamal
Cinnamyl alcohol
Citral
Citronellol
Cocamide DEA
Cocamide MEA
Cocamidopropyl betaine
Diazolidinyl urea
Diethanolamine (DEA)
DMDM hydantoin
Ethanolamine
Eugenol
Formaldehyde
Geraniol
Hexyl cinnamal
Hexylene glycol
Hydroquinone
Hydroxycitronellal
Imidazolidinyl urea
Isobutane
Isoeugenol
Kathon CG
Lanolin
Limonene
Linalool
Methylparaben
Mineral oil
PEG compounds
p-phenylenediamine
Propane
Propylene glycol

Sodium hydroxide
Sodium lauryl sulphate
Sulisobenzone
Thimerosol
Thioglycolic acid
Toluene
Triclosan
Xylene

Hair dyes and contact dermatitis

Severe cases of facial and scalp dermatitis have been reported through the application of permanent hair dyes. Chemical solutions used to highlight hair can corrode the scalp in some cases.[40]

One incredibly potent cause of allergic contact dermatitis in humans is a hair colourant called paraphenylenediamine (PPD), also referred to as p-phenylenediamine, used in permanent hair dyes.[41] This substance was prohibited for use in hair dyes in Germany, France and Sweden in the 20th century, because concerns developed about its damaging health effects. PPD is not approved for direct application to the skin,[42] yet when hair dye is applied it usually does come into contact with the scalp and very often the forehead and ears. According to Dr John P McFadden, senior lecturer at St John's Institute of Dermatology, patients with contact allergies to hair dyes often have dermatitis around the face or hairline and sometimes facial swelling is so severe that the patients must be hospitalized. He also highlights the growing number of individuals suffering allergic reactions to PPD in patch tests.[43] A survey of one London contact dermatitis clinic, where eczema patients were patch tested for reactions to PPD, found that allergy to the substance had almost doubled from 4.2 per cent in January 1999 to 7.1 per cent in December 2004. The study's authors state that the 'disturbing' increase in positive reactions to PPD over the six-year period where research took place 'may be due to subjects dyeing their hair in increasing numbers and perhaps at an earlier age'.[44] Patch testing data from other countries such as Belgium, Portugal, Denmark, Germany and Singapore support this pattern. Dr McFadden writes in the *British Medical Journal* that more than one million Thai adults and 1.3 million adults in Germany may be sensitive to PPD.[43]

Of those individuals who are allergic to PPD, 10 per cent also react to semi-permanent hair dyes. Those who have a sensitivity to PPD may also develop a cross-sensitivity to azo and aniline dyes (used in hair dyes, ballpoint pen inks, petrol, diesel oil and as a colorant in foods and medications), benzocaine and procaine (used in local anaesthetics), para-aminobenzoic acid (PABA – used in sunscreens and some face creams), para-aminosalicylic acid (used in tuberculosis treatment), sulphonamides (used in pharmaceutical drugs), carbutamide (used in diabetes medication) and hydrodiuril (a diuretic medication).[45]

According to the Scientific Committee on Consumer Products (SCCP) PPD sensitizes 100 per cent of laboratory animals used in predictive allergenicity testing at high enough concentrations.[46] When one particular study advertised for individuals suffering from adverse reactions to hair dye, 55 people with severe allergic contact dermatitis came forward. In some cases swelling of the scalp, ears and face was so acute that the people were originally treated for angio-oedema (allergic reaction causing swellings beneath the skin) and some had had to be admitted into hospital. The study concluded that this substance presents a significant health risk for the population,[47] yet it is authorized in hair dyes in concentrations of up to 6 per cent in the EU and 4 per cent in the US.

Did you know?

Abrasive substances are used in exfoliants, such as talc, fruit pits, crushed nutshells and aluminium oxide (in the case of microdermabrasion) to soften or remove the stratum corneum. The International Dermal Institute 'do not recommend the use of crushed fruit pits, shells or similar damaging substrates', due to their ability to cause skin irritation.[48] Dr Sandy Tsao, an instructor of dermatology at Harvard Medical School, points out that removing the stratum corneum leaves the skin vulnerable to sunburn, wrinkles, age spots and cancerous legions.[49] Aggressively rubbing exfoliating products onto the skin can cause broken capillaries and tiny skin fissures.

Skin lighteners

An increasing number of women are using skin lighteners either in an attempt to obtain lighter skin, or to lighten freckles, liver spots and age spots, or other hyperpigmented areas of skin. Skin lightening creams are incredibly popular in numerous African countries and amongst African-American and Asian women. Leading industry sources claim that up to 60 per cent of Japanese women use skin whitening products[50] while research conducted in 2004 by Synovate revealed that 38 per cent of 2,496 women surveyed in Hong Kong, Korea, Malaysia, the Philippines and Taiwan use skin lightening products.

Skin bleaching agents often use the chemical hydroquinone to decrease the skin's production of melanin, which gives skin its brown colour. However, melanin plays a vital role in protecting the skin from ultraviolet radiation. Hydroquinone is also known to cause cancer in laboratory animals, contact dermatitis in some cases, skin irritation and abnormal skin darkening.

The US Environmental Protection Agency (EPA) conducted research that found that this substance could cause skin tumours in mice exposed dermally[51] and the US National Toxicology Program identified carcinogenic activity in rats and female mice exposed to hydroquinone.[52] In high doses it can result in a disfiguring skin condition referred to as exogenous ochronosis, in which the skin progressively darkens and the collagen and elastin fibres degenerate. This condition has occurred following the use of 2 per cent hydroquinone, but in the US prescription skin lightening creams can contain up to 4 per cent of this agent. Occupational exposure to hydroquinone has caused eye injuries and impaired vision, and exposure to strong sunlight after using lightening products containing hydroquinone can reverse the effects of the cream.

In January 2001 the EU banned the use of hydroquinone for over-the-counter cosmetic products, restricting its use to prescription products used under medical supervision, and other countries have also restricted its use. However, this has not stopped hydroquinone-containing skin lightening products being made and sold illegally in the UK, as well as being exported from the UK to countries such as Nigeria, Ghana, Tanzania, Zimbabwe and South Africa.[53] Early in 2007 a couple in the UK were fined £100,000 and given a nine-month prison sentence each for selling skin whiteners to the value of £1 million.[54]

Illegal skin whitening creams often also contain steroids and mercury – a toxic chemical that affects the central nervous system, causing tremors, emotional alterations, insomnia, headaches and disturbed kidney function when inhaled, and which has been linked to reproductive toxicity, neuro-toxicity and cancer.

The prohibitions and restrictions on hydroquinone have led to an increasing reliance on other skin lightening agents, such as kojic acid, which has caused cancer when administered orally in studies on mice and rats,[55] and can result in skin irritation and contact dermatitis. In 2003 kojic acid was banned for use in cosmetic products in Japan, following a 1999 study that found that kojic acid fed to rats in high doses interrupted thyroid function and increased the production of thyroid stimulating hormone (TSH), causing enlargement of the thyroid glands.[56] Animal studies have also demonstrated that kojic acid can cause embryo and systemic toxicity. Kojic acid was also found to be genotoxic (able to cause damage to DNA that can lead to malignant tumours) in vitro by the International Agency for Research on Cancer (IARC).[57] Korea and Switzerland followed Japan's example by banning the substance as a cosmetic ingredient.

Did you know?

Astringent lotions intended for oily or acne-prone skin often consist of high concentrations of the alcohols ethanol and isopropanol (which are penetration enhancers), and include agents that exfoliate the skin, such as salicylic acid (used in the manufacture of aspirin), another penetration enhancer, that can also irritate the skin, eyes and respiratory tract. It has also caused reproductive and developmental toxicity in some animal studies and can increase the risk posed by UV radiation by stripping away the protective stratum corneum. Although astringent lotions tend to be aimed at those with oily/acne-prone skin, removing the skin's natural sebum can actually lead to the pores secreting excess oil as the skin attempts to counteract the loss of moisture, as well as more readily exposing the skin to bacterial and environmental assaults. Astringents can also alter the skin's pH level.

Protected by labelling? – The truth about 'hypoallergenic' and 'dermatologist tested'

If you have sensitive skin you may well choose products bearing these labels in the hope that your risk of experiencing any irritation will be reduced. 'Hypoallergenic' and 'dermatologist tested' are two frequently used terms – but unfortunately they may bear little or no relation to the product at hand.

As the *Manual of Dermatologic Therapeutics* clearly states, 'The term hypoallergenic does not necessarily imply that there are fewer antigens present. Any product may legally call itself hypoallergenic.'[58] In the House of Lords Select Committee on Science and Technology, Sixth Report on allergies, published in 2007, Professor Gawkrodger stressed in evidence submitted to the Committee, 'There is no regulation on the term "hypoallergenic" [and when these products are examined] I see a whole list of things which I know can cause allergy, so I am rather cynical about the label of hypoallergenic.'[59] Nearly 20 years ago the US FDA attempted to set standards for the use of this claim but two high profile brands challenged the suggested regulation and the proposal was dropped.

Again, 'dermatologist tested' can be a meaningless statement. It may simply be the case that a small number of individuals claiming to have sensitive skin have been patch tested and demonstrated no reaction to the product. The testing may not be scientifically valid and there is no guarantee that it will not cause reactions in others. As the Select Committee report remarks, 'the allergenicity of a substance is dependent on an individual person's response and their tendency to develop allergies'.[59]

In 2004 the product testing and campaigning charity 'Which?' wrote to ten leading UK cosmetics companies asking for evidence to back up their claims and an explanation for the use of claims such as 'dermatologist tested'. Eight companies replied and explained that such claims referred to tests intended to provide reassurance to consumers about product safety, but although general information about the tests was provided, none of the companies would provide specific details of trials conducted or test results.[60] 'Which?' did ask two expert dermatologists to examine the information provided to assess its validity, but because it was incomplete they were unable to do this comprehensively.

In the US manufacturers are not required to have *any* evidence to back up their claims.

Take home message

If you are experiencing any kind of skin irritation check the ingredients list on your personal care products. In particular look out for and avoid any products containing fragrance, the preservatives

quaternium-15, formaldehyde, imidazolidinyl urea and parabens, plus *p*-phenylenediamine and glyceryl monothioglycolate.

Photosensitivity

Photosensitivity is an abnormal sensitivity to ultraviolet (UV) radiation, or sunlight. It can be the result of a genetic predisposition, whereby the body cannot repair skin damage caused by exposure to sunlight or certain chemicals. The primary types are phototoxicity and photoallergy.

Phototoxicity (a non-immunologic reaction) occurs when skin exposed to sunlight or other UV radiation becomes damaged as a result of photoactive chemicals (chemicals that are able to absorb UV radiation) entering the viable (living) elements of skin and reacting under UV light to bring about cellular damage. The main symptom of phototoxicity is sunburn, which can lead to severe blistering. Acute phototoxic reactions include erythema (skin redness produced by capillary congestion), oedema (swelling caused by fluid in the body tissues), leading to hyper-pigmentation (where patches of skin grow darker in colour than the surrounding skin), and even skin cancer. The FDA have reported the discovery of potentially phototoxic agents in deodorants, antibacterial soaps, artificial sweeteners, cadmium sulphide (chemical injected into the skin during tattooing) and fluoroscent brightening agents for cellulose, nylon and wool fibres, mothballs and petroleum products.[61]

Photoallergy (an immunologic reaction) occurs on re-exposure to a chemical to which the individual has previously become sensitized. It is often characterized by an intense, eczema-like skin rash on exposure to sunlight. In a photoallergic reaction substances either made by the body or from outside are transformed by UV radiation into antigens (substances that prompt your immune system to generate antibodies against them).[62] Symptoms can appear within 20 seconds of being exposed to sunlight, although they may also be delayed.

The once commonly used sunscreen ingredient para-aminobenzoic acid (PABA) is known to cause photoallergic reactions, as are cinnamates, avobenzone, oxybenzone, padimate O, benzoylmethanes, musk ambrette and sandalwood oil. In fact, there are numerous cosmetic ingredients that have now been shown to cause phototoxicity. Research published in the scientific journal *Food and Chemical Toxicology* found that under sunlight six lipsticks and five facial creams generated reactive oxygen species (products of normal metabolism that can damage cell structures if levels become too high in the body), triggered haemolysis (the breakdown of red blood cells) and caused lipid peroxidation (cell damage caused by free radicals stealing electrons from fats in cell membranes).[63] It is thought that lipid peroxidation may play a vital role in certain aspects of the ageing process.[64]

Given that many ingredients used in cosmetics are marketed as anti-ageing miracles, it seems somewhat ironic that some of them can break down into toxic chemicals under UV light. Retinyl palmitate, a vitamin A derivative touted as an anti-ageing ingredient, decomposed under UVA light into chemicals that have been shown to be photomutagenic in mouse lymphoma cells.[65] Other vitamin A derivatives can also cause phototoxic reactions. The research authors concluded that repeated use of products containing phototoxic agents may lead to skin ageing, along with other problems such as erythema, oedema and photomutation (UV radiation-induced damage to DNA or sequence of a gene).

Bronopol (2-bromo-2-nitropropane-1,3-diol), used as a preservative and antiseptic in cosmetics, toiletries and topical medications, has been shown to be phototoxic in vitro, depending on the UV doses administered and concentration of the compound.[66] This suggests that it could potentially cause photosensitization when applied dermally.

Certain suntan accelerators and perfumes contain bergapten (or 5-methoxypsoralen), a phototoxic component of bergamot oil that can cause berloque dermatitis, a skin condition characterized by discoloration of the skin. According to one study, bergapten accounts for around 67 per cent of the absorption of UVA and UVB light by bergamot oil.[67]

Alpha hydroxy acids (AHAs), also commonly referred to as fruit acids, such as glycolic acid, malic acid, lactic acid and salicylic acid, have been lauded for their alleged 'anti-ageing' activity, because of their ability to remove the outer layer of skin revealing a 'younger looking you'. But they can also cause photosensitivity. In one study the AHA glycolic acid elevated the sensitivity of human skin to sunburn by as much as 50 per cent in some individuals.[68]

Other topically applied substances with phototoxic potential include: certain dyes (such as anthraquinone, Disperse Blue 35 and cosin dyes), fragrances, plant products (such as figs, limes, parsnips, fennel and dill) and coal tar components (such as acridine, anthracene, phenanthrene and pyridine). Certain pharmaceutical preparations such as particular antidepressants, antihistamines, antibiotics, antipsychotics, antiparasitics, diuretics, hypoglycaemics, non-steroidal anti-inflammatory drugs (NSAIDS), chemotherapy drugs and oral contraceptives can also cause photosensitivity. Various essential oils, such as bergamot and sandalwood (as mentioned above), citron, lavender and cedar can cause photosensitivity, as can the herb St John's wort.

Did you know?

Our staid styling friend, hairspray, pretty much glues our wispy strands together with 'liquid plastic', and perhaps worse. When you push that little button on an aerosol hairspray beads of polymer drip onto your hair shafts and bind them together, keeping your hair in a fixed position. Some individuals, having experienced repeat exposures to hairspray, suffer from symptoms such as acute upper respiratory infections, shortness of breath, frequent colds, chronic cough, and in certain instances, X-ray abnormalities.[69]

Asthma

Asthma is a common condition affecting the respiratory system. In the UK, as of July 2007, one adult in 13 was undergoing treatment for asthma,[70] and it is the most common chronic disease of childhood in the developed world.[71] In asthma sufferers, the airways that transport air into and out of the lungs become sensitive when they come into contact with something that causes them irritation (asthma trigger), such as allergens, cold, warm or moist air, exercise or emotional stress. This leads them to tighten and the muscles around them to constrict, resulting in inflamma-tion of the lining of the airways and often the overproduction of mucus or phlegm. The outcome is difficulty getting enough breath, causing symptoms such as wheezing, coughing and chest tightness.

Perfumes can trigger asthma attacks in some individuals and one very potent respiratory irritant is toluene, used in nail products, fragrances and other household products.[72] An Australian study investigating the link between domestic exposure to volatile organic compounds (VOCs) and asthma in young children found that toluene is a significant risk factor for asthma.[71] In 1991 toluene was added to Proposition 65 in the State of California as toxic to reproduction and some occupational exposures to toluene have been linked to spontaneous abortion or offspring with birth defects.[73] According to the US Environmental Protection Agency (EPA), the highest concentrations of toluene usually occur in indoor air from common household products, such as paints, paint thinners, synthetic fragrances and nail polish, as well as cigarette smoke.[73]

Benzene, a solvent sometimes used in nail polish removers and perfumes, and ethylbenzene, predominantly used to make styrene and in the production of rubber and plastic wrapping, were the strongest asthma triggers in the aforementioned Australian study, in that order. Benzene is a known carcinogen and has been shown to cause blood disorders, damaged bone marrow, aplastic anaemia, DNA damage and leukaemia in occupational settings. It is banned for use in cosmetic products in the EU and Canada.

Ammonium thioglycolate is used as a hair straightening agent, anti-oxidant and depilatory in hair-waving and straightening products, and in hair removing products. In an exposure study, 14 patients with asthma inhaled mists of ammonium thioglycolate at various concentrations. It was found that it caused asthmatic breathing, an uncontrollable cough and blocked nasal passages or nasal drip in 13 of the 14 patients.[74]

People who are exposed to high concentrations of chemicals on a regular basis through their employment can face higher risks of developing respiratory problems or exacerbating already existing conditions. Hairdressers, for example, are occupationally exposed to a wide variety of irritating and allergenic chemicals and have an increased risk of developing asthma and other respiratory symptoms.[75-77] In a 2002 study of hairdressers in Sweden, the hairdressers who most frequently conducted hair bleaching treatments or used hairspray had a slightly higher incidence of asthma, although the study states that the results are not conclusive.[78]

Other substances linked with asthma and lung disease include the following:

- **Persulphate salts** (sodium and potassium sulphate) added to hair bleaches to accelerate the bleaching processes can cause occupational asthma along with other respiratory problems and skin conditions.
- **PVP (polyvinylpyrrolidone)** or its co-polymers, used in many hairsprays to coat the hair, can cause lung diseases such as thesaurosis, a condition that arises out of the body storing up excessive amounts of a normal or foreign substance in the lungs, with PVP being discovered in lesions in the lungs and lymph nodes.
- Amines such as **paraphenylenediamine** and **ethylenediamine** used in the cosmetic and hair dye industries can cause occupational asthma.[79]
- Some **synthetic musks** can also promote asthma and accumulate in breast milk.
- Many other chemicals such as acetaldehyde, acetic acid, acrylates, aluminium powder, ammonia, benzoates, bisulphites, chlorhexidene, ethanolamines, fragrance materials, propane and quaternary ammonium compounds.

Take home messages

- If you suffer from asthma check the chemicals in your hairsprays, mousses and other setting agents. They may be aggravating your condition.

- Don't ignore any kind of skin reaction to a personal care product, however small. Stop using the product immediately. Be aware that what appears at first to be a minor reaction can become more severe with continued use of the product.

- Hair dyes are the most common cause of skin reactions. If you dye your own hair seek out natural dyes, always perform a patch test for any allergic reactions before dyeing your hair and check the dyes your hairdresser uses.

Chapter 3
The C word – Cancer

Did you know?

- In the USA the probability that an individual will develop or die from cancer over the course of a lifetime is one in two for men and one in three for women.

- Most cancers are not the result of inherited genes but from damage (mutation) to genes that takes place during an individual's lifetime.[1]

- Between 1973 and 1998 in the USA, breast cancer incidences rose by more than 40 per cent, and today a woman's lifetime risk of breast cancer is one in 8.2[2]

Cancer is the word everyone fears. It is the second leading cause of death in the USA after heart disease, and around one in four deaths in Europe are as a result of cancer. But what causes cancer and is there any evidence that over-use of certain personal care products might increase the risk of cancer developing? This chapter explores the latest research and examines the evidence.

The term 'cancer' refers to a cluster of diseases in which normal cells multiply beyond normal growth mechanisms, generating millions of similar self-multiplying cells that spread beyond their usual area (metastasis). There are over 100 types of cancer.

It is thought that every cancer develops from a single cell inheriting or acquiring DNA damage and failing to respond to normal processes that control growth. In the absence of control its offspring develop and multiply to create a tumour. In normal cells any damage acquired is repaired and the cells return to normal; if the damage cannot be repaired the cells do not divide. But in cancer cells there are cell cycle errors that are allowed to replicate.[3]

Research has revealed that two steps are needed for cancer to develop: initiation and promotion. In the initiation step a genetic change occurs in a cell. This may be something that you are born with or may be created by initiators such as viruses, hormones, chronic inflammation within the body, or exogenous (external) agents such as radiation, carcinogens (cancer-causing chemicals, biological or physical agents). In the second step promoters bring about rapid cell growth before the cell has had the chance to repair the DNA damage. Cancer promoters include chronic inflammation, radiation, hormones and environmental chemicals. It has also been suggested that extremely low-frequency electromagnetic fields (ELF-EMFs) may play a part in cancer promotion,[4] as does a high-fat diet and excess calorie intake.

It can take up to 20 years for cancer to appear after exposure to an initiator. If an individual is not exposed to many promoters, it may never materialize. Once the cancerous growth no longer requires exposure to a promoter, it grows independently (the progression phase). Sometimes two or more substances interact, heightening each other's effects and leading to more cancers than would be produced by the sum of the two substances' individual effects. This process is known as synergism. Exposure to certain occupational chemicals and smoking, or alcohol consumption and smoking, would be examples of this.

Environmental or genetic?

Studies have shown that environmental factors play a huge part in the onset of cancer, with only around 5 per cent of cases being genetically predisposed.[1] Environmental factors from this perspective can incorporate anything that people are exposed to, such as substances consumed, smoking, natural and medical forms of radiation, including exposure to the sun, workplace exposures, drugs, social and economic factors and substances existing in the air, water and soil.[5] In addition, ageing, alcohol, infections, hormonal factors, pollution, lack of exercise, sexual behaviour that elevates exposure to particular viruses and consumer products are all implicated in various types of cancers to different degrees.

Did you know?

Cosmetic products may contain toxic elements, such as metals, as impurities. A Finnish study found that 85 per cent of the eyeshadows assessed contained over 5 parts per million (ppm) of at least one of the metals lead, cobalt, nickel and chromium, plus the carcinogen arsenic. Levels of cobalt and nickel high enough to cause allergic symptoms in those previously sensitized were found in some eyeshadows, with long-term exposure to such levels being predicted to actually instigate sensitization.[6]

Chemicals and breast cancer

As the Breast Cancer Fund notes in its recent report, *State of the Evidence*, 'the increasing incidence of breast cancer over the decades following World War II paralleled the proliferation of synthetic chemicals …. An important body of scientific evidence demonstrates that exposure to common chemicals and radiation may contribute to the staggering incidences of breast cancer.'[2] Exposure to natural oestrogen present in the body during a lifetime is associated with breast cancer. Endocrine disrupting compounds (EDCs), which interfere with the actions of natural oestrogens, androgens and other hormones in the body, may present an increased breast cancer risk.[2] Scientists at the Silent Spring Institute in Massachusetts compiled scientific data linking chemicals with breast cancer and identified 216 chemicals associated with increased mammary gland tumours in animals, including industrial chemicals, chlorinated solvents, products of combustion, pesticides, dyes, radiation, pharmaceuticals, hormones, natural products and research chemicals. Almost all of the chemicals were mutagenic (capable of bringing about or increasing the frequency of mutations in an organism) and the majority caused tumours in multiple organs and species.[7]

Some of the compounds found in personal care products that have been associated with breast cancer include:

- **1,2-propylene oxide** – used as a fragrance.
- **1,3-butadiene** – plasticizer used in rubber sponges for cosmetic application. Cosmetics containers may contain this substance and it can be an impurity in butane, a propellant used in aerosol sprays.
- **1,4-dioxane** – petroleum-derived by-product of the ethoxylation process that can be present in shampoos, body wash and other foaming cosmetics as an impurity.
- **2,4-diaminoanisole sulphate** – aromatic amine used in hair dyes.
- **Benzene and other organic solvents** (such as toluene and formaldehyde) – used in nail polish, nail polish remover and perfumes.
- **Bisphenol A** – synthetic chemical used in the production of epoxy resins and polycarbonate plastics, used for food, drink and cosmetic packaging.
- **Ethylene oxide** – used in the production of non-ionic surfactants found in cleansing products; traces of this volatile chemical may remain.
- **Synthetic musks** – synthetic chemicals commonly used in a range of fragranced consumer products, including perfumes, aftershaves, cosmetics and personal care products as fragrances and fixatives.
- **n-Nitrosamines** – may be formed in cosmetic products in the presence of nitrosating agents.
- **Nonylphenol** – organic compound belonging to alkylphenol family. Can be found in various cosmetic products, although nonylphenol and nonylphenol ethoxylates have been banned for this purpose in the EU where they are classified as a hazard to health and environmental safety.
- **Parabens** – preservatives and antimicrobials commonly used in cosmetic products.
- **Phthalates** – used as plasticizers in a range of personal care and other consumer products.
- **Placental extract** – extracts from human and cow placenta found in hair conditioners, shampoos and other grooming products.
- **Polycyclic aromatic hydrocarbons** (PAHs) – common contaminants in petrolatum found in petroleum jelly, lipsticks, baby lotions and oils, and tobacco smoke (active and passive exposures).
- **Titanium dioxide** – white pigment used in sunscreens, mineral make-up and other cosmetics.

• **Triclosan** – organochlorine used as an antibacterial in soaps, tooth-pastes, mouthwash, etc.

• **Urethrane** (ethyl carbamate) – ester of carbamic acid used as a co-solvent in hair care products, sunscreens, nail polish, mascara and foundation.

Campaigners push for ban on chemicals linked to breast cancer

In the EU, campaigners have urged MEPs to strengthen chemicals legislation following a report suggesting that some chemicals may be associated with rising incidences of breast cancer. Professor Andreas Kortenkamp, head of the Centre for Toxicology at the University of London, has pointed to significant evidence that the rise in breast cancer is linked to environmental exposure to substances such as hormone-disruptive chemicals that mimic oestrogen. In the report commissioned by the health and environmental alliance HEAL and CHEM Trust, Professor Kortenkamp said:

> 'There is overwhelming evidence that oestrogens are strong determinants of breast cancer risks .... Given that natural oestrogens and man-made oestrogens used as pharmaceuticals have a role in breast cancer, concerns arise about the potential contribution of industrial chemicals and pesticides with hormonal activity.'[8]

Oestrogens occur naturally in the body and are required for breast development but they also play a role in the development of breast cancer. Natural oestrogens act on the 'end buds' of the epithelial ducts in mammary glands to promote growth. This takes place initially during the fetal stage and then again at puberty and finally during pregnancy. It is this growth of the end buds that links oestrogens to breast cancer. Oestrogens cause an increase in cells that can be prone to cancerous growth. The breast is most susceptible to cancer-causing influences during periods of growth, such as during puberty. In the womb, the mother's oestrogen levels affect the number of end buds that develop in the fetus, with higher levels of oestrogen causing more end buds to grow, and this effectively increases the cell pool from which cancer cells can be drawn.

Although Professor Kortenkamp acknowledges that numerous factors play a role in breast cancer, he continues:

> 'There is a case for relinquishing the dominant view of breast cancer as a life-style and genetic disease and for reappraising the role of environmental factors, including chemical exposures. With UK

breast cancer incidence at an all time high, risk reduction will not be achievable without considering preventable causes, particularly exposure to chemicals.'[8]

Chemical interactions

Although hormone-disrupting industrial chemicals such as polychlorinated biphenyls (PCBs) are now banned, they are still being detected in human tissues. There are also many other chemicals used in consumer products that have similar properties, including phthalates, bisphenol A, UV filters, commonly used preservatives such as parabens, and numerous others. Many of these have been found to act in a similar way to the natural sex hormone oestradiol, although the effect is much weaker.

Environmental pollutants such as PCBs and certain pesticides do not act alone, but in combination with natural oestrogens and other hormonally active chemicals in a woman's body, including chemicals released during the preparation of food (e.g. grilling meat, baking and roasting foods), cosmetic constituents (such as some synthetic fragrances, UV filters, antioxidants) and plant-derived oestrogens present in some foods. Although the hormonal strength of these chemicals is much lower than natural or pharmaceutical oestrogens, research has shown that quite a significant number of chemicals can enhance the effects of natural oestrogens.[9]

Professor Kortenkamp presented evidence that while low levels of certain individual chemicals may have no detectable impact on breast cancer, the combined additive effect of mixtures of these chemicals has a much greater impact. Testing a combination of 11 xenoestrogens (synthetic chemicals that behave like oestrogen in the human body) on the actions of the hormone oestradiol, Professor Kortenkamp found that the combined effect led to a dramatic enhancement of the hormone's action, even when each agent was present at levels that do not individually generate measurable effects.[10] Other research demonstrated that four organochlorines acted together to enhance the proliferation of human breast cancer cells, suggesting again that mixtures of certain chemicals work synergistically to produce a combined effect that is much stronger than the individual effects added together.[11]

As well as discussing the issue of chemical mixtures, Professor Kortenkamp also noted the importance of exposure levels at different times in a woman's life, such as development in the womb and puberty. Human studies have demonstrated that the daughters of women who were given the oestrogen diethylstilboestrol (DES) to lower the risk of miscarriage had an increased risk of breast cancer[12] and studies on laboratory animals have suggested that exposure to synthetic oestrogenic compounds in the womb can result in persistent alterations of the mammary gland, signifying that these compounds may increase susceptibility to breast cancer.[13,14] Professor Kortenkamp commented that the EU has funded a great deal of research on the subject but also said to *CORDIS News*, 'this is not entirely matched by an equally well founded and well thought out regulatory approach to complement this, to act on the basis of scientific evidence'.[15]

This report is currently being examined by MEPs in Brussels who are debating whether Europe-wide legislation could be used to help stall the rising incidence of breast cancer, which has increased by 50 per cent in some European countries over the last 20 years.[16]

How are cancer risks identified?

The cancer risks associated with numerous environmental chemicals are usually identified through studying individuals who are occupationally exposed to the substances at higher levels than the general public and through research conducted on experimental animals and human cells grown in a laboratory. Epidemiologists create studies to observe the effects of agents on specific human populations over a period of time and compare the results with unexposed groups of people.

Adverse effects of a particular chemical are often first identified in workers exposed to high levels through their occupation, such as painters, furniture makers and workers in the iron, coal, steel and rubber industries. There are very few epidemiological studies on carcinogenic substances used in cosmetic products because most people are exposed to the same or similar chemicals, so it is difficult to locate an 'unexposed' control group. It is also difficult to establish the health risks to humans from certain chemicals in epidemiological studies because researchers have to consider the effects of other causal agents, such as diet, smoking, radiation and other exposures. Health problems also frequently have a variety of interrelated causes and can take months or years to manifest, which makes it difficult to pinpoint the triggers.

There is ambiguity surrounding the precise role played by chemicals in cancer causation. Due to numerous interconnected factors that contribute to a person's risk of developing cancer it is not possible to accurately predict where exposure to a certain substance will definitely result in the development in cancer in a particular individual, although it is known that certain genetic and environmental factors elevate the risk of developing cancer.

In fact, experts estimate that at least 50 per cent of all cancers could be avoided by applying current knowledge of the causes, although proportioning risks to different factors is a common cause of disagreement. Exposure to a single agent may appear to be relatively low, but when you take into account that we are exposed to a myriad of carcinogens either at once or sequentially, it may not be safe at all.[17]

There are now numerous scientists who acknowledge that cancer can be drastically reduced by avoiding the introduction of carcinogenic agents into the environment in the first place and completely removing or minimizing exposure to carcinogenic agents already existing in the environment.[17]

Did you know?

Vaginal deodorants and douches can disturb the slightly acidic environment of the vagina and its population of healthy microorganisms (which helps to prevent infection). This can actually cause infections. The ingredients in vaginal deodorants are no less harsh than those used in other deodorizing products, often containing alcohol, propellants, talc, volatile silicones and the antistatic agent quaternium-18.

Douching has been linked to pelvic inflammatory disease (PID), ectopic pregnancies and infertility, as it forces pathogens into the uterus, tubes and pelvic cavity, increasing the risk of developing a serious infection that damages the tubes. A pooled relative risk from case-control studies found that women who douched regularly were at a 73 per cent higher risk of PID, a 76 per cent higher risk of having an ectopic pregnancy and potentially an 86 per cent higher risk of cervical cancer, than those who do not douche (although other risk factors may have been relevant for the cervical cancer).[18]

There is simply no need to introduce harsh agents into the sensitive genital area. Instead, eat healthily, bathe daily (but not with products containing harsh detergents), wear cotton underwear (preferably organic), to let your skin breathe and avoid wearing tight-fitting jeans or trousers.

Carcinogens in cosmetics

Mainstream beauty products contain a variety of known carcinogenic or potentially carcinogenic ingredients such as *p*-phenylenediamine, diethanolamine (DEA), acetaldehyde, certain azo and coal tar dyes, butylated hydroxyanisole (BHA), adipic acid, ethyl acrylate, organic solvents (such as formaldehyde, benzene and toluene) and lead acetate. In addition they may contain impurities in the form of nitrates, which can react with other ingredients in the product to form carcinogenic substances, for example, *N*-nitrosodiethanolamine (NDELA). Chemicals such as diazolidinyl urea, imidazolidinyl urea, DMDM hydantoin and quaternium-15 degrade to release the suspected carcinogen formaldehyde, and polyethylene glycol (PEG) can be contaminated with the carcinogens 1,4-dioxane and ethylene oxide, to name but a few.

Carcinogenic or potentially carcinogenic chemicals may only be used in cosmetic products at low concentrations, but we commonly use a myriad of such products on top of numerous other consumer products with cancer-causing ingredients. We are also exposed to many other carcinogens in our environment. Our exposure to cosmetic products is over a prolonged period of time and even prior to birth we are exposed to carcinogenic agents, through our mothers' use of cosmetic and other consumer products. For instance, in 1968 women who conceived after consuming cooking oil contaminated with polychlorinated dibenzofurans (generated from polychorinated biphenyls (PCBs)) gave birth to infants with 'oil disease' or Yusho,[19] so named because of the large-scale food poisoning incident in western Japan caused by these cooking oils.

The skin is highly permeable to toxic substances. According to Dr Samuel Epstein, chairman of the Cancer Prevention Coalition and author of *The Safe Shopper's Bible* and *Unreasonable Risk*, evidence presented at a 1978 Congressional hearing suggested that skin absorption of *N*-nitrosodiethanolamine (NDELA) is 100 times greater than absorption by mouth.[20] Dr Epstein points out that carcinogens taken in by mouth are absorbed from the intestines and transported to the liver, where they can be detoxified to different degrees, depending on the substance, but carcinogens absorbed through the skin can enter the bloodstream without this prior protective detoxification by the liver.[20]

In addition, numerous substances, known as penetration enhancers, increase the skin's absorption of toxic ingredients. The skin's outer layer (stratum corneum) is quite an effective barrier to the penetration of external substances but if it is stripped away its efficacy is lost and only re-established again after several days, when it grows back. Explicitly stated in a guide for cosmetic manufacturers is the fact that, 'many raw materials which are commonly found in cosmetic and toiletry products permeate into and through the stratum corneum; some can also act as penetration enhancers.'[21] Common penetration enhancers include sodium lauryl sulphate, polyethylene glycol (PEG), propylene glycol (PG), acetone, ceteareth compounds (including ceteareth-12 and ceteareth-20), cocoyl sarcosine, ethanol, limonene, lactic acid and disodium EDTA. A deficiency in essential fatty acids can also compromise the barrier properties of the stratum corneum.

Many studies have found that the risk of cancer developing is elevated if exposure to carcinogens begins in infancy, rather than later on in life. Young children have a greater susceptibility to carcinogens because the cells divide rapidly during childhood and if they are dividing rapidly following exposure to a carcinogen, any genetic mutation that has occurred is more likely to be fixed.[22] This all needs to be considered when looking at the potential adverse health effects of environmental exposures.

To be or not to be a carcinogen?

It would be more than a task and a half to comprehensively discuss all the known and potentially carcinogenic ingredients used in cosmetic products, but below you will find a smattering, along with a discussion on carcinogenic impurities that beauty products may contain. Concerns have also been raised in particular about the carcinogenic potential of phthalates (used as fixatives, solvents and fragrance carriers in cosmetics), certain UV filters (e.g. padimate O) and cosmetic-grade lanolin, which can be contaminated with carcinogenic pesticides such as DDT, dieldrin and lindane.

Bad hair days

As well as initiating allergic reactions in some users, permanent hair dyes have been associated with cancer risks.

A 39-year study of 38,866 female hairdressers and 6,824 male hairdressers in Sweden showed an increased risk of certain cancers. For the male hairdressers increased risks of cancer of the upper respiratory tract, lung and bowel were observed, and with the development of hair dyes in the early 1960s an increased risk of urinary bladder cancer was noticed, which then decreased as formulations were modified over the years. For the female hairdressers an increased risk of cancer of the pancreas, lung, cervix and skin, specifically affecting the scalp and neck which are typical contact areas for hair dyes, was found.[23] In research carried out between 1970 and 1987 the risk of non-Hodgkin's lymphoma among female hairdressers taking part in the study was elevated for that entire period.[24]

Various studies have linked permanent hair dye use to an increased risk of bladder cancer, particularly in cases of occupational exposure. Research published in 2001 by the University of Southern California comparing 897 patients with bladder cancer found that women who used permanent hair dyes at least once a month were twice as likely as non-hair dye users to have bladder cancer. Women who used hair dyes at least once a month for 15 years or more were three times more likely to develop bladder cancer. Hairdressers and barbers who had worked in those roles for ten or more years were five times more likely to have bladder cancer.[25]

However, such studies do not claim that hair dye use is a major cause of bladder cancer and suggest the need for further studies. Data analysis in Finland, Norway and Sweden found that male hairdressers in Norway and Sweden had an increased risk of both bladder and lung cancer, with the relative risks of bladder cancer being in the same range as the relative risks for lung cancer.[26] Several other studies have found no increased risk of bladder cancer from the use of permanent hair dyes or suggested that the risk factor is very weak.

An alternative to conventional hair dyes

Vegetable dyes are a safer option than those deploying a multitude of synthetic chemicals and are much less likely to cause allergic reactions (providing they don't contain permanent oxidation dye substances). Pure vegetable dyes are extracted from plants such as saffron, chamomile, black myrtle leaves and green walnuts. They are temporary, rinsing fairly easily out of the hair. Henna, used for centuries as a hair and skin dye, is extracted from the *Lawsonia inermis* shrub that grows in northern Africa and southern Asia. It has a more permanent effect because its molecules are able to penetrate the cortex of the hair shaft. In rare cases it has resulted in allergic contact dermatitis and occupational asthma. It can also cause skin sensitization in some individuals.

In 1997 Howard W. Mielke conducted a study into progressive hair colouring products (which dye the hair gradually) using the colour additive lead acetate. Given the potential for transfer of the toxicant lead into the body, he recommended that colouring agents containing this substance be removed from sale. Some of the products studied contained ten times the content of lead authorized for use in paint and, taking into account the frequent use of the product and amount of time left on the hair, lead contamination of the home and environment is likely to occur.[27] Lead acetate is classified as a Category 1 carcinogen in the EU and is banned for use in cosmetic products in Europe and Canada, but not the USA, although very few products actually incorporate this substance these days.

Permanent and semi-permanent hair dye use, especially of the black and dark brown colours, has also been linked with an increase in non-Hodgkin's lymphoma, multiple myeloma, leukaemia and Hodgkin's disease. A study of 1,300 women claimed that those who had reported the use of hair colouring products prior to 1980 were a third more likely to develop non-Hodgkin's lymphoma and those who used dark permanent hair dyes for over 25 years doubled their risk of developing the illness,[28] but this risk was confined only to those using hair dyes prior to 1980. Other research concluded that permanent hair dyes are not generally associated with an increased risk of fatal cancer, but the small minority who use dark, particularly black, hair dyes, for a prolonged period may have an elevated risk of fatal non-Hodgkin's lymphoma and multiple myeloma.[29]

Evidence for the association between hair dyes and cancer is hotly disputed by other studies. One published in 1994, involving over 99,000 women found no greater risk of haematopoietic cancers in women who had used permanent hair dyes compared with women who had never used them.[30] A meta-analysis of the personal use of hair dyes and risk of cancer featured in the *Journal of the American Medical Association* in 2005 again did not find strong evidence for an increased risk of cancer among personal hair dye users.[31]

Despite this, in 2001 the Scientific Committee on Consumer Products (SCCP), which advises the EU Commission on questions related to the safety of consumer products, expressed concern about the use of permanent hair dyes and recommended a safety assessment strategy for hair dyes, including the requirements for testing ingredients for their potential genotoxicity or mutagenicity. In 2005 the SCCP produced a report about personal hair dyes and cancer risks. Based on the evaluation of scientific evidence to date it was concluded that some studies suggest increased risks for hair dye users of developing acute leukaemia and chronic lymphoid leukaemia and an increased risk of bladder cancer for US women using hair dyes repeatedly over a prolonged period of time.[32]

As of September 2007 the European Commission has banned over 100 hair dye substances with a view to 'prohibiting all permanent and non-permanent hair dyes for which the industry has not submitted any safety files and those for which the SCCP has given a negative opinion'.[33] The cosmetics industry has failed to defend many of the subsequently banned substances for economic reasons.[34]

The cosmetics industry has so far submitted 117 safety files on hair dyes for risk assessment by the SCCP and based on their opinions the European Commission is, as I write, setting up a list of positively assessed hair dye substances that are proved safe for consumer health.[35]

Take home message

If you regularly colour your hair, try natural dyes as an alternative. Dark hair dyes in particular seem to have more question marks about their safety so consider a lighter shade or learn to love your natural colour.

Parabens

Parabens are a group of widely used preservatives added to food and cosmetics. They have come under scrutiny in recent years because of their ability to demonstrate a mild to moderate oestrogenic (hormonal) effect in studies on animals and cells. UK research published in 2004 by Dr Philippa Darbre, senior lecturer in oncology, School of Biological Sciences at the University of Reading, found concentrations of parabens intact in human breast tumours, with methylparaben being present at the highest level.[36]

Dr Darbre has been working on the role of oestrogen in breast cancer at the cellular level for around 26 years. One afternoon an undergraduate in her laboratory proclaimed out of the blue, 'Of course in our family we believe that it's underarm cosmetics that are the cause of breast cancer. You should see the sorts of chemicals they put in those things.' Dr Darbre explains, 'The more I read about it, the more I became convinced that this was at least part of the equation.' Some undergraduates brought shop-bought cosmetics into the lab so that they could test whether the formulations exerted any oestrogenic effects on cells in culture. It was found that they could, if they were diluted down far enough. Because the cosmetics contained a mixture of substances it was not possible to pin down the oestrogenic effects to parabens. As Dr Darbre says, 'There are plenty of other chemicals in these pots [of cosmetics] apart from parabens, which are also oestrogenic and we have to ask questions about additive effects. We are not exposed to one chemical; we are exposed to a mixture.'

Later, hearing about a study by Dr John Sumpter of Brunel University that had found that parabens were oestrogenic, Dr Darbre initiated a programme of study looking at whether parabens could be oestrogenic to breast cancer cells.

> *'We did a small study in 2004, which hit the headlines, demonstrating that parabens could be detected in human breast tissue. It was the first time an intact paraben had been found in the body and we were all led to believe that intact parabens could not get into the human body.'*

Other studies have since vindicated this finding. Two studies have identified parabens in raw sewage, demonstrating that they have passed through the human body. Parabens have been detected in human urine and a Danish study in which 26 healthy male volunteers applied cosmetic creams containing butylparaben, diethyl phthalate and dibutyl phthalate to their bodies, detected the substances in the bloodstream within one hour.[37]

Parabens are included in many consumer items and enter our bodies via multiple routes. Chronic exposure can result from repeated use of personal care products, especially underarm deodorants and antiperspirants. Such cosmetic items have been linked to breast cancer because they are applied very close to the breast, where they could potentially adhere to DNA and encourage the development of damaged cells,[38] and because oestrogen is known to play a part in the onset and progression of cancer.[39] A further issue is that deodorants and antiperspirants are often applied to shaved skin. This provides an easier route for chemicals to enter the body as shaving abrades the skin (i.e. strips away the protective outer layer).

Although no causal association has been conclusively proven, the *European Journal of Cancer Prevention* published a study that surmised that, 'Frequency and earlier onset of antiperspirant/deodorant usage with underarm shaving were associated with an earlier age of breast cancer diagnosis ... underarm shaving with antiperspirant/deodorant use may play a role in breast cancer.'[40]

Take home message

Avoid cosmetic products that contain parabens and encourage children and teenagers in particular to use natural products.

Talc

Cosmetic talcum powder, which is made up of more than 90 per cent mineral talc, is used in a range of beauty products, such as eyeshadows, baby powders and feminine hygiene products. Talc is used to help the product stick to the skin and for its translucency and spreadability. Some formulations consist of up to 75 per cent talc. Unfortunately talc can be contaminated with toxic asbestiform fibres, known to cause a variety of cancers and lung damage by prolonged exposure through inhalation. The cosmetics industry and the US Food and Drug Administration (FDA) consider cosmetic-grade talc to be safe, but in 1993 the National Toxicology Program (NTP) conducted toxicology and carcinogenicity studies of cosmetic-grade talc (free from asbestiform fibres), and found that rats exposed to this mineral via inhalation developed a range of inflammatory lung disorders, including cancer of the lungs and rare adrenal cancers. In mice, inhalation exposure caused chronic inflammation of the lungs.[41]

In addition, eight studies have indicated a 30–60 per cent increase in risk of developing ovarian cancer in women using talc-based body powder in the genital region.[42] The International Agency for Research on Cancer (IARC) has concluded that the use of talc-based body powder in the perineal (genital) region is possibly carcinogenic to humans. One study found that widespread exposure to talc when changing a baby's nappy, 'may contribute to the ubiquitous presence of talc in the ovarian tissue'.[43]

Silica

Amorphous silica, which is often added to cosmetics as an abrasive, absorbent, anti-caking, bulking or opacifying agent, may be contaminated with the carcinogenic crystalline form. Crystalline silica is included in the State of California's list of chemicals known to cause cancer, along with a multitude of other chemicals used in cosmetics.[44] The carcinogenic effects of crystalline silica have been shown in a range of studies on rats, in which exposure to crystalline quartz dust induced lung tumours.[45] Crystalline silica exposure is also associated with occupational silicosis (a lung disease caused by breathing in crystalline silica particles), lung fibrosis[46] and DNA damage in cell-based studies.[47]

Diethanolamine

Diethanolamine (DEA) and related compounds are used as emulsifiers, foaming agents and pH adjusters in shampoos, lotions, creams and other cosmetics. DEA is also used in dishwashing detergents, polishes, pharmaceuticals, agricultural chemicals, metalworking fluids and for a variety of other industrial applications. It is produced by reacting ethylene oxide with ammonia. This chemical can interact with amines and nitrites present in a product or nitrogen oxides in the air to form the carcinogen N-nitrosodiethanolamine (NDELA). In 1980 the US Food and Drug Administration (FDA) analysed 335 cosmetic products and found that 42 per cent were contaminated with NDELA.

The US National Toxicology Program (NTP) conducted a study in 1998 that found a link between the topical application of DEA and some DEA-related chemicals and increased incidences of liver and kidney tumours in laboratory mice.[48,49] Although it has been found to cause cancers in animal studies, DEA is not classified as a human carcinogen. Short-term exposure via inhalation can cause irritation of the nose and throat and dermal exposure can cause skin irritation. Dogs and cats repeatedly exposed to a flea repellant containing 53 per cent DEA for two days or more suffered severe neurological effects, including paralysis. This substance has been found to be toxic at multiple organ sites in rats and mice by oral or dermal exposure.[50]

Common ingredients that can contain diethanolamine (DEA)

The ingredients below are commonly used in a range of cosmetic products including shampoo, bubble bath, body wash, cleansers, liquid hand soap, bath oils, shaving cream, moisturizers, hair dyes and bleaches.

Cocamide DEA
Cocamide MEA
DEA-cetyl phosphate

DEA-oleth-3 phosphate
Lauramide DEA
Linoleamide MEA
Myristamide DEA
Oleamide DEA
Stearamide MEA
TEA lauryl sulphate
Triethanolamine (TEA)

Colour at a cost

Cosmetics just wouldn't be the same without colour: they are extensively used in cosmetic products to enhance the appearance of the product and temporarily impart colour to our skin. Colours are also used in food and drugs.

Manufacturers have a plethora of colours at their disposal. Colourants can be natural extracts, synthetic and water-soluble coal tar or azo dyes, or lakes (organic dyes that have been made water-insoluble, usually by interacting the dye with a metallic salt). Because lakes are water-insoluble they are often used when it is necessary to prevent a colour from 'bleeding', as with lipstick.

Natural colours are readily available for use but they are only soluble in water and fade readily because they are not lightfast. Some natural colours are derived from animal sources. The red colour carmine, for example, is obtained from crushed scale insects. The word 'natural' can be misleading; so-called 'natural' colours are often chemically synthesized rather than extracted from natural sources. Commercially used beta-carotene, for example, is often produced synthetically.

Organic colours are carbon based and were traditionally derived from coal tar or coal tar derivatives (such as aniline, benzene, naphthalene, xylene, quinoline and phenol). They are therefore still referred to as 'coal tar dyes', although they are now predominantly derived from petroleum. Inorganic colours (pigments) are composed of a mineral element with oxygen and other elements (usually sulphur, silicon or carbon) which are derived from naturally occurring sources or synthetically manufactured. The majority of inorganic pigments contain heavy metals or transition metals that can harm the environment and human health if certain levels are exceeded.[51] Organic colours tend to be used more frequently because inorganic colours are not available in as many and varied rich and bright shades.

In Europe colours are often designated by their Colour Index (CI) numbers, an international system of naming colours based on their chemical structure. Each colour has a five-digit number, for example CI 64500. There are over 150 colours permitted for use in cosmetics in the EU, although restrictions on usage apply to some of them.

In the USA colourants certified for use in foods, drugs and cosmetics are preceded by the prefix FD&C (e.g. FD&C Blue No. 1). If the number is preceded by the prefix D&C (e.g. D&C Red No. 33) it means that the colour is permitted for use in drugs and cosmetics. The prefix Ext D&C (e.g. Ext D&C Violet No. 2) means that the product is only certified for external use in drugs and cosmetics and is not to be applied to the lips or mucous membranes.

Artificial dyes tend to produce free radicals[52] (molecules with unpaired electrons that are unstable and can damage DNA, possibly leading to cancer) and some artificial colours used in hair dyes, such as Acid Orange 24 (CI 20170), Basic Violet 3 (CI 42555), Basic Green 4 (CI 42000) and Disperse Blue 1, are known or potential carcinogens. The above are all banned for use in hair dyes in the EU and Basic Violet 3 is also prohibited in Canada, but none of these are banned in the US, although restrictions apply to some of them.

Various coal tar dyes have been shown to induce cancer in studies on experimental animals and to penetrate human skin. These include uncertified colourants used in hair dyes such as 4-methoxy-m-phenylenediamine (4-MMPD 2,4-diaminoanisole), 4-chloro-m-phenylenediamine, 2,4-toluenediamine, 2-nitro-p-phenylenediamine and 4-amino-2-nitrophenol.[53] In 1979 the US Food and Drug Administration (FDA) proposed that hair dye products containing 4-MMPD should carry a cancer warning on the labels, but some hair dye manufacturers disputed the legitimacy of the regulation in court and the FDA withdrew the proposal and entered into a consent agreement with the hair dye manufactuers, many of which 'voluntarily' ceased their use of 4-MMPD. However, 4-MMPD was substituted with similar dyes that had not been tested for carcinogenicity. Coal tar dyes can also contain heavy metal impurities such as lead and arsenic, which are known carcinogens.

Despite studies revealing the carcinogenicity of many coal tar dyes used for hair products in animals, the FDA declared that they did not have the capacity to ban the suspect hair dyes. Although the 1938 Food, Drugs and Cosmetics Act was initially intended to sanction the prohibition of products considered harmful to the public, the hair dye industry lobbied to get exemption for hair dyes using coal tar colours. In addition, the FDA cannot take action against uncertified coal tar hair dyes that have been shown to be harmful if the label provides a cautionary statement suggesting that the product contains potentially irritant ingredients, that a patch sensitivity test should be conducted and that the product should not be used for dyeing the eyebrows or eyelashes.

Over the years various coal tar dyes used in cosmetics have been prohibited, and concerns about their safety have resulted in many manufacturers re-formulating their products. But some of these replacement compounds have also prompted concerns because of their similar chemical structures. Even colours used in cosmetic products touted as 'natural' alternatives, such as 'mineral make-up', undergo intense chemical processing.

Did you know?

Many of the coal tar colours used in cosmetics have been found to cause cancer in animals. Coal tar colours widely added to make-up products include:

- **FD&C Red No. 40 (CI 16035)** – p-credine used in the manufacturing of this colour is reportedly carcinogenic in animals.

- **FD&C Blue No. 1 (CI 42090)** – found to cause tumours in animals at the site of injection.

- **FD&C Yellow No. 5 (CI 19140)** – an azo dye that is referred to as E102 or tartrazine when used as a food additive and is known to cause allergic reactions, especially in asthmatics and those allergic to aspirin.

- **FD&C Green No. 3 (CI 42053)** – has caused sarcomas (cancers of connective tissues) in animals after repeat subcutaneous injections.

- **FD&C Red No. 4 (CI 14700)** – fed to dogs at levels of 2 per cent and 1 per cent of the diet caused adverse effects in the bladder and kidneys of the animals, with three of the five dogs being fed on the 2 per cent level dying after differing periods of time on the test. This is just a snapshot;

many other synthetic dyes are also associated with
adverse effects.

Fragrances

Some fragrance materials are carcinogens or suspected carcinogens. For
instance, in animal studies undertaken by the US National Toxicology
Program (NTP), coumarin demonstrated some evidence of carcinogenic
activity resulting in increased incidences of tumours in rats and mice.[54]
Synthetic coumarin is used in cosmetics as a fragrance material. It was
banned as a food additive in the USA in 1978[55] due to concerns about
liver and kidney toxicity, but it is not banned for use in cosmetic products.

Research sponsored by the US Environmental Protection Agency
(EPA) in 1991, studying fragrance chemicals in consumer products (such
as perfumes, soaps and deodorants) and enclosed spaces, associated with
sick building syndrome and chemical sensitivity, managed to identify 150
chemicals in 31 fragrance products. Although few of the chemicals
isolated had been tested for carcinogenicity, those conducting the research
noted that some mutagens (e.g. alpha-pinene) and substances toxic at high
concentrations (e.g. camphor) were detected.

Various chemicals were also detected in enclosed spaces, most
commonly the fragrance materials toluene, methylene chloride, ethanol,
1,1,1-trichloroethane, silane compounds, alpha-pinene, isopropanol, m-p-
xylene, n-undecane, n-decane, limonene, chlorodifluoromethane, acetone,
trimethylbenzene isomer and n-nonane.[56] Methylene chloride has been
found to cause cancer in animal studies and according to the US Food
and Drug Administration (FDA), 'the use of methylene chloride in
cosmetic products poses a significant cancer risk to consumers [and] may
render these products injurious to health'.[57] Thus cosmetics containing
methylene chloride are deemed adulterated.

Mineral make-up: A safe alternative?

**Make-up that was composed of inorganic pigments,
such as mica, zinc oxide and iron oxide, had a minor
revolution in the 1970s, fell out of favour in the 1980s
and has come back with a vengeance today, frequently
being touted as a 'natural alternative' to conventional**

make-up products, especially in North America. Manufacturers of such mineral make-up must process the ingredients carefully to avoid traces of toxic impurities. It is usually in loose powder form, making it easy to inhale, with some of the pigments, such as mica, potentially causing respiratory problems. There is a lack of industry regulation on mineral make-up and the term 'natural' can be a bit of a misnomer as the minerals have to go through chemical and purification processes to be included in cosmetic products.

Other controversial issues surrounding mineral make-up are the use of ultrafine particles in some mineral make-up products, which are nano-sized, and the sustainability of using mined minerals that cannot be replenished. The mining industry is also known for its exploitation of workers and polluting the environment with undesirable emissions such as dioxins. Some mineral make-up brands may also use potentially toxic minerals such as talc, aluminium and bismuth oxychloride – a by-product of lead and ore refining that can cause skin irritation and scratch the surface of the skin.

Having said that, if you are determined to use make-up, using mineral formulations made by certain brands will mean you are putting far fewer synthetic chemicals on your face than if you use conventional make-up. Just be careful of the misleading hype often surrounding this category of cosmetics. They are not 'organic' (unless you are referring to the chemistry definition of an organic compound, which has carbon-containing molecules!)

Imperfect impurities

Cosmetics can become contaminated with unwanted impurities through contaminated raw ingredients, during the manufacturing process (as a result of the breakdown products of cosmetic ingredients) or via absorption of nitrosamine precursors present in the environment, including packaging.[58] In a 1998 testing programme undertaken by the UK Department of Trade and Industry (DTI), carcinogenic impurities were discovered in 43 per cent of 128 products tested. Many of these impurities are readily absorbed by the skin, such as nitrosamines, which have also been found to induce cancer in experimental animals.[59] Five carcinogenic impurities that may be present in certain cosmetic products are described below. Other impurities include hydroquinone, acrylamide, lead, arsenic and mercury.

1,4-dioxane

1,4-dioxane is a trace contaminant of some chemicals used in cosmetic products.[60] Concerns about it initially came to light in the 1970s, when studies at the National Cancer Institute found an association between 1,4-dioxane and cancer in animals when administered at high levels in animal feed. During 1992–1997 the average concentration of 1,4-dioxane in some cosmetic products was found to be between 14 and 79 mg/kg, although a more recent survey by the Campaign for Safe Cosmetics found lower levels.[61] According to the FDA there are only low levels of 1,4-dioxane in cosmetic products, but because it can readily penetrate the skin and it evaporates easily, they have been monitoring the levels since the 1970s.[62] Nevertheless, the FDA have not set a limit on the level of 1,4-dioxane allowed in cosmetics, merely offering guidance on how to reduce the agent by vacuum stripping, leaving reduction of this impurity firmly in the hands of the cosmetics manufacturers.

There is also evidence that 1,4-dioxane can be absorbed via inhalation and ingestion and it may be found in tap water, leading to exposure through activities such as showering, bathing and laundering.[63] Low levels can cause eye, nose and throat irritation and high levels have been shown to target the liver and kidneys in studies on rats,[64,65] to cause vertigo and eye, nose, skin and respiratory irritation and result in death in some cases of occupational exposure in humans. The US Environmental Protection Agency (EPA) has classified 1,4-dioxane as a probable human carcinogen based on its ability to promote cancer in mice and guinea pigs.[66] It also caused cancer in a skin painting study.[59]

Cosmetic products that contain 1,4-dioxane as a contaminant may be those including ethoxylated ingredients that, according to the FDA, are identifiable by the prefix, word or syllable, 'PEG', 'polyethylene', 'polyethylene glycol', 'polyoxyethylene', '-eth', or 'oxynol'.[59]

Nitrosamines

Nitrosamines, also referred to as N-nitroso compounds, are carcinogens, recognized for their ability to readily penetrate human skin and cause cancer in all animal species studied[67] via interaction with DNA generating a mutation (genotoxic). They have been found in a variety of consumer products including pesticides, drugs, food and cosmetics. Surveys conducted in the USA found nitrosamines in some sunscreen products, especially ones containing a UV filter called octyl dimethyl PABA.

Nitrosamines are a class of chemical compounds formed from the reaction of two nitrogen–containing substances, an amine and a nitrosating agent. In cosmetic formulations nitrosamines can be formed when amines (e.g. monoethanolamine (MEA), diethanolamine (DEA) and triethanolamine (TEA)) or amino derivatives react with nitrosating agents either deliberately included in the formulation (e.g. 2-bromo-2-nitropropane-1,3-diol (bronopol, onyxide 500), 5-bromo-5-nitro-1,3-dioxane (Bronidox C) or tris(hydroxymethyl)nitromethane (tris nitro)) or present as contaminants (e.g. sodium nitrite) under conditions conducive to nitrosamine formation, usually during manufacture or product storage.

Nitrosamine contamination initially came to the FDA's attention in March 1977 through the presentation of a paper at an American Chemical Society meeting. The nitrosamine N–nitrosodiethanolamine (NDELA), which is formed from the nitrosation of diethanolamine, was detected in 27 out of 29 cosmetic creams and lotions at levels varying between 10 parts per billion (ppb) to 50 parts per million (ppm). Other FDA studies of over 300 cosmetic samples between 1978 and 1980 showed contamination up to 150 ppm in some products.

The FDA voiced its anxieties with the cosmetics industry about nitrosamine contamination in a notice published in the *Federal Register* of 10 April 1979 (44 FR 21365), stating that cosmetics containing nitrosamines may be viewed as contaminated and may be liable for enforcement action. Nearly two-thirds of cosmetic products tested between 1991 and 1992 contained NDELA in levels of up to 3 ppm.[68]

In the UK between 1994 and 1997 the DTI sponsored a survey of 128 consumer products, including cosmetic items, and almost half of all samples analysed and over half of the cosmetic products contained detectable levels of nitrosamines. The survey reported that certain cosmetic manufacturers may have been using inappropriate ingredient combinations. The study also found that four months after opening some of the products nitrosamine levels had doubled and that after 17 months they had quadrupled.

Many of the cosmetic products evaluated were re-formulated by the manufacturers and in some cases nitrosamine levels were drastically reduced. Recommendations for the avoidance of nitrosamine contamination were also established.[67]

The US Cosmetic Ingredient Review (CIR) concluded that the ingredients diethanolamine (DEA), triethanolamine (TEA), cocamide

MEA, 2-pyrrolidone-5-carboxylic acid (PCA) and sodium PCA should not be included in products that contain N-nitrosating agents. Despite this, many cosmetic manufacturers continue to include nitrosamine precursors in their products.

Ethylene oxide

Ethylene oxide is a volatile chemical predominantly used as a chemical intermediate in the production of ethylene glycol, along with other industrial chemicals. It is also used as a sterilizing agent, disinfectant, fumigant or insecticide. Ethanolamines used in soaps, detergents and textile chemicals are produced from ethylene oxide (on reaction with ammonia), as are non-ionic surfactants used in dishwashing products, detergents and industrial applications.

Other derivatives of ethylene oxide include polyethylene glycols (PEGs) used in a range of cosmetic formulations. The cosmetics industry's own Cosmetic Ingredient Review (CIR) panel highlighted in the *International Journal of Toxicology* that PEGs have been found to be contaminated with a number of impurities, including ethylene oxide, 1,4-dioxane, polycyclic aromatic compounds, and heavy metals such as lead, iron, cobalt, nickel, cadmium and arsenic.[69]

According to the Environmental Working Group (EWG) 25 per cent of personal care products may be contaminated with ethylene oxide, due to the pervasiveness of ingredients associated with ethylene oxide impurities (ethoxylated surfactants).[70] Ethoxylation is a chemical process whereby ethylene oxide is added to fatty acids to make them more water soluble; sodium dodecyl sulphate is ethoxylated, for example, to produce sodium laureth sulphate.

Ethoxylated surfactants are widely used in household and industrial cleaners, topical pharmaceuticals, cosmetics and laundry products[71] as foaming agents, emulsifiers and wetting agents.

Ethylene oxide is classed as a possible human carcinogen by the EU Council Directive (76/769/EEC) and the US Environmental Protection Agency[72] and as a known human carcinogen according to the US National Toxicology Program's Eleventh Report on Carcinogens, which states that 'the DNA damaging activity of ethylene oxide provides its effectiveness as a sterilant, and it is this same property that accounts for its carcinogenic risk to humans'. An association between exposure to ethylene oxide and an elevated risk of leukaemia, breast cancer and stomach cancer has been reported.[73] Occupational exposure to ethylene oxide has also been associated with lymphatic and haematopoietic cancer.[74] In studies on experimental animals ethylene oxide has caused tumours at multiple organ sites. There is limited evidence that ethylene oxide causes spontaneous abortion in humans and birth defects and testicular damage in experimental animals.[73]

As with 1,4-dioxane, cosmetic products that contain ethylene oxide as a contaminant may be those including ethoxylated ingredients, which, according to the FDA, are identifiable by the prefix, word or syllable, 'PEG', 'polyethylene', 'polyethylene glycol', 'polyoxyethylene', '-eth', or 'oxynol'.

What is a surfactant?

I use the term surfactant throughout the book, but what exactly do surfactants do? Most cleaning products contain surfactants (short for surface active agents), which lower the surface tension of the liquid in which they are dissolved, allowing it to spread more easily across and lift dirt from soiled surfaces such as textiles and the human skin. The surfactant molecules resemble tadpoles in shape; each has a water-loving (hydrophilic) head that is attracted to water molecules, and a water-hating (hydrophobic) tail, which attaches itself to the oil and grease particles. As the hydrophobic tails are buried in the oil and grease their hydrophilic heads are pulled towards the water, with the opposing forces drawing the oil and grease away from the soiled surface, suspending their particles in the water, so the dirt can be rinsed away.

Types of surfactants include wetting agents, foaming agents, cleansers, emulsifiers and solubilizers.

Formaldehyde

Formaldehyde is used as a disinfectant, germicide, fungicide, denaturant (to render the substance unfit for drinking) and preservative in nail polishes and hardeners, soaps and other cosmetic products. It is also used in household products such as furniture polishes and detergents. Preservatives such as imidazolidinyl urea, quaternium-15, DMDM hydantoin, sodium hydroxymethylglycinate and benzylhemiformal can release formaldehyde as a breakdown product. The Scientific Committee on Cosmetic and Non-food Products Intended for Consumers (SCCNFP), which previously collated scientific and technical information and produces opinions for the European Commission on the safety of cosmetic and non-food products intended for consumers, states that the aforementioned preservatives, 'decompose very rapidly to release formaldehyde when dissolved in aqueous/polar solvents',[69] releasing some or all of the formaldehyde they contain. The level of formaldehyde released from imidazolidinyl urea in a solution dissolved in water increases with a more alkali pH and when the temperature of the solution and storage time is increased.[76] This is very telling given the prolonged shelf-life of cosmetic products containing synthetic chemicals and the significant length of time we store and continue to use our products.

Formaldehyde is a suspected carcinogen and common skin and eye irritant. The International Agency for Research on Cancer (IARC) has concluded that there is adequate evidence that formaldehyde causes nasopharyngeal cancer in humans and strong but not sufficient evidence for a link with leukaemia.[77] Studies have shown that occupational exposure to formaldehyde increases the incidences of respiratory cancers. It is also a common contact allergen and can cause skin sensitization.

The FDA, although aware of its allergic and irritant potential, does not object to the use of formaldehyde in cosmetics provided certain restrictions on its concentration and application are adhered to, along with safety cautions being included on the product.[68] It is banned for use in cosmetic formulations in Sweden and Japan and restrictions apply in Canada and the EU – where finished products containing formaldehyde or substances that release formaldehyde must be labelled with the warning 'contains formaldehyde' if the concentration exceeds 0.05 per cent.

Take home message

Formaldehyde is one chemical you are well advised to avoid given its potential to cause allergies and irritation and identification as a potential carcinogen. Check your product labels for its presence and seek alternatives wherever possible.

Polycyclic aromatic hydrocarbons (PAHs)

Polycyclic aromatic hydrocarbons (PAHs) are a group of more than 100 chemicals formed by the incomplete combustion of coal, oil, petrol, wood, tobacco, charbroiled meats, garbage or other organic materials, including anthracene, chrysene, naphthalene and benzo(a)pyrene. The primary source of PAH emissions is petroleum refineries, fossil fuel power plants, coal tar production plants and aluminium production plants, among others.[78] PAHs are widespread environmental contaminants and a variety of consumer products can contain PAHs, including plastics, medicines, dyes, pesticides and wood preservatives. They are present in tobacco smoke and are common impurities in petrolatum, also known as petroleum jelly. Petrolatum is present in 7.1 per cent of cosmetic products available for purchase, including 15 per cent of all lipstick and 40 per cent of all baby lotions and oils.[70] Cosmetics, shampoos and hair dyes that contain coal tar may contain PAHs. Coal tar is banned from inclusion in cosmetics in the EU and Canada.

Some individuals who have been chronically exposed to PAHs via inhalation or skin contact have developed cancer.[79] Occupational exposure to PAHs has been linked with an elevated risk of prostate cancer,[80] lung cancer, bladder cancer[81] and breast cancer.

One study into the effects of PAHs on breast cancer tissue found that the incidences of PAHs bound to DNA (DNA adducts) was 2.56 times greater for breast cancer tissue than for non-cancerous breast tissue.[82] The US National Toxicology Program has listed 15 PAHs reasonably anticipated to be human carcinogens.[73]

The most widely investigated PAH is benzo(a)pyrene, which has been shown to cause tumours in mice, rats, guinea pigs, hamsters, rabbits, monkeys, newts and ducks.[83] Dietary exposure to PAHs in human beings has been linked to elevated risks of colorectal adenoma and pancreatic cancer.[84,85]

Petrolatum is classified as a carcinogen: category 2 (may cause cancer) in the EU Dangerous Substances Directive and was thus prohibited for use in cosmetics in 2004. However, the qualification note N was applied, which means that 'the classification as a carcinogen need not apply if the full refining history is known and it can be shown that the substance from which it is produced is not a carcinogen'.[86] Penreco (a leading producer and marketer of various chemicals) has interpreted this to mean that as long as the petrolatum is refined and meets or exceeds the FDA purity standards for food, as determined by a UV (ultraviolet) light test, it can be included.[87] Therefore petrolatum or petroleum jelly is still used in cosmetic products.

There is no requirement for petrolatum to be refined for use in personal care products in the USA. Obviously some manufacturers will take it upon themselves to ensure that the petrolatum in their products is refined with minimal PAH impurities, but this does not make it any easier for the consumer to discern whether the ingredients contain minimal PAHs or otherwise.

Take home message

The number of substances linked to cancer can appear overwhelming at times and it's important not to work yourself into a state of unnecessary panic. However, the rise in breast cancer in particular is grounds for concern for all of us and there is evidence of a possible role being played by personal care products we use regularly. Avoiding products containing parabens and aluminium compounds in your underarm antiperspirant/deodorant in particular may be a wise precaution.

Chapter 4
Feeling hormonal – Endocrine disruption

Did you know?

- Sperm counts have declined over the past 50 years in many countries.

- Infertility may now affect 15–20 per cent of couples in industrialized countries compared with 7–8 per cent in the early 1960s.[1]

- The impacts on animals of certain chemicals in our environment include birth defects, cancers and damage to their nervous, reproductive and immune systems.

Endocrine disrupting chemicals (EDCs) are external chemicals that can detrimentally alter the function of the endocrine or hormone system in humans and animals, even at very low doses. These chemicals range from pesticides and pharmaceuticals to flame retardants, plasticizers and synthetic chemicals commonly used in cosmetic and other consumer products, and include plant-based oestrogens. The rise in the incidence of several cancers in humans (such as breast, testicular and prostate cancer) and male genital defects, alongside the increased observation of endocrine, developmental and reproductive effects in wildlife that has occurred over the last 60 years coincides with a period during which huge amounts of hormonally active synthetic chemicals have been introduced into the environment.

Researchers from Brunel University and the Imperial Cancer Research Fund explain,

> 'Untimely exposure to natural or synthetic oestrogens can adversely affect human health, particularly with regard to the reproductive cycle and reproductive function. In addition to decreased sperm counts in men and increased incidence of disorders of the male reproductive tract, recent epidemiological studies suggest that cumulative exposure to oestrogenic chemicals is related to the incidence of reproductive cancers.'[2]

The endocrine system is involved in the regulation of countless bodily functions and maintains internal equilibrium within the body. Endocrine disruptors can interfere with the 'production, release, transport, metabolism, binding, action or elimination of natural hormones in the body responsible for the maintenance of homeostasis and the regulation of developmental processes'.[3] The most prominent endocrine disruptors identified thus far either mimic the structure of normal hormones produced by the endocrine system (e.g. oestrogen and androgens) and bind to a cell receptor, causing the cell's normal response but at an incorrect time or to excess (**agonistic effect**), or bind to the cell receptor and block the binding of the natural hormones (**antagonistic effect**).

Did you know?

- **Oestrogens** are a family of chemicals with similar compositions that are predominantly in charge of female sexual development and reproduction. They are generated by the ovaries, along with adipose (fat tissue) and the adrenal glands.

• **Androgens** are in charge of the developing and preserving of the male sexual characteristics. Their structure is similar to the structure of oestrogens, as oestrogens are generated from androgenic precursors. Testosterone is the main human androgen and is chiefly produced by the testes.

Humans are regularly exposed to chemicals that have been shown to disrupt hormones, generating concerns about their potential contribution towards problems in many Western countries such as declining sperm counts, birth defects, increases in testicular cancer and breast cancer, undescended testes, altered thyroid functioning and the feminization of fish. A scientific paper presented at the Symposium on Oestrogens in the Environment, III: Global Health Implications, states 'data showing a lowering of sperm quality and quantity, increased infertility, and spontaneous abortion rates in humans suggest that environmental oestrogens play a role in the toxicology of human reproduction and development'.[4] External chemicals capable of exerting reproductive effects have been unendearingly termed 'gender benders' by the media.

A varied group of synthetic endocrine disrupting chemicals known as **xenoestrogens** have been found to interfere with normal hormone functioning and have entered the environment in a number of ways. Herbicides and pesticides, such as DDT and lindane, are released via agricultural spraying, polychlorinated biphenyls (PCBs) are by-products of the electrical industry, dioxins are by-products of waste disposal and alkylphenols are discharged from treatment systems. Xenoestrogens can also be present in household products including bisphenol A and phthalates in plastics, polybrominated organics in flame retardants and parabens, aluminium salts, triclosan and cyclosiloxanes in cosmetic items. Food items can also contain certain xenoestrogens.

Contaminants often find their way into the environment via sewage. Contributary factors include the release of liquid effluents into rivers and oceans, deposition of dry sludge onto the land and the release of volatile organic compounds (VOCs) into the atmosphere. Sewage effluents are reported to be oestrogenic.[2] The occurrence of hermaphrodite (having both male and female sex organs) fish in the lagoons of sewage treatment works caused researchers to hypothesize that sewage effluent may contain substances oestrogenic to fish. Studies on rainbow trout placed in the effluent from sewage treatment works revealed that concentrations of a trout protein called plasma vitellogenin, which is associated with egg production, increased over 1,000-fold in three weeks, indicating oestrogen stimulation in the liver. Subsequent results obtained from 15 sewage treatment works across England demonstrated that in all instances, exposure of trout to effluent caused a significant increase (500- to 100,000-fold) in the concentration of plasma vitellogenin.[5] It was hypothesized that the oestrogenic substances causing this could be ethynyloestradiol, which is used in pharmaceuticals, or alkylphenol ethoxylates (APEs).

Although we are only exposed to small quantities of these chemicals, because they are lipophilic (fat-loving) and not easily metabolized they tend to build up in our fatty tissues throughout our lifetime. A significant number of xenoestrogens have been identified in breast fatty tissue and human milk. Similarly acting oestrogenic chemicals, even in low concentrations, when combined can produce more significant effects than would be anticipated by the sum of their individual effects. This has been shown in research on fish led by Professor John Sumpter of Brunel University, in which a mixture of synthetic oestrogens had a greater effect on sexual development than individual oestrogens.[6]

As far back as the 1930s scientific studies on experimental animals have highlighted the oestrogenic propensities of a variety of industrial chemicals, including bisphenol A[7] and in the 1950s the pesticide DDT (dichlorodiphenyltrichloroethane), which was found to have a feminizing effect in roosters.[8] The pharmaceutical preparation diethylstilboestrol (DES), originally used for its oestrogenic properties, was found to cause the masculinization of female rodent's brains and in 1969 became associated with an increased risk of vaginal cancer in women, as well as being linked with other female and male genital tract abnormalities in the offspring of women given DES during pregnancy.[9,10]

The degradation products of surfactants known as alkylphenol ethoxylates (used in cosmetics, detergents, paints and herbicides) can persist in surface waters and aquatic sediments and have been found to have an oestrogenic effect in male fish, for example, causing male roach, trout and flounder to produce eggs in their testes. When fish are simultaneously exposed to a variety of oestrogenic chemicals the effects can be enhanced.[11]

Developing embryos and fetuses are exquisitely sensitive to hormonal variations. Chemicals polluting a mother's body can cross the placenta, leaving the fetus exposed to chemicals in the mother's blood. For instance, bisphenol A has been found in amniotic fluid, confirming passage through the placenta.[12] Lipophilic oestrogenic pollutants can also be passed on to babies in milk fat through breast feeding.[13]

A study conducted for Greenpeace and the World Wide Fund for Nature (WWF) by the Netherlands Organization for Applied Scientific Research (TNO) confirmed that there are eight chemical groups commonly present in umbilical cord blood. These are synthetic musks, alkylphenols, bisphenol A, brominated flame retardants, perfluorinated compounds, phthalates, organochlorine pesticides and triclosan. Exposure to low levels of external hormones or toxicants can lead to irreversible physiological alterations, as opposed to the reversible changes generated in adults temporarily exposed to the same levels.[14]

Damaging our children?

Genital malformations and other reproductive problems often arise during development in the womb, when reproductive organs are forming. The organ systems are exquisitely sensitive to hormonal signals at this stage and endocrine disruptors can easily disturb these processes.

As highlighted in the section on cancer (Chapter 3), some chemicals can interfere with the production of oestrogen, possibly leading to the development of breast cancer in women and disturbing pubertal development in girls[15] – for instance, bringing about early breast development and menarche (first menstrual period). During pregnancy, contaminants present in a women's body can be transferred across the placenta to the fetus; they can also be passed on via human breast milk.

A growing body of evidence for endocrine disruption

A trend towards an increase in some potentially hormone-related conditions has been observed in recent years, and although behavioural and nutritional factors may provide a degree of explanation for this it is possible that fetal exposure to endocrine disrupting chemicals has contributed.[16] According to Dr Shanna Swan, professor in the Department of Obstetrics and Gynecology and director of the Centre for Reproductive Epidemiology at the University of Rochester School of Medicine and Dentistry, 'the evidence that environmental chemicals can affect reproductive outcomes in males and females is quite strong now'. However, Dr Swan points out that evidence is primarily based on rodent studies and although outcomes can translate from the animal to the human, it is not really possible to

> 'conduct studies on humans in a randomized way, in a controlled trial on environmental exposures. .... You cannot tell a group of individuals to expose themselves to phthalates and pesticides. There is no control over that and so we always have to deal with the problem that the associations we are observing may be due to other unmeasured variables, related to the chemicals and exposures that we are looking at.'

Dr Swan also points out that 'when for example you take phthalates syndrome, which was first identified in rodents through randomized studies and you see observationally that it is happening in humans, although it doesn't conclusively prove that the same thing is going on, it does make it much more plausible. It is as close as we can come in a human study.'

It is not only industrial and pharmaceutical chemicals that have demonstrated endocrine disrupting activity: various cosmetic ingredients are also suspected endocrine disruptors, as described here.

Did you know?

In 1991, researchers at Tufts University, Boston, found that a chemical was leaching from polystyrene laboratory tubes (used in routine laboratory procedures) and causing the proliferation of breast cancer cells in vitro, even though oestrogens had not been added to the cells. It was subsequently discovered that the substance causing the oestrogen-like effects was the alkylphenol p-nonylphenol (a substance used as a plastic additive and surfactant).[17]

UV screens

Ultraviolet (UV) filters – used in concentrations of up to 10 per cent. in sunscreens and in a variety of other cosmetics such as face creams, lipsticks, skin lotions, hair dyes, shampoos and bubble baths – are highly lipophilic (fat-loving) and as such can persist in the environment, in wildlife and in humans. We are not only exposed to sunscreens via our application but also through the food chain. Dr Philippa Darbre, senior lecturer in oncology at the University of Reading says, 'measurements in fish have shown these UV screens to be present at a level comparable with that of PCBs and DDT'.[18]

There are two types of sunscreens – physical and chemical.

Physical sunscreens contain materials that coat the skin with a thin membrane, scattering and reflecting UV rays in the visible and UV spectrum. Those typically used in sun protection products are the naturally occurring minerals zinc oxide and titanium dioxide. This has prompted concerns because sun protection products including these substances may contain nano-sized particles. Nanoparticles of titanium dioxide have been shown to cause damage to DNA in vitro and in human skin cells when exposed to UV light and water.[19] The smaller the particles the more toxic they are to cells, for instance 20nm particles of titanium dioxide can completely destroy supercoiled DNA at low doses and without exposure to UV, but 500nm particles can only cause slight damage to DNA.[20] This is relevant given that super-tiny nanoparticles of titanium dioxide are being employed in sunscreens and cosmetics because they are colourless on the skin, whereas larger particles give the skin an undesirable white tinge.[21]

Chemical sunscreens include substances such as benzophenones and cinnamates. These absorb UV rays and dissipate their energy. The UV-absorbing chemicals are slowly broken down by the energy and sunscreen products must be constantly reapplied. Chemical sunscreens are added to sun protection products in concentrations of up to 10 per cent. They are also commonly used in a host of other cosmetic products, particularly moisturizers. Many chemical sunscreens can cause irritant reactions. Some have been associated with the production of free radicals, which can harm DNA and may even cause endocrine disruption.

Chemical constituents of sunscreens have reached detectable levels in freshwater and seawater systems, with experts estimating that around a quarter of the sunscreen ingredients applied to the skin are released in water over the course of a 20-minute submersion.[22] Certain sunscreen and personal care ingredients have been found to cause coral bleaching, even at low concentrations, promoting viral infection in coral reefs and threatening the survival of endangered tropical ecosystems. The preservative butylparaben and the UV filters octyl methoxycinnamate, benzophe-none-3 (oxybenzone) and 4-methylbenzylidene camphor caused complete bleaching even at very low concentrations.[22]

The use of sunscreens is increasing despite doubts about their ability to protect against melanoma. In fact, the results of some studies have discovered an increased rather than decreased risk of melanoma.[23,24] In humans sunscreens can be absorbed through the skin and have been identified in urine and breast milk. Both in vitro and in vivo investigations have demonstrated that several widely used sunscreens cause oestrogenic effects.[25]

Benzophenone-3 (oxybenzone), frequently used in sunscreens and tanning agents, has been shown in studies on experimental rats to insti-gate a dose-dependent reduction in litter size, survival rate and testes weight of male rats.[26] In an in vitro cell-based study five out of six commonly used sunscreens (benzophenone-3, homosalate, 4-methylben-zylidene camphor, octyl-dimethyl-p-aminobenzoic acid and octyl methoxycinnamate) demonstrated oestrogenic activity. Homosalate and benzophenone-3 have also been reported to have anti-androgenic effects (preventing or inhibiting the biological activity of male sex hormones) in particular types of cells.[27] One two-week human study investigated whether the sunscreens benzophenone-3, octyl methoxycinnamate and 3-(4-methylbenzylidene) camphor (4-MBC) were absorbed and influ-enced reproductive hormone levels naturally present in humans after topical application. It was found that all the sunscreens were detectable in urine and a minor, intermittent but statisitically significant drop in testos-terone levels was observed in the male participants.[28]

The low-down: Chemical sunscreens and their adverse effects

Anthranilates – UVA filters. Menthyl anthranilate is used in the USA in concentrations of up to 5 per cent. It is not authorized for use in Europe or Japan. It has been shown to produce reactive oxygen species (ROS) under UV light. Menthyl anthranilate lacks safety data.

• **Benzophenones** – UVA filters. Benzophenone-3* (oxybenzone) has been found to significantly penetrate the skin and has been detected in human urine and human milk. Research has shown that up to 10 per cent of the applied dose can penetrate the skin.[29] Concerns about its potential oestrogenicity have been raised. Benzophenone-3 produces free radicals under UV light, which can potentially damage DNA. It is also a photoallergen and may cause skin sensitization. A study of 2,517 Americans over the age of six conducted by the US Centers for Disease Control and Prevention (CDC) as part of the 2003–2004 National Health and Nutrition Examination Survey, detected oxybenzone in the urine of 97 per cent of study participants. Women and girls had higher levels of oxybenzone in their body than men and boys. This was attributed to the different uses of personal care products according to sex, race and ethnicity.[30] The use of oxybenzone is not restricted to sunscreen products; it is used in various other personal care products including moisturizers, lipstick and hairspray. Other benzophenones include dioxybenzone and sulisobenzone.

- **Camphor derivatives** – UVB filters. 4-methylbenzylidene camphor (4-MBC)* is not approved as an active ingredient in sunscreens in the USA. It is authorized for use in Europe, although concerns have been raised due to evidence that 4-MBC may be an endocrine disruptor and lead to hypothyroidism. 4-MBC is listed as a substance of possible concern by the OSPAR Commission, because it is potentially very persistent and bioaccumulative in the environment. The OSPAR Commission are responsible for managing work carried out under the Convention for the Protection of the Marine Environment of the North-East Atlantic. It can also cause photoallergic dermatitis.

- **Cinnamates** – UVB filters. The best known is 2-ethylhexyl-p-methoxycinnamate (octyl methoxycinnamate),* which has been detected in human milk. In an in vitro study on mice cells octyl methoxycinnamate added to an ethyl alcohol was found to kill 50 per cent of the cells (only 10 per cent were killed with ethyl alcohol alone). When the solution was placed underneath a UV lamp cell additional cell mortality was noted. Octyl methoxycinnamate is also a penetration enhancer. Cinnamates can cause skin irritation and contact allergies. Other well-known cinnamates are isoamyl-*p*-methoxycinnamate and cinoxate.

- **Dibenzoylmethanes** – commonly used UVA filters in the EU. The most widely used derivative is avobenzone (also known as Parsol 1789 and 4-*t*-butyl-4'-methoxydibenzoylmethane – a combination of octyl methoxycinnamate and butylmethoxydibenzoylmethane). Avobenzone can result in the production of free radicals under UV light, which can lead to DNA damage. It is unstable under UV light, breaking down into several chemicals, including benzoic acid, benzaldehyde, acetophenone, dibenzoylmethane and others. Avobenzone can also cause contact allergies.

- **Octocrylene** – UVB filter that is chemically related to cinnamates. Results in increased levels of ROS because it is absorbed into the nucleated epidermal layers after a certain amount of time. It can cause skin irritation and in some cases contact dermatitis. Researchers found concentrations of octocrylene and 4-MBC in the muscle tissue of brown trout from seven Swiss rivers receiving effluent from wastewater treatment plants.[31]

- **Para-aminobenzoic acid (PABA)** – UVB filter. This used to be a very popular sunscreen ingredient but its use has declined as a result of problems with allergic dermatitis and photosensitivity. It is banned for use in sunscreens in Canada. PABA results in increased levels of ROS. It has been found to increase the formation of potentially mutagenic thymine dimers, damaging links between DNA strands in human cells that some people lack the mechanism to repair, thereby increasing their risk of skin cancer. A derivative of PABA called octyl dimethyl PABA (padimate O)* is often used in sun protection products in place of PABA, but it is expected to produce similar free radicals to PABA, such as hydroxyl radicals, which are highly reactive and can attack a variety of molecules within living organisms, including DNA. Padimate O is also mutagenic to yeast cells[32] and a penetration enhancer. Other PABA derivatives include ethyl dihydroxypropyl PABA, pentyl dimethyl PABA, padimate A and glyceryl PABA.

- **Salicylates** – UVB filters. The penetration enhancer octyl salicylate (octisalate) does not offer effective sun protection for the skin. Homomenthyl salicylate (homosalate)* is used in concentrations of up to 10 per cent in the EU. Along with octyl methoxycinnamate and various other sunscreens, it was found to increase the penetration of herbicide into hairless mouse skin.[33] Homosalate can also break down under sunlight to form salicylic acid and trimethylcyclohexanol. Other salicylates used in sunscreens include, isotridecyl salicylate and trolamine salicylate.

*Note: These sunscreens have been found to be weakly oestrogenic, increasing the proliferation of breast cancer cells and inducing in vitro a protein called pS2 that is associated with breast cancer. Application of 4-methylbenzylidine camphor in olive oil to the skin of immature hairless rats led to increased uterine weight at concentrations of 5 and 7.5 per cent.[25]

Butylated hydroxyanisole

Butylated hydroxyanisole (BHA) is used as an antioxidant in foods, pharmaceuticals and cosmetics such as lipsticks and eyeshadow. Not only is this substance considered as a possible human carcinogen by the World Health Organization, the US National Toxicology Program (NTP) and the International Agency for Research on Cancer (IARC), among other organizations, but it has also been found to be oestrogenic.[17] Butylated hydroxyanisole is banned for use as a fragrance material in the EU but is authorized for other purposes.

High doses of BHA administered to male and female rats has instigated mild dysfunction and underdevelopment of the reproductive system, altered testosterone and thyroid hormone (T4) levels, affected sex organ weights and delayed sexual maturation.[34] In another study on experimental rats BHA was found to increase the relative organ weights of the liver, kidney, adrenal glands and the brain, decrease weights of the vagina, spleen and prostate gland and reduce the number and motility of sperm. For one generation of rats the number of male rats was reduced due to the administration of BHA, with the study concluding that BHA is a disruptor of the androgen and thyroid hormonal system, both in the animals and cells analysed.[35]

Parabens (para-hydroxybenzoic acids)

Parabens have been used as preservatives for over 80 years to prevent bacterial growth and extend shelf-life in a multitude of consumer products including foods and cosmetics, skin and hair products, perfumes and soaps. Although parabens are generally readily metabolized and excreted, some have been found to be oestrogenic. Ethyl-, propyl- and butylparaben have been shown to possess oestrogenic effects in a study on fish, with propyl- and butylparaben demonstrating an oestrogenic effect as potent as was found in tests on bisphenol A.[36] Research has suggested that repeated and long-term topical application of parabens could possibly result in prolonged oestrogenic effects in skin and that the anti-ageing benefits of a range of cosmetics and pharmaceuticals may be partly a product of the oestrogenicity of parabens.[37]

Parabens have been shown to be oestrogenic in vivo and in vitro[38–41] and have been detected in human breast tumour tissue,[42] cord blood and breast milk.[43] As mentioned in Chapter 3, UK scientists have reported concentrations of parabens found in breast tumour samples.

In a paper looking at the deficiencies in toxicology testing and research assessments for endocrine disrupting chemicals with regards to human health, authors Dr Philip W. Harvey and Dr David J. Everett state,

> 'The parabens regulatory toxicology database is deficient ....
> Critical toxicology data gaps also have been noted for cosmetic uses
> of parabens .... Parabens are readily dermally absorbed and escape
> skin metabolism, have been detected in human breast tissue and
> are oestrogenic.'[44]

Dr Philip Harvey, toxicologist and editor-in-chief of the *Journal of Applied Toxicology*, has suggested that regular daily application of body lotion containing parabens around the chest and breast area would result in enough parabens being absorbed to be equivalent to a significant amount of oestradiol (the natural oestrogen found in the body) when compared to the natural concentrations of oestradiol in human breast tissue.[44]

Take home message

There are a number of deodorant and cosmetic products in the market that are paraben-free. Given the question marks about the safety of parabens it makes sense to choose paraben-free products.

Phthalates

Phthalates (pronounced tha-lates) used as plasticizers (to increase the flexibility of plastics) are lipophilic (fat-loving) compounds present in a wide range of products, such as polyvinyl chloride flooring, detergents, plastic clothing, lubricating oils, pharmaceuticals, blood bags and tubing, children's toys and cosmetics. The main phthalates in cosmetics are dibutyl phthalate (DBP), dimethyl phthalate (DMP) and diethyl phthalate (DEP) used in products such as nail polishes to reduce chipping, hairsprays to avoid rigidity, moisturizers to help the product spread easily across the skin and as solvents and perfume fixatives in a range of other beauty products. Diethyl phthalate and dibutyl phthalate are extensively used in perfumes, nail polishes and hairsprays and may be inhaled and absorbed into the lungs.[45]

Phthalates are also present in our diet through food production processes and packaging. Research conducted by Greenpeace discovered phthalates in the top layer of certain food products that had migrated from the plastic wrappers.[46] Phthalates have also been detected in indoor air and dust and human urine and blood samples, with levels being highest in children between the ages of six and 11, and in women.[47] Several phthalates cause testicular and liver damage, liver cancer and fetal malformations in studies on experimental rats.[48]

Since 2005, the phthalates diethylhexyl phthalate (DEHP), dibutyl phthalate (DBP) and benzyl butyl phthalate (BBP) have been prohibited in Europe in children's toys and other products in concentrations exceeding 0.1 per cent, while diisononyl phthalate (DINP), diisodecyl phthalate (DIDP) and di-*n*-octylphthalate (DNOP) have been banned from toys and childcare products intended for children under the age of three that can be put in children's mouths.[49] Imported items may still contain higher levels of phthalates. Additionally under an amendment to the EC Cosmetics Directive in January 2003, chemicals classified as carcinogenic, mutagenic or as toxic to the reproductive system are banned for use in cosmetic products. The phthalates benzyl butyl phthalate (BBP), dibutyl phthalate (DBP) and diethylhexyl phthalate (DEHP), classified as toxic to reproduction,[50,51] are thus prohibited from use in cosmetic products in the EU and its member states.

Despite this regulation cosmetics manufacturers often use these chemicals in cosmetics intended for the US or other markets, and when used as fragrance carriers there is no legal requirement to feature phthalates on cosmetic ingredients labels. There is also still a risk of contamination. In a study conducted by the Women's Environmental Network (WEN), the Swedish Society for Nature Conservation and Health Care Without Harm 34 well-known cosmetic products were tested for phthalate levels by an independent laboratory. Phthalates were identified in almost 80 per cent of the products, none of which had them listed as ingredients on the labels.[52]

The Environmental Working Group (EWG) in the US studied phthalate levels in 72 personal care products and detected diethyl phthalate in 71 per cent of the products and dibutyl phthalate in 8 per cent of the products tested.[53]

Several phthalates have been shown to have oestrogenic activity and have been identified in urine, breast milk samples and infant formula. In one recent study scientists measured the levels of metabolites of seven commonly used phthalates in urine samples across a selection of 289 adults. Worryingly, they found that women of reproductive age (20–40 years) had higher levels of monobutyl phthalate, a metabolite of dibutyl phthalate, in their urine than the other age and gender groups.[45]

The phthalates BBP, DBP and DEHP have also been found to mimic oestrogen, inhibiting apoptosis (programmed cell death) in breast cancer cells induced by the chemotherapeutic drug tamoxifen (used to treat breast cancer), promoting resistance to the drug's effects.[54]

Scandinavian scientists have found a significant association between mothers with high levels of phthalate contaminants in their breast milk having sons with decreased reproductive hormone levels.[55] DBP, DEP and

DEHP were all linked with reduced testosterone levels in the blood. Various phthalates, including DBP, have also been shown to adversely affect reproductive tract development in male rats in an anti-androgenic manner. The phthalate ester DEHP has been shown to reduce male testosterone levels to female levels in male rats.[56]

Epidemiological studies have revealed potential safety concerns about human exposures to phthalates. Researchers comparing phthalate metabolites in urine samples collected from adult male participants in the National Health and Nutrition Examination Survey (NHANES) between 1999 and 2002 discovered significant correlations between high levels of certain phthalate metabolites and abdominal obesity with insulin resistance,[57] providing a potential link between phthalate exposure and diabetes.

In a study on premature breast development among young Puerto Rican girls under the age of eight, significantly high levels of the phthalates DMP, DEP, DBP and DEHP and its major metabolite mono-(2-ethylhexyl) phthalate were discovered in 68 per cent of samples, suggesting a possible link between endocrine disrupting plasticizers and premature breast development in a human female population.[58]

Men are also potentially at risk from exposure to certain phthalates. Testicular dysgenesis syndrome, which comprises male reproductive disorders that develop at birth, such as cryptorchidisim (undescended testis), hypospadias (where the opening of the urethra is abnormally positioned on the underside of the penis), or during young adulthood, such as low sperm counts, fertility problems, testicular cancer and testicular atrophy (shrinking of the testicles), has been linked in some scientific studies to fetal exposure to oestrogenic chemicals such as phthalates in the womb. In fact, the term 'phthalate syndrome' has been coined, according to Professor Richard M. Sharpe, 'to cover the range of abnormalities that are seen after in utero exposure of rats to certain phthalates'.[59]

Dr Shanna Swan, professor in the Department of Obstetrics and Gynecology and director of the Centre for Reproductive Epidemiology at the University of Rochester School of Medicine and Dentistry, led a study to ascertain the reproductive effects of exposure to phthalates in the male babies of mothers recruited in California. The research demonstrated an association between high exposures to four phthalates in 85 mothers and a short anogenital distance in their baby boys. The boys with a shorter anogenital distance tended to have smaller penises and were more likely to have incompletely descended testes. The study also suggested that 'humans may be more sensitive to prenatal phthalate exposure than rodents'.[60]

The industry fights back

Question What is the Cosmetic, Toiletry and Perfumery Association's view of phthalates and parabens, which have been linked with endocrine disruption and cancer in some studies?

Answer 'Both phthalates and the parabens, as used in cosmetics, are safe and any suggestion that they are not is based on misinformation rather than scientific fact. Not all phthalates are the same. Not all phthalates are capable of mimicking hormones. Those that can and which might represent a theoretical risk of harm to human health are banned from cosmetic products. The remaining use of specific phthalates is without any risk of hormonal effects.

To help put this into perspective, the most potent of the phthalates that was used was in nail polish or nail varnish. It was banned in 2005 because it had a theoretical potential to mimic the hormone oestrogen. That potential was, however, vanishingly weak. Indeed, a calculation showed that you would need to paint your nails 35,000 times a day to be exposed to a dose that might have a potential to mimic oestrogen. There was simply not enough time in the day to be at risk.

Similarly with the parabens, the two most widely used parabens have no ability to mimic oestrogen. This has been shown repeatedly and so cannot pose any risk. The others are incomplete mimics, meaning they are not actually able to produce the same effects as oestrogen no matter how high the dose, and are also very low in potency.

The complete argument is long and complex but in essence, you would need to use something like a quarter of a ton of cosmetics a day to be exposed to a potentially oestrogenic dose, but in fact virtually none of the parabens applied to the skin is absorbed intact. The study claiming to have found parabens in breast tumour tissue has been robustly criticized by the

scientific community at large and is simply not
considered a credible study.'

*Dr Christopher Flower, director-general, the Cosmetic, Toiletry
and Perfumery Association (CTPA).*

Triclosan

Triclosan, developed in the 1960s, is an organochlorine widely used as a
preservative to zap microbes in personal care and cosmetic products
including toothpaste, deodorants, soaps, liquid hand soap and body
washes. Organochlorines contain carbon, chlorine and sometimes other
constituents and they are characterized by their stability, lipophilicity
and ability to bioaccumulate. Triclosan is registered with the US
Environmental Protection Agency (EPA) as a pesticide.[61] Concerns have
arisen about triclosan's potential to encourage resistance to antibiotics by
targeting bacteria in the same way as medical drugs.[62] Europe's Scientific
Committee on Consumer Products (SCCP), while questioning the
weight of evidence in favour of resistance and cross-resistance arising
from the use of triclosan in cosmetic items and acknowledging its effectiveness in preventing hospital-acquired infections such as MRSA (methi-
cillin-resistant *Staphylococcus aureus*), states that, 'no current data
demonstrate any extra health benefits from having anti-bacterial
containing cleansers in ordinary households'.[63] Regular soap and warm
water is sufficient for everyday use according to the US Centers for
Disease Control and Prevention (CDC).

Triclosan is very toxic to aquatic animals and algae and could disrupt
the balance of the ecosystem if released into the environment at high
levels.[64] It has been detected in human plasma and breast milk, with
concentrations higher in those mothers who used personal care products
containing triclosan than in those who did not.[65]

A study on North American bullfrogs found that triclosan disrupted
the thyroid hormones at very low levels.[66]

When triclosan was added to the Mississippi River and exposed to UV
light some of it was converted to dichlorodibenzo-*p*-dioxin.[67] This may
explain the presence of some of the dioxin found in the environment. It had
previously been established that triclosan could be converted to dioxin in a
laboratory setting and that sunlight results in the degradation of triclosan.
Although dichlorodibenzo-*p*-dioxin is not one of the dioxins that have
prompted safety concerns, repeated exposure to chlorine in the wastewater

treatment process could chlorinate triclosan, which might then be converted to more dangerous dioxins under sunlight when released from the treatment facility. One of the researchers, Kristopher McNeill, associate professor of the Department of Chemistry at the University of Minnesota, explains, 'The toxicity of the dioxins increases with the number of chlorine substituents, so the more chlorinated dioxins are generally more toxic than the less chlorinated dioxins.' The dioxin formed by triclosan is one of the less toxic dioxins but Dr McNeill explains, 'Our concern is that in the wastewater treatment process sometimes chlorine is used to kill pathogens as a secondary treatment. This can add chlorine atoms to triclosan.' This could result in the formation of a dioxin more toxic than the dichlorodibenzo-p-dioxin, presenting an environmental threat, especially as dioxin readily accumulates in organisms.

Triclosan has also been shown to cause reproductive effects, such as fetal death in rats when administered orally at high doses.[68]

A number of UK antiperspirant/deodorant brands no longer include triclosan in their products and some manufacturers have switched to alternatives in toothpastes. In 2003 major high street retailers such as B&Q, Marks & Spencer and Asda agreed to phase out the use of triclosan in some of their own-brand products.

A triclosan-free zone

Given all the concerns about triclosan does it really need to be used in cosmetic products? That's a good question. Kristopher McNeill, associate professor of the Department of Chemistry at the University of Minnesota says, 'It is worrisome that we are incorporating this chemical into consumer products when it has the potential to make toxic by-products. My own feeling is that it is unnecessary, when soap works just fine without these compounds and toothpaste probably works just fine without triclosan.'

Alkylphenols

Alkylphenols (APs) are synthetic chemicals mainly used to produce alkylphenol ethoxylates (APEs) – non-ionic surfactants that were once widely used in household and industrial detergents to help products clean effectively, and are still used in cosmetic products such as shaving creams and shampoos. The alkylphenols known as nonylphenol (NP) and octylphenol (OP) are reacted with ethylene oxide to produce nonylphenol ethoxylates (NPEs) and octylphenol ethoxylates (OPEs) respectively.

Alkylphenol ethoxylates break down into alkylphenols (such as nonylphenol and octylphenol) which are around ten times more toxic than APEs. Alkylphenols can cause skin irritation (which usually clears up once use of the product stops), skin reddening, contact dermatitis and photosensivity. They are toxic to aquatic organisms and oestrogenic to fish.[69] Synthetic oestrogenic compounds, such as APEs are now commonly detected in sewage effluents and surface waters in Europe, the USA and Japan.

APEs were first shown to have oestrogenic effects in the 1930s[7] and later in 1978 more evidence of their endocrine disrupting effects came to light.[70] Nonylphenol has been found to leach out of plastic containers and can be formed by the breakdown of certain chemicals found in cosmetic products. In a 1987 study by Ana M Soto. nonylphenol showed oestrogen mimicking effects in cultured human breast cells, causing oestrogen-sensitive breast cancer cells to multiply[17] and it has also caused permanent reproductive damage in the fish most strongly affected by the compound.[71] Octylphenol administered to male rats via drinking water caused a reduction in testicle size.[72]

A voluntary ban on the use of APEs has existed since 1995 in the EU (although some cosmetic products still contain APEs) and an EU risk assessment of nonylphenol and nonylphenol ethoxylate products was conducted, with the European Commission drafting a proposal to restrict their uses in 2002. Some manufacturers agreed to phase them out through a voluntary agreement. Subsequently, in July 2003 EU Directive 2003/53/EC banned the use of nonylphenol ethoxylates in cosmetic products. This directive came into effect in January 2005. Nonylphenol and 4-nonylphenol branched are directly banned by the Cosmetics Directive. APEs have not been added to domestic detergents in the UK since 1976 and alkylphenols will eventually be banned in many applications, but the process has been a very slow one.[73] There are no bans on the use of APEs in the USA.

Why do we develop underarm odour?

The skin has two types of sweat glands: eccrine and apocrine. Eccrine sweat glands exist over most of the body and open out onto the surface of the skin. These regulate body temperature by secreting sweat onto the skin, which cools the body down as it evaporates. Apocrine sweat glands develop during puberty and are predominantly present under the armpits, around the nipples of the breast and the genital area. Emotional stress leads the apocrine glands to push the fatty sweat produced in the gland tubule onto the surface of the skin, which causes a strong odour as bacteria decompose the organic compounds in the sweat. Underarm hair exacerbates the odour problem by providing a larger surface area for the bacteria to flourish on.

• Antiperspirants – are used to reduce, block or absorb the secretion of sweat onto the skin's surface and inhibit underarm odour, with their exact mechanism being uncertain.

• Deodorants – are designed to prevent or mask underarm odours, through the addition of fragrances and antimicrobial agents such as triclosan, quaternary ammonium compounds, farnesol and alcohols, which are used to kill the bacteria on the skin. However, the bacteria rapidly return and so in a vicious cycle we apply yet more deodorant.

Deodorants may be combined with antiperspirants (deoperspirants), with the aim of tackling perspiration, bacteria and masking odour.

Aluminium salts

Aluminium is the most abundant metal in the earth's crust and we are all exposed to low levels of aluminium in our environment. Aluminium compounds are used in a variety of applications and consumer products such as saucepans, foil, astringents, antacids, buffered aspirin, food additives, cosmetics (as colour additives) and antiperspirants.

Aluminium salts, most commonly aluminium chlorohydrate, aluminium sesquichlorohydrate, aluminium zirconium chlorohydrate, aluminium zirconium trichlorohydrate, aluminium zirconium tetra-chlorohydrate, aluminium zirconium pentachlorohydrate, aluminium zirconium trichlorohydrex glycine complex and aluminium zirconium tetrachlorohydrex glycine complex, are authorized in high levels in antiperspirants, sometimes making up to 25 per cent of the volume of the product.

We regularly apply antiperspirants to our underarms, which are left on the skin. In the case of women, antiperspirants are usually applied on shaved and therefore more sensitive skin, possibly enabling the aluminium to be more readily absorbed in close proximity to the breast. Dermal absorption of antiperspirant aluminium salts applied to the skin has been identified in studies on mice and the human underarm.[74] Results from research have found that aluminium binds to oestrogen receptors in the breast, mimicking the effects of oestrogens.[75]

A survey of 437 females diagnosed with breast cancer found that those who frequently used antiperspirants along with shaving their underarms from an early age were diagnosed with breast cancer at an earlier age, suggesting that antiperspirant use may play a role in breast cancer.[76] Kris G. McGrath, associate professor of clinical medicine at the Feinberg School of Medicine, Northwestern University, who led this study, says 'I truly believe in a link between underarm hygiene and breast cancer, with my biggest concern about aluminium being [that it's] applied so close to the breast, often preceded by underarm shaving.'[77]

Large amounts of aluminium have proven to be harmful to unborn developing animals, causing delays in neurological and skeletal development. Aluminium from a mother can enter her unborn baby via the placenta and breast milk. Exposure to high levels of aluminium has also been linked to Alzheimer's disease in some studies, although others have found no association.[78]

Prolonged used of antiperspirants and deodorants based on aluminium zirconium and zirconium has been linked to the development of underarm granulomas (nodular tissue inflammation). Evidence also suggests that certain zirconium compounds have caused toxic effects in the lungs and other organs in experimental animals. The US Food and

Drug Administration's (FDA) Code of Federal Regulations for Cosmetic Products comments:

> 'When used in aerosol form, some zirconium will reach the deep portions of the lungs of users. The lung is an organ, like skin, subject to the development of granulomas. Unlike the skin, the lung will not reveal the presence of granulomatous changes until they have become advanced and, in some cases, permanent. It is the view of the Commissioner that zirconium is a deleterious substance that may render any cosmetic aerosol product that contains it injurious to users.'[79]

A toxic mess

'I am not quite sure why anyone in their right mind would want to spray a 25 per cent solution of aluminium under their arms everyday. We are worried about a trace of aluminium in a cooking pan that might cause Alzheimer's, so why do we shave our underarms and apply a 25 per cent solution to that area every single day? It is absolute madness. People need to understand what is really in a pot of underarm cosmetics. It is just a toxic mess really!'

Dr Philippa Darbre, senior lecturer in oncology, Biomolecular Sciences Section, School of Biological Sciences, the University of Reading.

Musk fragrances

Polycyclic and nitro musks are synthetic chemicals commonly used in a range of fragranced consumer products, including laundry detergents, air fresheners, household cleaners, perfumes, aftershaves, cosmetics and personal care products as fragrances and fixatives. They are not specified on ingredients labels, instead being covered by the broad terms 'fragrance', or 'parfum'. Synthetic musks were initially detected in environmental samples nearly 20 years ago.[61] Certain nitro and polycyclic musks have been detected in human adipose (fat) tissue,[80] breast milk[81] and blood.[82]

The polycyclic musks AHTN and HHCB, known to be ubiquitous and bioaccumulative in the aquatic environment, due to their lipophilic (fat-loving) properties, have been shown to have an anti-oestrogenic effect in zebrafish.[83]

The nitro musks known as musk xylene and musk ketone and again the polycyclic musk AHTN have been found to increase the proliferation of human MCF-7 breast cancer cells, suggesting that these substances demonstrate oestrogenic activity.[84] The discovery of musk xylene and musk ketone in women's blood has been associated with different clinical parameters of the endocrine system, including elevated numbers of miscarriages in women with higher concentrations of musk xylene.[85] Polycyclic musks have been detected in Norwegian outdoor air samples.[61] Research prepared by the Dutch organization TNO Environment and Geosciences for Greenpeace in 2005 detected phthalates and artificial musks in every brand of perfume that was tested.[86] The inclusion of nitro musks in perfume compounds has been associated with cases of extreme intolerance to sunlight.

Due to concern in the EU about the potential adverse health and environmental effects of nitro musks, some of these chemicals have been banned for use in cosmetic products, resulting in an increased reliance on polycyclic musks. However, polycyclic musks have similar health and environmental concerns.

The industry fights back

Question Why are fragrance houses exempt from disclosing the ingredients used in their perfume products? Isn't it a consumer right to know what substances we are putting into our bodies?

Answer 'We have to make sure we understand the implications of the supply chain here. We are the fragrance creators. The labelling of the finished products, what the consumers see, is the responsibility of the finished product manufacturers, acting under the respective laws that apply to their products.

When we were requested, by new legislation in Europe, to disclose the ingredients out of a list of 26 potential sensitizers, we complied with it. We are happy to disclose ingredients when it is necessary and helpful to the consumer, but the limit to it is the confidentiality of the formula, which cannot be protected by patent or copyright, hence our need to be careful with disclosure.

Some market research has shown that rightly or wrongly the majority of consumers, with the exception perhaps of those who are more sensitive, do not bother to look at ingredients labels. It's hard to understand what the ingredients are, unless you are a chemistry graduate. We are obliged to put a name following international nomenclature rules but it is of more interest to a dermatologist than the consumer.

This labelling legislation is less to inform the consumer and more the dermatologists, the ones who can understand the identity of the chemical behind the name.'

Jean-Pierre Houri, director-general of the International Fragrance Association (IFRA).

Dioxins

Dioxins are persistent and bioaccumulative toxic substances and are banned by the Stockholm Convention on Persistent Organic Pollutants (POP) treaty as of 17 May 2004. They are unwanted by-products mainly formed from industrial processes involving heat.

The manufacture or incineration of certain cosmetic ingredients can produce dioxins and cosmetic packaging may transfer dioxins to the product.

As well as being readily stored in adipose (fatty) tissue, dioxins are stored in breast milk and can be passed on to fetuses during pregnancy and young infants during breast feeding. In humans, exposure to dioxins can disrupt the endocrine system, damage the nervous system and immune system, cause reproductive damage, birth defects and various cancers and lead to a skin disease called chloracne, along with numerous other adverse effects.[87]

Did you know?

In 2005, following a meeting of international experts and scientists on endocrine disruptors, approximately 200 scientists signed the Prague Declaration on Endocrine Disruption, which calls on governments and the public to address the risks posed to human health and wildlife by endocrine disruptors. These experts signed a position paper intended to update European citizens, policy makers and researchers on the shortcomings and flaws in current regulation and highlight constructive suggestions that could result in better protection of humans and wildlife.[15]

Take home message

There is a growing body of evidence pointing to the harmful effect of the endocrine disrupting chemicals on the environment and human health. It is up to all of us to try to reduce their usage. Some of the things you can do include: limit your use of sunscreens – wear a hat and cover-up instead; avoid products containing phthalates and parabens; replace your antibacterial wash with soap and choose an aluminium-free antiperspirant.

Chapter 5

Nanotechnology – Technological breakthrough or nightmare?

Nanotechnologies involve engineering matter at the scale of atoms and molecules, measuring in the range of 0.2–100 nm. To give you an idea of the scale we are talking about, a nanometre (nm) is one-billionth of a metre. One human hair is around 80,000 nm wide, a red blood cell is around 7,000 nm wide and a water molecule is approximately 0.3 nm across.[1]

Nanotechnologies and nanoscience are not uniform disciplines; the terms encompass a range of disparate technologies that intersect a variety of traditional scientific fields including materials science, engineering, physics, medicine and environmental sciences. There is no standard definition for nanotechnologies but the Royal Society and the Royal Academy of Engineering have defined nanoscience as 'the study of nanomaterials' and nanotechnologies as the design, production and application of 'structures, devices and systems by controlling shape and size at the nanometre scale'.[1] Nanoscale structures exist naturally, for example nanomaterials occur as a result of combustion processes such as forest fires and volcanoes.[2] Nanoparticles (microscopic particles, each with one or more dimensions that are less than 100 nm) are also naturally produced by plants and algae, and certain proteins within the body are nano-sized.

There are two groups of nanoparticles: those that break down into their molecular constituents upon application to the skin (e.g. liposomes, microemulsions, nano-emulsions) and soluble particles (e.g. titanium dioxide, fullerenes, quantum dots).[3] A nanomaterial is a material that has one or more external dimensions, or an internal structure, on the nanoscale.[4]

Nanotechnologies are not novel, but have expanded since advances were made in our ability to examine and manipulate atoms and molecules with astonishing accuracy. They now have a number of current or planned applications; for example, titanium and zinc oxide nanoparticles are used in sunscreen to reflect and absorb UV light, nanomaterials are used in active surfaces (for example, self-cleaning windows), carbon nanotubes are used to strengthen tennis racquets, paramagnetic nanospheres are used as drug delivery systems in medicine[5] and nanomaterials are used in chip-resistant paint and imaging technology.

Runaway innovation often leaves safety legislation floundering as it attempts to keep up with the new advances in technology, and nanotechnology is no exception. Worldwide, corporations are introducing thousands of tons of nanomaterials into the environment and into the bodies of millions of people, despite an absence of knowledge about their safety and in the face of mounting evidence indicating the potential toxicity of certain nanomaterials. Dr Andrew Maynard, chief science advisor of the Project on Emerging Nanotechnologies at the Woodrow Wilson International Center for Scholars, explained to me, 'Nobody's really quite sure what these nanomaterials might do in the environment and yet companies are already using them in products.'

Fixed nanomaterials, such as computer chips that are rigid in structure, cannot escape into the environment, but free engineered nanomaterials that are able to travel around in a product, such as those used in cosmetic products, have prompted health and environmental concerns. Nano-emulsions contain similar ingredients to regular emulsions but have much smaller droplet sizes (as low as 10 nm), making them transparent and giving them other novel properties. However, when applied to the skin, nano-emulsions are not stable and disintegrate into their component ingredients. Some cosmetic products use mineral-based materials for product performance. For instance, sunscreen products contain zinc oxide and titanium dioxide nanoparticles, as UV filters. According to the Scientific Committee on Consumer Products (SCCP), it is unclear what other kinds of nanomaterials are being used in cosmetic products.[4]

Friends of the Earth have suggested that at a conservative estimate, there are at least several hundred cosmetics, sunscreens and personal care products on the global market that contain nanomaterials.[6] The Nanotechnology Consumer Products Inventory, featured on the website of the Woodrow Wilson International Center for Scholars, lists hundreds of nanomaterial-containing products, including sunscreen for babies and adults, socks, children's toys, contact lens cleaners, moisturizer, slippers, skin cleanser, food containers, refrigerators and tennis racquets.

To add to consumer confusion there are a number of companies that have co-opted the term 'nano' for their products, although nanotechnology has not been applied. A distinct lack of a standard definition for nanotechnology causes difficulties for regulators as well as consumers.

In 2003 the UK government commissioned the Royal Society and the Royal Academy of Engineering to conduct independent research into developments in nanoscience and nanotechnologies, along with their impacts. Their 2004 report notes,

> 'If nanoparticles penetrate the skin they might facilitate the production of reactive molecules that could lead to cell damage .... There is insufficient information about whether nanoparticles used in cosmetics (such as zinc oxide) penetrate the skin and there is a need for more research into this .... There is virtually no information about the effect of nanoparticles on species other than humans or about how they behave in the air, water or soil, or about their ability to accumulate in food chains.'[5]

Because free engineered nanomaterials are used in personal care products that are routinely washed off, they can habitually enter the environment.[3] Political scientist Dr Terry Clarence Davies, senior advisor to the Project on Emerging Nanotechnologies and a senior fellow at Resources for the Future explains, 'Once nanotechnology materials get into the ambient environment it may be impossible to contain them. The concerns about exposure are not theoretical. Many of the current commercial applications of nanotechnology are high-exposure uses such as cosmetics, clothing and drugs.'[7]

The 2004 Royal Society report recommended that, 'Chemicals in the form of nanoparticles or nanotubes be treated as new substances,'[1] and that 'ingredients in the form of nanoparticles undergo a full safety assessment by the relevant scientific advisory body before they are permitted for use in products.'[1] In addition, the report suggests that the use of nanomaterials in cosmetics should be highlighted on the labels of consumer products.[1] Despite these cautionary statements, in a regulatory void cosmetic companies are increasingly deploying nanomaterials in cosmetic products.

Nanotechnology – The health risks

'Once inside the body [nanoparticles] seem to have unlimited access to all tissues and organs, including the brain and likely also the fetal circulation, and may cause cell damage that we don't yet understand .... Current regulations fail to guarantee consumers that these new technologies are safe to use.'[8]

National Resources Defense Council (NRDC), Nanotechnology's Invisible Threat, *December 2006.*

What's the problem?

Nanoparticles' strength may also be their curse. The toxicity and reactivity of particles depends on their surface area-to-mass ratio, which increases as the particles become smaller. Their tiny size gives them unique and useful properties. For example gold is inert in bulk form but in nanoparticle form it becomes reactive, making it a useful catalyst for use in the automobile and chemical industries, but when the particles reach around 2 nm they are small enough to bind to DNA, which could present health concerns. As nanoparticles decrease in size and the surface area increases, they have a greater ability to produce reactive oxygen species (ROS) – molecules formed naturally in the body through the metabolism of oxygen, which can cause oxidative damage in cells, tissues or organs, if there are too many for the body's repair mechanisms to cope with.

Dr Andrew Maynard says,

> 'There is research on particles in lungs, which shows a clear correlation between the impact on the lungs and the surface area of the particles for a given chemistry. We also know from research that the actual chemical make-up of the particle is important as well, so

the chemistry as well as the overall surface area is important.'

Researchers who collected ambient ultrafine (nanoscale) particulate pollutants in the Los Angeles Basin in California found ultrafine particles located in the mitochondria (energy-producing organelles) of macrophages and epithelial cells, causing 'major structural damage,' which may contribute to oxidative stress.[9] Inhalation of combustion-derived nanoparticles (CDNP) is associated with fibrosis, chronic inflammatory lung disease, metal fume fever and cancer.[10] Inhaled ambient air pollution ultrafine particles may play a part in the respiratory and cardiovascular mortality associated with particulate air pollutions.[11,12]

The tiny size of nanoparticles means that if they are able to penetrate the outer layer of skin, access the deeper layers and enter the bloodstream, they can be readily taken up by the human body, crossing membranes and, for example, entering the nucleus or the mitochondria and damaging the DNA.[13] Nanoparticles may reach the heart, if they are bloodborne, the brain after inhalation (particle exposure can potentially alter the brain structure), cross the placenta and enter bone marrow (where they could affect immunity).[13] Researchers found that certain nanoparticles translocated into the brain via the olfactory bulb (a structure of the brain involved in detecting odours) in mammals and fish.[14] They are also 'efficiently deposited by diffusional mechanisms in all regions of the respiratory tract,'[2] and the smaller the particles the further they are transported into the lungs.[15] Studies in rats and humans have shown that inhaled nano-sized particles are swiftly transferred to the bloodstream.[2] Nanoparticles could also reach lymph nodes, the spleen, access the central nervous system and may be absorbed through the skin. A variety of nanoparticles have caused elevated oxidative stress (which has been implicated in the cause of numerous illnesses), the release of pro-inflammatory mediators such as cytokines (protein molecules released by cells of the immune system), DNA damage and cell death in human tissue and cell cultures. Concerns have arisen over the use of nanoparticles in aerosol products, such as deodorant, due to the potential effects of inhalation.

Titanium dioxide is a white chemical used in sunscreens to reflect and scatter UV light and in various cosmetic products. In water, however, nano-sized particles of titanium dioxide result in the production of hydroxyl radicals, which can cause strand breaks in DNA. Nano-titanium dioxide also stimulates the production of reactive oxygen species under UV light, which is of concern given its use in sunscreens. The widespread use of nano-titanium dioxide and its possible entry into the body via inhalation, through the skin and through ingestion indicate that it presents a significant risk to humans, wildlife and aquatic organisms.[16]

Nano-titanium dioxide is much more chemically reactive than conventional titanium dioxide. Research has also shown that if administered to the lungs of rats it caused a significant inflammatory response at very low dose compared with rats inhaling larger titanium dioxide particles at the same mass dose.[2] Various studies have concluded that titanium dioxide used as a UV filter in sunscreens does not penetrate through the outermost layer of healthy skin, but if large amounts of nanoparticles are administered (as is often the case with repeated body applications of sunscreens over a prolonged period) a small uptake of nanoparticles may be of significance.

Zinc oxide, another chemical used in cosmetics in the form of nanoparticles, can also result in oxidative DNA damage under UV light, and mice fed nanoscale zinc powder for two weeks showed increased symptoms of lethargy, vomiting and diarrhoea compared with those given microscale zinc powder. Two of the mice exposed to nanoscale zinc powder died after one week.[17]

Cosmetics manufacturers routinely contest that the toxicity of nanoparticles does not present a problem because they remain in the stratus corneum (outer layer) of dead skin cells, but at this stage we cannot be entirely sure that this is the case. Dr Andrew Maynard suggests that:

> 'the current data is really inconclusive. The weight of evidence is on the side of most nanoparticles not penetrating the deeper layers of skin, but there are a number of studies that have suggested that certain types of nanoparticles go through. One study shows that if you start flexing the skin, there's a greater chance of particles penetrating through the surface and another study has shown that if you can change the surface chemistry of particles, you can do so in a way that will encourage the particles to go through the skin. So, while the chances are in most cases that these very small particles stay on top of the skin, more research is needed to understand what circumstances might encourage them to pass through.'

It is known that broken skin is a poor particle barrier, so the presence of acne, eczema, shaving cuts or severe sunburn may help the absorption of nanoparticles.[18] It is also important to bear in mind that a number of cosmetic ingredients are penetration enhancers, which may allow nanoparticles to reach deeper layers. The Scientific Committee on Consumer Products (SCCP) point out in their nanotechnology report produced for the EU Commission that, 'nanomaterials constituents (such as lipids or surfactants) may act as penetration enhancers by penetrating individually into the stratum corneum (after particle disruption on skin surface) and subsequently altering the intercellular lipid lamellae within this skin layer.'[4]

The intercellular lipid lamellae (internal structure) of the stratum corneum is thought to provide the permeability barrier of the epidermis,[19] ensuring the low water permeability of intact skin.[20] Although the SCCP consider it highly unlikely that nanoparticles will be passively transported through intact skin, they also suggest that 'if the skin is damaged, and the normal barrier disrupted, then the probability of entry of particles may be substantially increased.'[3] Unfortunately few studies have explored the absorption of nanoparticles through damaged skin. As Dr Andrew Maynard says, 'All the studies have focused on healthy skin and there has always been a concern that if you've got damaged skin you're going to have a set of conditions which will further enable nanoparticles to go through and reach the layers where you have the lymphatic system or blood system.'

Fullerenes

In 1985 a form of carbon known as the C60, fullerene or buckyball was discovered. Up until this point only two forms of carbon were known – diamond and graphite. The C60 molecule is shaped like a sphere, with 60 carbon atoms organized in a geodesic dome, or perhaps more recognizably, a standard, football-like pattern of 12 pentagons and 20 hexagons. Other carbon fullerenes studied include C70, C76 and C84 and cylindrical fullerenes are known as carbon nanotubes or buckytubes.

Fullerenes are being considered for a variety of applications. In fact, engineered C60 molecules are being used in some cosmetic products, such as facial moisturizers and creams, and are touted as powerful antioxidants. The toxicity of fullerenes has not been widely researched but they have been reported to be mutagenic (capable of bringing about or increasing the frequency of mutations in an organism) in *Salmonella typhimurium* bacteria (Ames test).[21] More shockingly, they have been shown to cause brain damage in fish. Nine juvenile largemouth bass were exposed to water containing modest concentrations (500 parts per billion) of fullerenes and after only 48 hours it was found that the fish had raised levels of 'lipid peroxidation', a type of oxidative degradation of lipids that has been linked in humans to Alzheimer's disease. Researchers also detected chemical markers in the liver indicating inflammation.[22] Environmental toxicologist Eva Oberdörster of Southern Methodist University in Dallas who conducted this research said, 'It is possible that effects in fish may predict potential effects in humans.'[14,23]

In another study, water-stirred fullerenes caused increased lipid peroxidation in the brains and gills of fathead minnow fish.[24] Other reported effects include oxidative damage in rat microsomes exposed to UV and visible light and photosensitization, DNA cleavage, mutagenicity, cancer initiation, cell toxicity under photoirradiation,[25] damage to lung tissue of mice if inhaled and a 50 per cent mortality rate among water fleas (tiny crustaceans that are a food source for other aquatic species).

Carbon nanotubes have demonstrated cytotoxicity to alveolar (lung) macrophages. The cytotoxicity of fullerenes depends on their structure. If the structure is slightly changed it can increase the toxicity by ten million. C60 molecules have been found to generate more reactive oxygen species (ROS) than other fullerenes.

Did you know?

• In 2006 sales of nanotechnology-related products reached almost €744 million. While just three years ago less than 40 nanopackaging products were on the market, now there are over 400.[26] Nanopackaging, such as food packaging, uses nanotechnology to enhance the performance of packaging materials, for instance by prolonging a product's shelf-life.

- The worldwide market for nanotechnologies is predicted to reach $1 trillion by 2015.[5]

- Since 2000 the US Federal Government has spent $1 billion a year on nanotechnologies research.[5]

Regulating nanotechnology

Culminating in 2007 the Council for Science and Technology, a top-level government advisory body, conducted a two-year review of the UK government's promise of progress on investigating the health and environmental consequences of nanotechnology, following the government's response to the Royal Society and Royal Academy of Engineering report, *Nanoscience and Nanotechnologies: Opportunities and Uncertainties*.[1] The CST stated that 'there has been virtually nothing done by government to resolve this problem.'[27] The review chairman said 'It's totally absurd to have a report ... and then not do the research that was your number one target.'[27]

Over the last five years the UK government has spent £10 million on nanotechnology, with only £3 million spent on toxicology and the health and environmental implications of nanomaterials.[5] This is a drop in the ocean compared with the £40 million per annum awarded by the Engineering and Physical Sciences Research Council (EPSRC) for nanotechnology progress and £90 million invested over a six-year period by the Department of Trade and Industry (DTI) for commercialization of nanotechnology.

In 2005 the UK government set up the Nanotechnology Research Coordination Group (NRCG) to establish and oversee the implementation of a research programme into the possible health and environmental risks associated with free engineered nanomaterials. It did isolate research priorities but cannot award research funding that relies on scientists applying for research council grants.[5] Funding is available to assess the health and environmental risks of nanotechnology, but few researchers have actually applied for it.[5]

In September 2006 the UK Department for Environment, Food and Rural Affairs (Defra) set up a voluntary reporting scheme, enabling the industry to divulge information about the potential risks of free engineered nanomaterials to the government, but according to the CST report, so far only a few organizations have disclosed data.

The report also notes that there is little documentation explaining how current regulations will be applied to nanotechnology. The REACH (Registration, Evaluation, Authorisation and Restriction of Chemicals) legislation described in Chapter 1 has not provided a separate classification for nanomaterials, apart from fullerenes, and the CST states that the 1 tonne per annum stipulation in REACH is not appropriate for nanotechnology.[5]

The UK's Royal Society, the Nanotechnology Industries Association, Insight Investment and the government-sponsored Nanotechnology Knowledge Transfer Network are currently consulting on a global voluntary code of conduct that would offer guidance on what companies can do to demonstrate that they are using nanotechnology responsibly, in the absence of comprehensive legislation. The aim is to protect researchers, plant workers and consumers from the potential adverse health effects of nano-engineered products and packaging.[26] A draft code is available for consultation.

The EU Commission has also consulted on a European Code of Conduct for Responsible Nanosciences and Nanotechnologies Research, following on from the responsible strategy endorsed by member states in 2004 and the Nanotechnologies Action Plan 2005–9, which proposes a code of conduct. The document for consultation advocates a precautionary approach and culture of responsibility in which in the event of uncertainty, member states work to ensure the safety of individuals.[28]

The EU Commission has developed the Seventh Framework Programme (FP7) for scientific research into nanotechnology and technological development, following on from previous programmes to this end, and has allocated around €3.5 billion for funding research related to nanotechnology over six years, out of €50.5 billion available. This includes funding for other areas as well as health and environmental effects. Funding has increased from previous programmes from €120 million under FP4 to the €3.5 billion under FP7, so the issue is being taken seriously, but since 1998 only around €28 million has been expressly dedicated to the possible impact of nanotechnologies on health and the environment.[29] The EU Commission is currently intending to review current regulation to ascertain whether new regulatory action is necessary to cover the possible risks presented by nanotechnology.

In the USA, the Project on Emerging Nanotechnologies at the Woodrow Wilson Center in Washington DC, has served as a forum for debate about the Responsible Nano Code. Chief scientist of the Project on Emerging Nanotechnologies, Dr Andrew Maynard, is not totally convinced that the US government is doing enough to ensure the safety of nanomaterials, stating at a hearing held by the US Congress's House Science Committee,

CHAPTER 5: NANOTECHNOLOGY   127

'There is a yawning knowledge-gap between nanomaterials entering commerce now, and what we know about their safety, and this uncertainty over how to develop nanotechnologies safely is hamstringing regulators, paralysing nano-businesses and confusing consumers.'[30]

In 2006 the US Food and Drug Administration (FDA) announced the formation of an FDA Nanotechnology Task Force, charged with establishing how best to regulate this technology and promote the ongoing development of innovative and safe FDA-regulated products that use nanotechnology materials. A report was released by the task force in July 2007, recommending that the FDA consider developing guidance for manufacturers about when the use of nanoscale ingredients may require extra data to be submitted and consider 'pursuing regulatory measures that take into account the potential importance of material size and the evolving state of the science,'[31] along with adopting other strategies to address the benefits and risks of FDA-regulated products using nanotechnology.[31]

However, as a report (prepared by the Congressional Research Service (CRS) for the US Congress) highlights, much of the data held by companies developing nanomaterials is proprietary and they 'will not voluntarily reveal details about production processes or even the chemical composition or physical structure of their nanomaterials, due to concerns about competition, potential effect of regulatory decisions, and potential liability'.[32] This hinders the scientific evaluation of nanoscale materials along with the diverse nature of nanotechnology, which means that academics are usually only familiar with certain fields of research and cannot even agree among themselves on a common terminology.[32] Nanotechnology may be little understood, but this hasn't stopped governments investing billions of dollars into developing the technology and its field of application.

Director David Rejeski of the Project on Emerging Nanotechnologies indicates that the FDA Task Force report is a small step forward, but 'the agency must act rapidly to adopt and fully implement the Nanotechnology Task Force's recommendations', to keep up to speed with this rapidly developing area of technology.[33] Some might say they are already too far behind to ever catch up, especially in the realm of cosmetics, where the FDA lacks resources, funding and regulatory oversight. Michael R. Taylor, former FDA deputy commissioner for policy and a professor at the University of Maryland School of Medicine, remarked in a 2006 report commissioned by the Project on Emerging Nanotechnologies that the FDA is not 'nano ready' due to dwindling resources and capacity caused in part by inadequate funding from Congress, which could potentially lead the agency to miss safety concerns or discover them too late, potentially putting the public's health at risk and hindering innovation.[34]

Friends of the Earth have called for the labelling of nanoparticle-containing products, but the FDA Task Force report concluded that mandatory labelling was unnecessary 'because the current science does not support a finding that classes of products with nanoscale materials necessarily present greater safety concerns than classes of products without nanoscale materials'.[31] Meanwhile, the general public continue to serve as nanotech guinea pigs as the the global market for nanotechnology (currently estimated at $62 million and expected to grow to $2.6 trillion in manufactured goods by 2014[24]) skyrockets.

The industry fights back

Question Does nanotechnology used in cosmetic products pose a risk to consumers because the miniscule nanoparticles can enter deeper layers of the skin and have been shown to cause DNA and lung damage in animal studies?

Answer 'Nanotechnology is a very broad term and covers many different things. Nanomaterials are only used in cosmetics where the company involved can (and must be able to) demonstrate the safety of the product, including those actual ingredients in use. This means any cosmetic product currently on the market that includes nanotechnology won't pose any risk to consumers.

Nanotechnology in cosmetics is currently used to a very limited degree but is certainly being investigated to see if there are any beneficial effects to using it more widely. There are some nano-emulsions that in use, break down into oil and water phases; it is used simply to give unusual texture to the product and a clarity not possible with conventional emulsion technology. Indeed, milk is a nano-emulsion and ricotta cheese is largely composed of man-made nanoparticles, and yet neither of these cause concern.

The most widespread use of nanomaterials in cosmetic products at present is in sunscreens where titanium dioxide in micro- and nanoparticle sizes help to provide a high level of protection against the sun's rays. Extensive testing has shown conclusively that these particles do not penetrate the skin. Whilst some studies have shown that some other nanoparticles may be absorbed into the body, such studies are not relevant to cosmetic ingredients. Remember that nanoparticles are many times larger than molecules and we are well aware that not all molecules behave identically. In the same way, each nanomaterial should be considered a unique substance and investigated on its own merits. Only those whose safety can be demonstrated are allowed in cosmetic products.'

Dr Christopher Flower, director-general, the Cosmetic, Toiletry and Perfumery Association (CTPA).

Chapter 6
What *is* a natural beauty product?

What is a synthetic chemical?

The United States Department of Agriculture (USDA) Organic Standard defines the terms synthetic and non-synthetic (or natural) as follows:

• **Synthetic** – a substance that is formulated or manufactured by a chemical process or by a process that chemically changes a substance extracted from naturally occurring plant, animal, or mineral sources, except that such term shall not apply to substances created by naturally occurring biological processes.

• **Non-synthetic (natural)** – a substance that is derived from mineral, plant, or animal matter and does not undergo a synthetic process as defined in section 6502(21) of the Act (7 U.S.C. 6502(21)). For the purposes of this part, non-synthetic is used as a synonym for natural as the term is used in the Act.[1]

With all the concerns about chemicals in beauty products can we safely turn to products labelled 'natural' and 'organic' instead? Unfortunately all is not as it seems in the world of natural beauty. 'Organic' and 'natural' have become lucrative marketing claims in the 21st century. Consumers generally associate these two words with products that are healthier, derived from more ethical and environmentally friendly sources and minus synthetic additives. Market analysts Euromonitor International stated in 2007 that 'cosmetics companies are forgetting glamour and going back to nature as natural and organic brands become among the most sought after on the market'.[2] We are becoming increasingly concerned about the content of our food, cosmetics and other consumer products.

Defining natural and organic

- **Natural** – ingredients extracted directly from plants, animal products or the earth, which have undergone minimal or no processing. In practice, a cosmetic product containing a single natural ingredient in a low concentration amid a myriad of synthetic chemicals could still be labelled as natural.

- **Organic** – usually refers to non-genetically modified ingredients that have been derived from crops grown in an ecological manner, with respect for the environment, without the use of artificial pesticides, herbicides, fertilizers and other toxic synthetic ingredients and processed using natural ingredients. In reality, the term organic may be used even if a cosmetic product contains as little as 1 per cent organic ingredients.

Marketers spoon-feed us what we want to hear, which is dependent on their large-scale consumer research. Alisa Marie Beyer, CEO of the Benchmarking Company, Washington DC says:

'To maintain a solid place in [the female consumer's] heart, brand managers should evaluate the use of applicable marketing messages

> *she likes to hear most, such as reduces wrinkles, hypoallergenic,*
> *natural/organic/pure ingredients, and works with her own body*
> *chemistry.'[3]*

Unfortunately there are no official government standards for what some of the marketing terms above should represent, so companies can, largely speaking, get away with liberally using them, substantiated or otherwise.

Despite the growing demand for 'organic' and 'natural' consumer products, the past lack of an official definition for the terms led to a proliferation of pseudo-natural brands. Over recent years the United States Department of Agriculture (USDA) has allowed personal care products to be certified to the standards of their National Organic Program, which were originally developed for agricultural products. These standards contain legal definitions of synthetic and natural (non-synthetic) substances, generating angst for brands who wish to continue misusing the terms 'natural' and 'organic', without raising suspicions about the integrity of their product compositions. Many of these brands use the terms liberally for products that may contain a small percentage of, or even no organic and natural ingredients whatsoever. Even more astonishingly, some of the products advertised as 'certified organic' (but without genuine USDA organic certification) are almost entirely composed of synthetic ingredients, with floral waters counted as organic components in the percentages of organic content. This is misleading for consumers who often assume that organic food standards also apply to cosmetic products labelled as 'organic'.

Even products sold in health food stores often contain cheap water extracts of organic herbs and perhaps a few other token organic ingredients amidst synthetic cleansers and conditioners that are frequently derived from petrochemicals. Diana Kaye and James Hahn, founders of USDA-certified organic beauty brand Terressentials faced innumerable obstacles to getting their range stocked by health retailers:

> *'We thought that they would be very interested in healthier*
> *products. We couldn't have been more wrong. We learned, first-hand,*
> *that the vast majority of the store owners and managers did not*
> *want to learn about the toxic chemicals used in beauty products*
> *and, curiously, did not want to offer our products. For years, this*
> *situation had us baffled. Finally, one store owner told us the truth.*
> *She said that, though our products were the best that she had seen*
> *in years, she wasn't going to bring them into her store, because to do*
> *so would make her other products look bad!'[4]*

Healthy skin naturally

'Healthy skin is dependent on good digestion and effective de-toxing so it's important to ensure your digestive tract and liver are in good working order first. To keep your skin healthy you should, on a daily basis, drink at least six glasses of water, eat five daily servings of colourful fruit and vegetables, consume a tablespoon of mixed fresh seeds and a tablespoon of cold pressed seed oils. In addition you should eat three servings of oily fish a week, ensure you consume plenty of fibre-rich foods, try to sometimes use alternatives to dairy such as soya milk and tofu, include vegetables sources of protein such as beans and lentils and have low-fat, live, organic yoghurt.'

Patrick Holford, leading nutritionist, founder of the Institute of Optimum Nutrition and author of Solve Your Skin Problems.

The oleochemical con

Many 'natural' and 'organic' brands contain oleochemicals, which are principally derived from vegetable oils (palm and coconut) or less frequently, animal fats (such as tallow) but are structurally similar to petrochemicals. They are often used as surfactants in cleansing products, such as shampoos, body washes, household detergents and industrial cleaning products. Oleochemical emollients are also used to soften the skin. Because they are derived from renewable resources, oleochemicals are often lauded as an environmental friendly alternative to petrochemicals. Products containing oleochemicals may be labelled as '100 per cent organic' when in reality a single ingredient in the formulation is organically produced.

Both petrochemical and oleochemical surfactants are derived from natural sources: while oleochemicals come from plants, petrochemicals are derived from crude oil which, originates from fossilized vegetation.

A significant stage in the manufacture of oleochemicals is the hydrogenation of vegetable oils, during which they are heated to around 200°C in the presence of hydrogen and a metal catalyst, such as copper chromate, nickel, palladium or platinium. Following hydrogenation the waxy fats produced are filtered to remove the catalyst, bleached and deodorized.

Hydrogenated fats, fatty acids and emulsifying waxes are commonly used in cosmetic products because they are cheap, have a long shelf-life and give the formulation a pleasing feel, but they are not authorized for use in certified organic food products because they are produced through chemical processes and may be contaminated with petrochemicals or metal catalyst residues.

Diana Kaye, director of organic beauty brand Terressentials says,

> *'Most people would be surprised to learn that the ingredients —
> vegetable emulsifying wax (a.k.a. soy wax), coconut fatty acids, cetyl
> alcohol and jojoba butter/beads — that are frequently used in 'all
> natural' and even 'organic' personal care products are hydrogenated
> synthetically-reacted materials. These hydrogenated fats are synthetic
> waxy substances that are virtually indistinguishable from ordinary
> shortening.'*[5]

It has been suggested that the topical application of 'trans fats' (a term used in the food industry to refer to a nutritionally undesirable type of fat) may disrupt normal prostaglandin function. Prostaglandins are lipid compounds with hormone-like effects that serve vital functions in the body such as controlling inflammation and blood pressure, relaxing the muscles in the walls of blood vessels and regulating acid secretion of the stomach. Trans fats or trans fatty acids are primarily produced by partially hydrogenating vegetable oils. We know the health risks associated with consuming hydrogenated fats in food, such as elevated levels of 'bad' cholesterol and increased risk of heart disease and type 2 diabetes, so why would we want to apply them to our bodies?

Oleochemicals are often represented as a 'green' alternative to petro-chemicals but researchers studying the energy and material requirements and environmental releases for surfactants used in European consumer detergents concluded that:

> *'The production of each surfactant has an impact on the
> environment via the consumption of a broad variety of resources
> such as crude oil, natural gas, agricultural products and minerals for
> material feedstock, energy generation and transport purposes. Also,
> environmental emissions occur during the production and transport
> of all surfactants. Based on the findings of this study, no technical
> or scientific basis exists to support a general environmental*

superiority claim, either for an individual surfactant or for the various options for sourcing from petrochemical, oleochemical or agricultural feedstocks and minerals.'[6]

In addition, a palm oil-based surfactant used in the USA or Europe will have involved producers in South-East Asia who grow the palm trees. The international trade in palm oil is a key factor in rainforest destruction and large-scale human rights abuses in Malaysia and Indonesia,[7] where without compensation or consultation the indigenous peoples' land is seized and handed over to companies for the development of monoculture palm oil plantations. Between 1985 and 2000 as much as 87 per cent of the deforestation in Malaysia can be attributed to palm oil plantations.[8]

Oleochemical manufacturers often claim that palm oil plantations bring much needed employment and infrastructural development to these regions, but the plantation work is usually poorly paid and exposes workers to illegal agrochemicals, such as the toxic herbicide paraquat. Nearby villagers report the decline of local fish stocks, contaminated drinking and bathing water and rises in birth defects and fertility problems.[8] The reality is that oleochemicals and 'organic' are not synonymous and the increasing reliance on palm oil as a raw material, or as the industry call it, a 'feedstock', is most certainly not environmentally or human friendly.

Some organic brands cold-press the natural plant oils used in their cosmetics, which is considered a healthier and less energy-intensive alternative to oleochemical and petrochemical production. Hector Bolanos, joint managing director of organic beauty brand Raw Gaia, says,

'Raw, living ingredients are better for you and your skin simply because the natural ingredients retain all their life energy, antioxidants, minerals, vitamins and essential fatty acids. The crucial aspect is that in order to ensure that all these nutrients are retained products must be made at temperatures below 40°C. If ingredients are heated above this level during the manufacturing process, most of the antioxidants, minerals and vitamins in the ingredients are destroyed. One of the best examples of this is oils and fats, which when heated produce highly toxic trans fatty acids and lead to the creation of free radicals. In contrast, cold-pressed fats and oils retain all the natural goodness of the ingredient.'[9]

Although cold-pressed oil should be produced at lower temperatures, the lack of labelling regulation means that companies can market oils as 'cold-pressed' when they have been heated to temperatures of up to 243°C in the USA (the EU has imposed standards for the terminology of cold pressing). While cold pressing seems to be a preferable alternative to oleochemicals or petrochemicals from the consumer's viewpoint, it is more costly because heating oil produces a higher yield than cold pressing, so it is not the processing method of choice for most manufacturers.

Pure and natural?

Most organic ingredients are produced in the same facilities as synthetic ingredients, using the same equipment. Bob Durst, consultant at Simple Organic Solutions, who inspects organic processing plants, says, 'Very few of the facilities are solely organic. They may only do a couple of runs a year or a couple of runs a week organically and the rest of the time they process conventional ingredients.' There is always a risk of contamination, according to Bob Durst, 'that is one of the reasons why the inspectors go in and look at these things, to check whether contamination is a possibility and whether procedures are in place to prevent that from happening'.

Natural doesn't necessarily mean organic either. There is no guarantee that natural ingredients within a product are derived from, for example, crops grown without the use of artificial pesticides and fertilizers, or produced without chemical intermediates and intensive chemical processes. The natural substance shea butter, for example, is often extracted with solvents, chemically bleached, deodorized and then treated with synthetic preservatives such as butylated hydroxyanisole and butylated hydroxytoluene. Glyceryl caprylate, manufactured by a chemical reaction known as esterification and commonly used in recognized 'natural' and 'organic' products, is also used as an agricultural pesticide to target mites and fungi on crops.[10]

Grapefruit seed extract

Grapefruit seed extract – a natural compound found in grapefruit pulp – is converted into synthetic compounds via an intensive chemical process. Some commercial grapefruit seed extracts have been found to contain the synthetic antimicrobial agent benzethonium chloride, commonly used in cosmetic products, along with the synthetic chemicals triclosan and methylparaben.[11] The Swiss Toxicological Information Centre state that grapefruit seed extracts containing benzethonium chloride in concentrations of 7–11 per cent may present a major health risk, if significant amounts of a concentrated solution are ingested. Skin or eye exposure may also cause toxic symptoms.[12] This is particularly of concern because the USDA detected benzethonium chloride in commercial grapefruit seed extracts at concentrations of 8 per cent.[11] The Scientific Committee on Cosmetic Products and Non-food Products Intended for Consumers (SCCNFP) evaluated benzethonium chloride based on research conducted and found that the effects of this substance on experimental animals (depending on the dose administered and route of administration) included signs of liver damage, growth retardation, skin lesions, decreased thymus weights, decreased body weight of rat pups, maternal toxicity, fetal mortality, skeletal malformations and gastrointestinal lesions. In conclusion, the SCCNFP stated that 'benzethonium chloride has moderate acute toxicity by the oral route and high toxicity following parental exposure ... the data provided in the submitted dossier does not support the requested use of benzethonium chloride as a preservative in leave-on products'.[13]

Essential oils

Essential oils, routinely used in conventional and 'natural' or 'organic' cosmetics, are extracted by various processes including cold pressing, distillation, steam distillation, hydrodiffusion extraction, carbon dioxide extraction and solvent extraction – which yields more essential oil at a lower cost than the other methods, but can leave behind residues of the solvent. Some essential oils can cause skin irritation, contact allergies, photosensitivity and cytoxicity to human skin cells. The topical application of certain essential oils, such as lavender and tea tree oil has been linked to cases of gynaeco-mastia (development of prominent breast tissue in males) in three pubertal boys. Once the topical use of products containing these oils was discontinued the gynaecomastia resolved. Researchers at the US National Institute of Environmental Health Sciences discovered that both lavender and tea tree oil demonstrate weak oestrogenic and anti-androgenic activities in cultured human breast cancer cells.[14] Citral and geraniol may possibly interact with oestrogen receptors, but this is at very high concentrations.[15] There is a need for more research addressing the potential adverse health effects of essential oils.

'Natural' preservatives?

Formulations containing water require some form of preservative to inhibit microbial growth. Products labelled as 'natural' and 'organic' often contain synthetic preservatives such as:

- **Benzoic acid** – a carboxylic acid that can cause skin irritation and aggravate asthma symptoms. It is produced commercially by partial oxidation of toluene with oxygen, using cobalt or manganese naphthenates as a catalyst.

- **Benzyl alcohol** – a volatile flammable liquid prepared by heating a mixture of benzyl chloride, sodium carbonate and water or by hydrolysis, benzyl alcohol may contain benzaldehyde as an impurity. It is a skin irritant and severe eye irritant linked to contact dermatitis and urticaria. Benzyl alcohol affects lipid bilayers and has caused benign tumours of the adrenal gland in mice when given in high doses. Its vapours can irritate the nose and throat and ingestion can cause central nervous system depression.

- **Dehydroacetic acid** – is readily absorbed by the skin and classified as 'harmful' by the European Commission. A material safety data sheet (MSDS) for this substance suggests that it may be toxic to the kidneys, liver and central nervous system and may cause cancer based on animal test data. Repeated or prolonged exposure may result in target organ damage.[16]

- **Diazolidinyl urea** – is produced by the reaction of allantoin and formaldehyde in the presence of sodium hydroxide solution and heat, after which the mixture is neutralized with hydrochloric acid and evaporated. It may cause contact dermatitis in some individuals and is a formaldehyde releaser.

- **DMDM hydantoin** – can cause skin irritation, contact allergies and skin sensitization. In products where DEA or DEA-containing compounds are present, the carcinogenic chemical N-nitrosodiethanolamine (NDELA) may be generated. It is also a formaldehyde releaser.

- **Parabens** – these esters of para-hydroxybenzoic acid have been shown to be oestrogenic in various studies and may cause contact allergies in some individuals. All commercially used parabens are chemically synthesized.

- **Phenoxyethanol** – a glycol ether produced by reaction between phenol and ethylene oxide at elevated temperature and pressure. Phenol is a toxic agent that is associated with a risk of lung cancer in those occupationally exposed. It is also a penetration enhancer and can adversely affect the central nervous system and cause severe burns at concentrations of 1–2 per cent. Ethylene oxide is a known human carcinogen and probable neurotoxicant. It can also cause skin, eye and respiratory irritation.

- **Sodium benzoate** – produced by reaction between benzoic acid and sodium hydroxide or sodium carbonate, sodium benzoate has caused endocrine disruption in experimental animals, although this was at high doses, along with reproductive effects such as fetotoxicity, skin irritation and brain and nervous system effects.

- **Sodium hydroxymethylglycinate** – a synthetic substance derived from glycine (aminoacetic acid) that lacks safety data on the health risks associated with chronic exposure. It may cause skin and eye irritation and is a formaldehyde releaser.

Diana Kaye, co-founder of organic beauty brand Terressentials suggests that natural ingredients such as organic grain alcohol and vinegar can be used to preserve products, but many brands opt for cheaper ingredients. Bob Durst, consultant with Simple Organic Solutions and member of the Organic Trade Association (OTA) Personal Care Task Force and NSF Personal Care Joint Committee, adds:

> *'There are a lot of people who are opposed to change and will claim that they cannot possibly produce organic personal care products without synthetic preservatives, when in fact they may have not tested thoroughly, are being over-cautious, have not looked at alternatives, or have considered alternatives but found them to be not quite as effective or more expensive. I think there is a lot of resistance in the marketplace to making changes that they feel might be somewhat detrimental to either the shelf-life of the product or to their bottom line.'*

Obstacles to organic

Manufacturers of organic beauty products also face the problem of limited availability of organic raw materials and ingredients. Common ingredients tend to be non-organic and if they are organic it can be difficult to acquire large quantities. People can be put off by the premium prices of organic beauty products and the costs of production tend to be higher for organic farms due to the avoidance of cheap chemicals, crop rotations and better animal welfare standards. That said, non-organic farms result in environmental deterioration, culminating in extra costs, so the variance is not as great as it would initially seem.

The Natural Ingredient Resource Center has defined a natural ingredient as 'present in or produced by nature, produced using minimal physical processing, directly extracted using simple methods, simple chemical reactions or resulting from naturally occurring biological processes', with natural ingredients being, 'grown harvested, raised and processed in an ecological manner, not produced synthetically, free of all petrochemicals, not extracted or processed using anything other than natural ingredients as solvents, not exposed to radiation and not genetically modified'.[17] This definition is nice in theory, but not typically the kind of 'natural' ingredients used in most cosmetic products.

Watered down: Greenwashing synthetic products

Natural beauty is becoming big business and some brands are prepared to stoop very low in order to convince consumers that their products are truly organic. One practice used to mislead consumers is making the water component of a cosmetic formulation a diluted infusion of numerous herbs (in order to justify their organic claim) and filling the rest of the product with cheap synthetic chemicals. Ingredients must be listed on cosmetic products in descending order of weight, so the herbal infusion will appear first on the ingredients label to give the illusion of a natural product.

Another crafty trick used by some pseudo-natural brands is including the water component of their products when determining the percentage of organic materials. Water is not organic, it's an agricultural product and certification bodies such as the USDA disallow this practice in their regulations. By combining a weak herbal tea infusion with a variety of synthetic chemicals a manufacturer can claim, for instance, that their product 'contains 70 per cent organic ingredients', when in reality it contains around 70 per cent water and 30 per cent synthetic chemicals.

Floral water (or hydrosol) is the leftover water collected when plants are distilled to produce essential oils and and is often used to make fraudulent organic claims, when in reality only a residue of the floral water is actually organic, because the rest is just plain old water! Craig Minowa, environmental scientist with the US Organic Consumers Association (OCA) says, 'Current fraudulent labeling on organic body care products has resulted in a small handful of large cosmetics companies taking the lion's share of market sales for organics by taking standard synthetic products and watering them down with poorly regulated and overly diluted hydrosols.'[18]

There is nothing inherently wrong with using water in beauty products when the remaining ingredients are organic, but there is something very wrong with fooling consumers into believing that a synthetic chemical concoction with watered down hydrosols is a natural, organic product.

Natural v. synthetic

Not everyone is convinced that natural means better. Philippa Darbre, senior lecturer in oncology at the University of Reading says, 'A natural chemical for me is no different from a synthetic chemical, whether it is extracted from a natural or synthetic source. A chemical is a chemical. A compound is defined by its chemical structure.'[19]

Synthetic versions of natural substances are identical in structure and cheaper to produce. Methyl salicylate (oil of wintergreen) is extracted from plants but it is more cost effective for manufacturers to synthesize it from raw materials derived from coal tar and petroleum. As well as copying chemicals found in nature, scientists also try to enhance them by making modifications; for example, vanillin can readily be converted to ethyl-vanillin, which is considerably more potent.[20]

Craig Minowa, environmental scientist with the US Organic Consumers Association (OCA) suggests that the argument in favour of synthetically producing natural ingredients,

> 'completely walks outside the perimeter of the simple logic of what an "organic" and a "natural organic" ingredient is. Natural means that it is naturally derived, it hasn't been chemically synthesized in a laboratory, for example, extracting an oil directly from a plant, versus chemically formulating the same chemical composition in the laboratory with synthetic ingredients. Sure you can make the exact same chemical composition but as far as the definition goes and what consumers are expecting of the farmer's role in that whole process, it's a completely different world.'

A standard definition of 'natural' in the *Oxford English Dictionary* is 'existing in or derived from nature; not made, caused by, or processed by humankind'. This seems to be pretty far removed from the conventional *and* 'natural' cosmetics industry's interpretation of the term.

Did you know?

A 2007 consumer survey implemented by the US Organic Consumers Association (OCA) and taken by over 5,500 consumers who frequently purchase organic products, found that:

• Nearly 50 per cent of respondents incorrectly believe that a product labelled as 'Made with organic ingredients', contains either 'all' or 'nearly all' organic ingredients.

• Seventy-six per cent of survey respondents also indicated that products labelled as 'organic' should be 100 per cent organic.

• Almost 42 per cent of survey respondents felt that products labelled as '70 per cent organic' should not contain synthetic ingredients unless they are made from organic agricultural material.[21]

It's natural ... I swear!

Some brands can be very disingenuous with the language they use in their marketing copy, on ingredients labels and even brand names. Claims that products are sodium lauryl sulphate free, petrochemical free, paraben free, and so on, do not necessarily indicate that these products are completely free from synthetic chemicals, simply that they have chosen to eliminate the specific synthetic compounds mentioned. Cosmetic ingredients derived from animal or vegetable sources often undergo significant chemical processing before finding their way into our products. Some products labelled as 'organic' actually contain petroleum-derived compounds. Also beware of the claim 'chemical free' often used on products branded as natural. Everything contains chemicals! A natural substance is still a chemical. It is the demarcation between a natural and synthetic chemical that is the vital issue, not the fact that it is a chemical.

Many companies are opting to use surfactants derived from plant sources instead of petroleum, such as olefin sulphonate (derived from coconut oil) and cocamidopropyl betaine and oleyl betaine (derived from coconut and palm oils). Although these compounds are derived from natural substances they still need to be processed using the same chemical reactions as petroleum-based surfactants, and the end product is synthetic.

Cocamidopropyl betaine, commonly used in cosmetic products labelled as 'organic' and 'natural', is an important occupational hazard for hairdressers,[22] causing sensitization and allergic contact dermatitis. It may contain residues of the chemicals used in its production and some allergic reactions are believed to be a consequence of the impurity dimethylaminopropylamine, which has been identified as a contaminant in many cosmetics, shampoos and detergents.[23] Dimethylaminopropylamine is a high production petrochemical compound manufactured and distributed by large petrochemical corporations, also used as a petrol additive, an intermediate in the production of corrosion inhibitors for aviation fuel and wastewater treatment. It is believed to be corrosive to the skin and eyes and a sensitisizing allergen. Russian researchers have found this compound, which may be toxic to aquatic species, in wastewaters in close proximity to petrochemical plants and oil refineries.[23]

That's not to say that all synthetic ingredients are inherently unsafe. Bob Durst, consultant with Simple Organic Solutions and member of the Organic Trade Association (OTA) Personal Care Task Force and NSF Personal Care Joint Committee, says:

> 'When you get into processing, particularly with personal care products, there are a lot of synthetic reactions that are necessary to produce the category of products. You can't make soap without saponification. That is just a fact of life. Saponification, transesterification etc. are chemical processes and there are changes in the molecular make-up of the feedstock so you don't recognize the end product from the feedstock going in. The same thing happens on the food side. Baking is a chemical process. Lots of things in the food industry are chemical processes.'

Some of the organic standards for personal care products (such as the recent NSF International Draft Standards) aim to use the most benign processes, and require organic agricultural materials as feedstock, 'so it's a compromise or a sell-out to the organic fanatic, but if you are going to have this category of products it's necessary', says Bob Durst. Despite this fact, including the term 'organic' in a brand name or producing products labelled as 'organic' seems somewhat erroneous when there is a lack of due regard for product composition.

Going against the grain

Amidst a dearth of genuinely natural cosmetic products, lies the brand Eselle. Founder, Sarah McIntyre, explains why she developed a 100 per cent organic beauty range.

'The Eselle brand was set up in 2006. It grew from my personal feeling of despair at how the consumer was hoodwinked into buying products that stated they were natural and were anything but! I would look up the MSDS (material safety data sheets) on various chemical additives and found them to be toxic. From this intensive research I developed a 100 per cent organic range of Soil Association certified products in the UK, and I am pleased to still be completely hands on in the developing and making of the products.'

Chapter 7
Organic labelling initiatives

Organic crop production (for foodstuffs) has been regulated in the UK since 1993 but there is no European legislation pertaining to the certification of organic ingredients for cosmetic products. The organic research organization Organic Monitor has forecast a shake-up of the natural cosmetics industry in 2008, as a number of new natural and organic standards are introduced, primarily in the USA, and private European certification bodies undertake the harmonization of standards for certified natural and organic beauty products. The most rigorous standards internationally are those of the US Department of Agriculture (USDA).

Some individuals and organizations have criticized the proliferation of 'organic' certification standards as a flagrant attempt to undermine official USDA standards with diluted versions, effectively legitimizing the explosion of organic-labelled products containing synthetic ingredients. Craig Minowa, environmental scientist with the US Organic Consumers Association (OCA) says, 'Currently, various big body care companies and interests are using their influence to shape weak and watered down organic standards for body care products. This is being done in a manner that serves to dramatically increase their profit margins at the expense of public health and the environment, while putting legitimate organic farmers and body care producers out of business.'[1]

Why the US standards are the best

What are the USDA standards? In the USA, the Organic Foods Production Act of 1990 required the USDA to develop national standards for organically produced agricultural products. This Act, along with the National Organic Program (NOP) – a marketing programme within the USDA, requires that agricultural products labelled as organic are derived from farms certified by a USDA-accredited State or private agency. The National Organic Standards (NOS) in the USA were finally disclosed in December 2000 and implemented in 2002, with organic foods sold in the USA displaying the USDA organic seal.

There are various types of organic labelling ranging from products with less than 70 per cent organic ingredients to those with 100 per cent organic ingredients:

- Processed agricultural products sold or labelled as '100 per cent organic' must contain 100 per cent organically produced raw or processed agricultural products (excluding water and salt) and may bear the USDA organic seal.
- Products sold or labelled as 'organic' must not contain less than 95 per cent organically produced raw or processed agricultural products and additional ingredients should be organically produced unless they are not available in this form, in which case they should be non-agricultural ingredients or products that meet the requirements of the standards (i.e. on the NOP's National List of allowed substances) and may bear the USDA organic seal.
- Products containing at least 70 per cent certified organic ingredients can be labelled as 'made with organic', and the remaining 30 per cent of contents may include non-organic agricultural ingredients that do not contain synthetic compounds. They cannot bear the USDA organic seal.[2]

Although the standards were initially developed to certify agricultural products, a 2002 USDA directive opened the door to producers of non-food products containing agricultural ingredients (such as personal care products, pet food, dietary supplements and textiles) allowing them to certify products compliant with the NOP standards. Despite pressure to remove personal care products from the jurisdiction of the USDA-NOP standards, the USDA seal remains available to those products that are able to meet the standards. This means that products bearing this seal are your best bet for legitimate organic beauty. Be aware that some brands fraudulently use the seal on their website when their products are not certified, so always check that the product itself carries the seal.

Adherence to organic industry standards is not enforced by the USDA, but beauty brands fraudulently using the USDA organic seal for their products can be fined.

Call yourself organic?

Here is a list of ingredients for a cleansing body mousse by a well-known brand that exclusively sells products marketed as 'organic' and 'natural', which are certified as 'organic' by a recognized certification body. This particular certified product contains only two organic ingredients.

- **Aqua** – water.

- **Aloe barbadensis leaf juice★** – gel obtained from the leaves of the aloe vera plant.

- **Coco glucoside** – produced by the condensation of coconut alcohol with glucose. It has not been assessed for safety but is considered to be a very mild surfactant.

- **Parfum (fragrance)** – the product doesn't specify whether the fragrance ingredients are natural, only that 99.4 per cent of the content is derived from natural origin, which means that numerous synthetic fragrance ingredients derived from natural sources may potentially be present.

- **Limonene** – colourless terpene present in certain trees and bushes that can also be synthetically produced. It can cause skin, eye and respiratory irritation, skin sensitization and contact allergies.

- **Linalool** – terpene alcohol present in many flowers and plants. Can cause skin, eye and respiratory irritation and skin sensitization.

- **Citral** – yellow liquid present in the oils of several

plants. Can cause skin irritation and skin
sensitization.

• **Eugenol** – occurs in various plant essential oils. Can
cause contact dermatitis, skin irritation, inhibition of
peripheral sensory nerve activity at low doses and
result in neurotoxicity at high doses.

• **Geraniol** – occurs in various plant essential oils. Can
cause contact allergies and skin irritation.

• **Cocamidopropyl betaine** – synthetic chemical that
may contain dimethylaminopropylamine as an
impurity, which can cause sensitization and allergic
reactions and may be contaminated with carcinogenic
nitrosamines.

• **Benzyl alcohol** – volatile flammable liquid prepared
by heating a mixture of benzyl chloride, sodium
carbonate and water, or hydrolysis. Can be made
with other alkali salts. Benzyl alcohol may contain
benzaldehyde as an impurity (see page 187 for
further information). Can cause skin sensitization
and allergic reactions and may be a neurotoxicant.

• **Citric acid** – derived from citrus fruits and naturally
present in living creatures. Its chemical name is
2-hydroxy-1,2,3-propanetricarboxylic acid. Can cause
skin irritation and has caused brain and nervous
system effects, such as tremors, at low doses in
experimental animals.

• **Glycerin** – a polyhydric alcohol. Commercially it
can be synthesized from the petrochemical propene
and natural materials. It is a by-product of soap
manufacture and also produced by trans-
esterification. Can cause skin irritation and dryness
(see Chapter 1 for more information).

• **Butterfly bush extract*** – butterfly bush is a fast-
growing bush from China.

- **Dehydroacetic acid** – a derivative of pyrone. Used as a preservative to kill microorganisms. Readily absorbed by the skin (see page 138 for more information).

- **Sodium benzoate** – produced by reaction between benzoic acid and sodium hydroxide or sodium carbonate. Benzoates have been associated with asthma, urticaria (hives or nettle rash), eye irritation and angioedema (spontaneous swelling of areas of skin or the mucous membranes).

- **Potassium sorbate** – the potassium salt of sorbic acid produced by reacting sorbic acid with potassium hydroxide. May cause skin, eye and respiratory irritation. It caused chromosome abnormalities in cultured hamster cells.

*From organic farming.

Pseudo-natural brands exposed – The US story

The Organic Consumers Association (OCA), a US non-profit public interest organization, in conjunction with Dr Bronner's and David Steinman, co-author of *The Safe Shopper's Bible*, commissioned a study during 2007 and 2008 into the presence of the carcinogenic impurity 1,4-dioxane (a product of ethoxylation) in 100 personal care and other consumer products produced by leading 'natural' and 'organic' brands. Researchers found that around 50 of these products contained this toxic contaminant (some of the product manufacturers are listed below).

365 Everyday Value
Alba
Aura Cacia
Circle of Friends
Citrus Magic
Earth Friendly Products
Earth Therapeutics
Eco Bella
Ecover
Emerald Forest

Giovanni Organic Cosmetics
Grandpa's
Healthy Times
Hugo
JASON Pure Natural & Organic
Kiss My Face
Life Tree
Method
Nature's Gate Organics
Nature's Gate
NutriBiotic
Origins
Rainbow
Sea-Chi Organics
Seventh Generation
ShenMin
Shikai
Ultra

For the past three years the OCA has been putting pressure on various industry members that are profiting from marketing pseudo-organic products. The OCA has called for brands that use ethoxylated ingredients or otherwise include synthetic petrochemical preservatives, to omit all organic claims from both their labelling and branding. Ethoxylation necessitates the use of the petrochemical ethylene oxide, a known carcinogen and suspected kidney toxicant, neurotoxicant and respiratory toxicant. Craig Minowa, environmental scientist with the OCA says, 'Prior to the investigation we had already talked to industry members on this subject, because we knew they were ethoxylating their ingredients and 1,4-dioxane is almost always a by-product of that process.'

Products certified by the USDA did not contain detectable amounts of 1,4-dioxane because ethoxylation is proscribed in the USDA standards. Consequently, the OCA recommend purchasing USDA certified products to ensure the absence of petrochemical compounds and propose that products labelled as 'organic' and 'organics', although not technically suggesting complete compliance with NOP Organic Standards, should still be free from petrochemicals. Cleansing ingredients should be produced from organic agricultural material and the product should contain certified organic materials obtained through conventional agricultural methods.[3]

Other standards prohibiting ethoxylation exist but many of these still sanction the hydrogenation and sulphation of conventional material.

According to the OCA, two of these weak standards are Ecocert and Organic and Sustainable Industry Standards (OASIS), which do not ban the use of all petrochemicals in cleansing ingredients.[4]

Permissible cleansing ingredients according to Ecocert standards include olefin sulphonate, cocamidopropyl betaine and sodium myreth sulphate, made in significant part with petrochemicals such as ethylene oxide. Some Ecocert certified products sold by recognized 'natural' brands that are branded as 'organic' or even '100 per cent organic' contain petroleum compounds along with other synthetic ingredients. The OCA state, 'the primary organic content in most Ecocert certified products comes from "flower waters" where up to 80 per cent of the "organic" content is just regular tap water that Ecocert counts as organic'.[5]

Along with Dr Bronner's (whose products were found to be clear of 1,4-dioxane) the OCA filed cease and desist letters with companies that 'misleadingly' label their products as 'organic', demanding that prior to 20 April 2008, these companies commit in writing to eliminate 'organic' and 'organics' branding and labelling from product packaging by 1 September 2008 to avoid litigation. Subsequently, the OCA and Dr Bronner's drew up a settlement offer enabling the brands to retain their organic branding provided they reformulate their products to USDA-NOP Organic Standards, using organic materials and without petrochemical compounds in their primary ingredients.[6] The contract also addresses the practice of including water as 'organic' content in personal care products containing heavily diluted hydrosols.

So far, relatively few of the brands have agreed to re-formulate their products. Craig Minowa, environmental scientist with the OCA, sheds some light on the situation,

> 'Bigger companies have thumbed their noses at us. I would think they have made millions of dollars from these products that are misleadingly labelled as organic and they have big pockets to defend themselves against litigation. Both the USDA and the FDA have turned their backs on the whole issue because neither of them have the capacity to deal with the ubiquitous nature of this mislabelling in the marketplace, so I would imagine that these big companies are just hoping that government agencies will end up not caring and consumers will not pay any attention to it.'

Confusing consumers?

A boom in agencies and companies developing organic standards may well prove to be a significant source of confusion for consumers, especially as many of these standards are less rigorous than those of the USDA-NOP. NSF International – a not-for profit, non-governmental organization that develops national standards – made their proposed NSF Draft Standard 305 for organic personal care products available for public comment in January 2008. These have been modelled and built on the USDA-NOP standards.

Craig Minowa of the OCA says, 'The NSF standard is supposed to be a more balanced process of creating standards, but there are things in the labelling programme that are not to the level that we would expect for organic products. It won't be federally regulated. The OCA's position is really that we already have an organic standard and there is no need to confuse consumers.'

Over the last several years the OCA and Dr Bronner's have engaged in efforts to strengthen the 'made with organic' personal care category under the NSF International standards, in order to ensure the exclusion of petrochemical compounds as per the USDA-NOP model. The OCA are now concerned that the process is being threatened by the Organic and Sustainability Industry Standards (OASIS), introduced in March 2008.

These personal care product standards were introduced by a trade group consisting of predominantly mainstream companies such as Estée Lauder, L'Oréal, Aveda, Hain Celestial Group (Jason and Avalon Organics), Cosway Company (cosmetics manufacturer) and Cognis Corp (a speciality chemicals company). In these standards is a provision permitting products containing 85 per cent organic ingredients to be labelled as 'organic' (rather than 'made with organic'), even though the remaining substances may include sulphated and hydrogenated cleansing ingredients and certain synthetic petrochemical preservatives such as phenoxyethanol (made by treating the toxic substance phenol with the carcinogen ethylene oxide) and 1,3-propanediol (a skin sensitizer also used in antifreeze, paints and polymers), generally produced via an expensive petrochemical process from propylene and ethylene oxide.[7,8] The OCA clarify, 'The OASIS standard was spearheaded and created exclusively by conventional industry members without any input or comment period from organic consumers, organic farmers or personal care companies who have achieved USDA National Organic Program certification for the majority of their products.'[9]

Just prior to the announcement of the OASIS standards, privately owned, Toronto-based organization Certech Registration promulgated their own cosmetic organic certification standards for the Canadian and American market with the same flexible requirements as Ecocert.

The European story

There are various unofficial certification bodies in Europe. Recently, an industry group called NaTrue (European Natural and Organic Cosmetics Interest Group or EEIG), representing natural cosmetic companies (including Lavera, Logona, Primavera, Santaverde, Dr Hauschka and Weleda) has also released its own standards. The NaTrue group was set up to lobby for the interests of the leading 'natural' cosmetics companies in Europe and has formed what it calls a 'strategic alliance', with Körperpflege- und Waschmittel e. V. (IKW) the German Cosmetic, Toiletry, Perfumery and Detergent Association, to establish a label for natural cosmetics. This is a conventional industry body including members such as Avon Cosmetics, Colgate Palmolive, GlaxoSmithKline and Johnson & Johnson. NaTrue cite the lack of a clear regulatory definition for 'natural' as a reason for establishing the group. The worldwide proliferation of cosmetic standards has partly been attributed to lack of a legal definition for the words 'natural' and 'organic', even though there is clearly a legal definition of natural, organic and synthetic provided by the USDA.

The NaTrue Standards[10] give manufacturers very wide latitude to use a range of synthetic ingredients. There are categories for 'natural,' 'nearly natural' and 'nature-identical' preservatives (e.g. benzoic acid, salicylic acid) and inorganic pigments. The term 'nearly natural' refers to materials derived from a natural substance apart from mineral oil. What it fundamentally means is synthetic substances derived from natural substances, using a term that is more appealing to consumers than the word synthetic. 'Nearly natural' substances permitted include aluminium stearate, ammonium lauryl sulphate, hydrogenated substances (such as hydrogenated coco-glycerides and hydrogenated palm oil), sodium lauryl sulphate and suphated castor oil.

Three labelling systems are designated under the standards:

- **Natural cosmetics** – this includes a table listing the minimum 'natural' and 'nearly natural' substances permitted in products bearing this label, ranging from a minimum of 0 to 90 per cent for natural substances. Unbelievably, cleansing products containing surfactants are allowed to contain only 3 per cent 'natural' substances, so the remaining ingredients can be primarily synthetic. Soap may contain no natural substances whatsoever.
- **Natural cosmetics with organic proportion** – products must contain at least 15 per cent 'natural' ingredients (70 per cent of which should be from organic farming). At most 15 per cent of ingredients can be 'nearly natural'.

- **Organic cosmetics** – products must contain at least 20 per cent 'natural' ingredients (95 per cent of which should be from organic farming). At most 15 per cent can be 'nearly natural'.

It is quite shocking that a product labelled as 'natural' can contain as little as 3 per cent natural substances and that a product labelled as 'organic' can contain as little as 20 per cent natural ingredients with only 19 per cent of those required to be organic. Would you be happy if you purchased a product labelled as organic only to find that a mere 19 per cent of the ingredients are, in fact, organic?

Various retailers are getting in on the 'let's cobble together our own standards' act with the Whole Foods Market announcing its Premium Body Care Standard.

Other standards

Perhaps further contributing to consumer confusion about which standards are the most reliable, there are numerous organizations worldwide certifying products to their own unofficial organic cosmetic standards. The main organic certification body in the UK is the Soil Association. Other well-known organizations offering certification of beauty products include Organic Farmers & Growers (in the UK), Ecocert (in France), BDIH (in Germany), AIAB (in Italy), NASAA (in Australia), Australian Certified Organic (ACO) and the Organic Food Chain (OFC).

Europewide efforts are under way to harmonize organic and natural standards for beauty products with international organic cosmetics standards working group members, comprising the certification associations Ecocert, Naturland, Cosmebio, Ecogarantie, AIAB and BDIH, attemping to thrash out a single set of standards. As yet details of these organic cosmetics standards have not been defined, although general principles have been established. Once the standards have been delineated and agreed upon they will probably be submitted to the European Commission.

Below is a summary of several European and Australian organizations offering organic and natural standards for personal care products. These vary in stringency. You'll notice I have listed a smattering of positive and negative points following each précis. These lists are by no means exhaustive and I cannot vouch for how effectively the standards and inspection protocols are enforced. When sourcing natural beauty products keep in mind that currently the most rigorous standards are the official standards of the United States Department for Agriculture – National Organic Program.

Did you know?

The International Federation of Organic Agriculture Movements (IFOAM) (www.ifoam.org) is an international organization made up of regional bodies that promote the expansion of sustainable and organic agriculture around the world. IFOAM advises governments, the EU and the UN with regards to organic agriculture and their standards have been used to inform voluntary and statutory standards worldwide. IFOAM has in place systems to guarantee organic standards of production and processing. The primary method is the Organic Guarantee System (OGS) based around the IFOAM Basic Standards and Accreditation Criteria. This allows third party certification while ensuring an international guarantee of these standards. IFOAM supports other methods of organic quality assurance that do not involve third party certification such as self-declaration and Participatory Guarantee Systems (PGS).

Certification bodies – The lowdown
The Soil Association

The Soil Association (www.soilassociation.org), founded in 1946 by a group of farmers, scientists and nutritionists, is a UK campaigning and certification organization for organic food and farming. The standards for health and beauty products were launched in May 2002 and the Soil Association currently certifies around 65 companies and 1,500 products to these standards. Prior to this, products had to conform to the Soil Association's organic food standards.

The Soil Association symbol

- A product labelled as '100 per cent organic' and bearing the Soil Association symbol must contain 100 per cent organic ingredients.
- A product labelled as 'organic' and bearing the Soil Association symbol must contain at least 95 per cent organic ingredients.

- A product labelled as 'made with xx per cent organic ingredients' and bearing the Soil Association symbol must contain at least 70 per cent organic ingredients.[11]

Positives

- Products labelled as 'organic' must contain at least 95 per cent organic ingredients. Some Soil Association-certified products contain 100 per cent organic ingredients.
- Sulphonation, hydrogenation, ethoxylation and propoxylation are prohibited.
- Water must be excluded from the calculation of organic content (but for flower waters the organic residues can be included in the percentage of organic ingredients).
- Sodium lauryl sulphate (SLS), sodium laureth sulphate (SLES), parabens, cosmetic solvents and synthetic fragrances and colours are prohibited.
- Ingredients derived from a specific list of endangered or vulnerable species must not be used.
- Animal testing should not be conducted on ingredients in used or finished products unless required by law.
- The standards exclude the addition of manufactured nanoparticles.

Negatives

- Non-organic glycerol and herbs are permitted if not available in organic form.
- Petrochemical and synthesized ingredients are authorized as reagents.
- The petrochemical compounds phenoxyethanol and cocamidopropyl betaine are authorized.
- Complex fragrances may not contain a full list of ingredients on the label, making it difficult for consumers who want to avoid specific chemicals in a product.
- In products labelled as 'made with xx per cent organic ingredients' water is excluded from the calculated percentage of ingredients, which only pertains to the non-water components. For example, if a product is 60 per cent water it can be labelled as 'made with 80 per cent organic ingredients', even though only 32 per cent of the ingredients are organic, the remaining content is water and synthetic ingredients.
- Organic ingredients transformed by chemical processes may be listed on the label followed by the words 'made with organic [name of ingredient]', which is a bit misleading for consumers, who may think that the end product itself is organic and natural.
- Until January 2010 manufacturers of surfactants are not required to undergo inspection and certification.

Organic Farmers & Growers (OF&G)

OF&G (www.organicfarmers.org.uk) is a UK certification body accredited by Defra and approved to inspect organic UK-based production and processing. Its national headquarters are in Shrewsbury, Shropshire. This body has established its own Organic Assurance Scheme and is able to inspect and certify a range of operations. The OF&G recently directed its expertise towards creating its Cosmetic and Bodycare Standard, which is based on the EU Regulation (EC2092/91) and the Nordic Ecolabelling Standards.

Labelling

- **95 per cent rule** – a product may be labelled as 'organic' when at least 95 per cent of the agricultural ingredients (excluding minerals and water) are organic and the remainder come from lists of Approved Ingredients, Additives or Processing Aids in the OF&G Control Manual.
- **70 per cent rule** – a product label may make reference to organic ingredients where 70 per cent of the agricultural ingredients are organic and the remainder come from lists of Approved Ingredients, Additives or Processing Aids in Section 10 of the OF&G Control Manual.[12,13]

Positives

- Products labelled as organic must contain at least 95 per cent organic ingredients.
- Sulphonation, hydrogenation, ethoxylation and propoxylation are prohibited.
- Genetically engineered organisms or products derived from them are prohibited.
- The final product must not have been tested on animals within five years of the application to register it as organic. No further testing should be conducted on the ingredients used, unless required by law.
- SLS, SLES, parabens and synthetic fragrances and colours are prohibited.
- Non-organic solvents such as mineral oils, benzene, hexane and propylene glycol are prohibited.
- Alumina and chemically synthesized sunscreens are prohibited (although titanium dioxide and zinc oxide are authorized).

Negatives

- Non-organic glycerol and herbs are permitted if not available in organic form.
- The petrochemical compounds phenoxyethanol and cocamidopropyl betaine are authorized.
- Petrochemical substances are authorized as reagents.

- If a product is predominantly composed of a mineral (such as chalk) it may be labelled in the same manner as a 70 per cent organic product if the mineral ingredients are required for functionality.
- In products labelled as 'xx per cent organic' water is excluded from the calculated percentage of ingredients, which only pertains to the non-water components (see Soil Association section for more information).
- Certain items not considered to be cosmetic ingredients, such as impurities, solvents and carriers, do not have to be listed on the ingredients label.

Biodynamic agriculture

Biodynamic agriculture is a method of natural and organic farming based on Rudolf Steiner's spiritual science belief system called Anthroposophy. Rudolf Steiner (1861–1925) was an Austrian philosopher, scientist and social reformer. Biodynamic agriculture sees the soil, plants and animals as parts of one living and self-sustaining system. Farming with this method excludes the use of artificial pesticides, herbicides, fertilizers and any other man-made chemicals. The health of the soil is of paramount importance, so organic manure and compost are used to nourish the soil. Biodynamic preparations based on Steiner's original concept are used as part of the process. Although similar to organic farming, there are some differences, such as the most favourable times for planting, cultivating and harvesting are determined by an astrological calender; biodynamic farms aim to be self-sufficient, so a variety of crops and animals are used to ensure the minimum need for external inputs; natural preparations are used to improve both soil health and crop quality; specific herb, mineral and cow-dung based compost preparations are used; ecological diversity is also promoted as part of biodynamic farming.

Ecocert – French (and international) organic certifier

Ecocert (www.ecocert.com), established in 1991, is a control and certification body governed by the public authorities and legislation that currently conducts inspections and certification services in over 80 countries covering all continents. It is accredited for structure and procedures by COFRAC (French Committee for Accreditation). Cosmetics are certified via the Ecological and Organic Cosmetics standards. Ecocert aims to ensure that standards on products, systems and services are complied with and certifies a variety or products including food, cosmetics, detergents, perfumes and textiles.

Ecological and Organic label

A product labelled as Ecological and Organic must contain a minimum of:

- 95 per cent natural ingredients or ingredients 'of natural origin' in the finished product
- 10 per cent certified organic ingredients in the finished product.

At least 95 per cent of the plant ingredients must be certified organic and the maximum amount of synthetic ingredients is 5 per cent in the finished product.

Ecological label

A product given the Ecological label must contain a minimum of:

- 95 per cent natural ingredients or ingredients 'of natural origin' in the finished product
- 5 per cent certified organic ingredients in the finished product.

At least 50 per cent of the plant ingredients must be certified organic and the maximum amount of synthetic ingredients is 5 per cent in the finished product.[14]

Positives

- Raw materials extracted from living or dead animals are prohibited.
- Animal testing of the finished product is prohibited.

Negatives

- To be labelled as Ecological and Organic, only 10 per cent of the total ingredients are required to be organic (but this can include floral waters as a plant ingredient so in reality the organic content may be much lower). The remaining contents can be chemically processed because 'of natural origin' simply means that the ingredient is *derived* from a natural substance. It may have undergone various chemical reactions and, by the USDA definition of synthetic found in the NOP standards, actually be a synthetic substance.

- When the term 'natural ingredients' or 'of natural origin' is used, this includes water as it makes the percentage of natural ingredients higher, without the requirement to include more natural plant ingredients. As mentioned earlier, floral water in totality is considered an organic ingredient, so a product may contain purely floral water and synthetic chemicals and be labelled as Ecological and Organic.
- Ingredients arising from cloning, cell cultures and fermentations with microorganisms are authorized for inclusion as ingredients 'of natural origin'.
- Phenoxyethanol and parabens are permitted as preservatives for the ingredients (not exceeding 0.5 per cent).
- The regulations actually state that the following 'pseudo-natural' substances may be used: benzoic acid and its salts, propionic acid and its salts, salicylic acid and its salts, 4-hydroxybenzoic acid, its salts and its esters, 2-phenoxyethanol, benzylic acid and sorbic acid.
- Chemical processes such as hydrogenation and sulphation are permitted.
- Certain minerals such as aluminium, hydrated silica and sodium fluoride are permitted.
- Plant-based synthetic compounds such as sodium lauryl sulphate and sodium coco sulphate are permitted.

BDIH

BDIH (www.kontrollierte-naturkosmetik.de) is the Association of German Industries and Trading Firms for pharmaceuticals, health care products, food supplements and personal hygiene products. In 1996, along with producers of natural cosmetics, BDIH established guidelines for certified natural cosmetics. These guidelines, to which products must comply with in order to obtain BDIH certification, include the conditions below:

- Botanical ingredients of organic origin, or wild-harvested, should be used where possible.
- Animal testing is not permitted on any finished products or ingredient added to the market after 1 January 1998. This does not include animal testing carried out by third parties with no affiliation to BDIH.
- Ingredients and raw materials must not be derived from dead

vertebrates (e.g. spermaceti, terrapin oil, mink oil, marmot fat, animal fat, animal collagen or living cells).

- Inorganic salts and mineral ingredients (such as sodium chloride) are usually permitted.
- Components for natural cosmetic products can be used if they are obtained by the hydrolysis, hydrogenation, esterification or trans-esterification of fats, oils and waxes, lecithin, lanolin, monosaccharides, oligosaccharides, polysaccharides, proteins and lipoproteins.
- Synthetic colorants and fragrances, ethoxylated ingredients, silicones, paraffin and other petroleum products are not permitted.
- Preservatives identical to those found in nature are authorized to ensure product safety and stability. These include: benzoic acid and its salts and ethylester, salicylic acid and its salts, sorbic acid and its salts, and benzyl alcohol. When these products are used, the product label must state 'preserved with [name of preservative]'.
- Natural ingredients and finished cosmetic products must not be disinfected by radioactive treatment.
- Compliance to the guidelines is evaluated by the independent testing institute Ecocontrol in Osterode, Germany.[15]

BDIH only make their full guidelines and positive list of ingredients available to manufacturers so I am unable to comment on how stringent the standards are.

Australian organic standards

In Australia the Australian Quarantine and Inspection Service (AQIS), which is part of the Australian Government Department of Agriculture, Fisheries and Forestry (DAFF), administers a nationally agreed organic standard known as the National Standard for Organic and Bio-dynamic Produce (NSOBP – first implemented in 1992), which stipulates minimum requirements for organic production, processing, transportation, labelling and importation. A cosmetics section was added to the Standard in 2007. Certifying bodies accredited by AQIS apply the standard as a minimum requirement to all products. The seven certification bodies accredited by AQIS to implement the standard include the National Association for Sustainable Agriculture, Australia (NASAA), Australian Certified Organic (ACO), Organic Growers of Australia (OGA), the Organic Food Chain (OFC), Safe Food Queensland, Tasmanian Organic-Dynamic Producers (TOP) and the Bio-dynamic Research Institue (BDRI).

Unfortunately, although the standard outlines the procedure for organic certification, it does not impose restrictions on the labelling of a product as 'organic' (as opposed to 'certified organic'), so as in other countries, largely synthetic and uncertified products may be misleadingly labelled as 'organic'. Furthermore, the Export Control (Organic Produce Certification) Orders 1997 require every person who produces or manufactures organic produce for *export* to be certified, but certification is not mandatory for the dosmetic market.[16] A specific domestic certification framework and relevant authority is notably absent. A report compiled for the Rural Industries Research and Development Corporation suggests that while Australia compares favourably to key international partners in terms of regulatory standards, 'the lack of a clear domestic organic standard is seen as a significant shortcoming to be overcome for industry to meet consumer expectations'.[17] The terms 'organic', 'natural' and 'synthetic' are defined in the standard; for instance organic is defined as 'the application of practices that emphasize the: use of renewable resources; and conservation of energy soil and water; and recognition of livestock welfare needs; and environmental maintenance and enhancement, while producing optimum quantities of produce without the use of artificial or synthetic chemicals'. This, along with the definition for 'natural', is slightly ambiguous.

The certification bodies can prescribe their own specific standards, which must meet the terms of the NSOBP, but may differ between certification bodies, confusing consumers as to which standards are the most legitimate.

Standards Australia. a non-government standards body established in 1922, is in the process of drawing up a new Australian standard for organic food produce, which will also cover cosmetics and skincare products, following an application from the Organic Federation of Australia. This process is in part a result of the confusing variations on what is accepted as organic. The National Standard for Organic and Bio-dynamic Produce is being used as a base document for the standard. Most certifiers support the new standard but some have raised concerns that it will not mandate inspection and certification, leaving the marketplace open to fraudulent organic claims.[18]

Biological Farmers of Australia (BFA)

Biological Farmers of Australia (www.bfa.com.au) is the biggest representative member-based organization for organic agriculture in Australia, promoting trade, development and organic standards. The BFA's organic standard, known as the Australian Organic Standard (AOS), details the requirements for selling produce as certified organic in Australia. It is based upon the AQIS (Australian Quarantine and Inspection Service) export standard and other international organic standard guidelines. Once certified, products can display the BUD logo. The BFA has in place an existing cosmetics standard, which is based on their food standards. More recently the BFA prepared a working document specifically on the processing of cosmetics, which will be included in the next version of AOS to be published in 2008.

Australia Certified Organic (ACO), set up in 2001, is the certification arm of the BFA conducting audits on businesses to ensure compliance with the standards. This certification organization conforms to AQIS regulations and therefore to EN 45011, USDA-NOP, JAS, ISO 65 and IFOAM/IOAS criteria for organic certification organizations. ACO is a USDA-accredited certifier.

Labelling

- Processed agricultural products sold or labelled as '100 per cent organic' must contain 100 per cent organic ingredients (excluding water and salt) and reference may be made to 100 per cent organic on the label.
- Products sold or labelled as 'certified organic' must contain a minimum of 95 per cent organic ingredients and additional ingredients permitted are specified in the standard.
- Products containing a minimum of 70 per cent certified organic ingredients may make reference to the organic ingredients on the label. The remaining 30 per cent of contents must be from a list of authorized substances outlined in the standards.
- Products containing less than 70 per cent certified organic ingredients may not make a reference on labelling to certification or organic content.[19]

Positives

- Products labelled as 'certified organic' must contain at least 95 per cent organic ingredients.
- 'Natural' is clearly defined to the same standards as the USDA-NOP standards, excluding ingredients that have undergone chemical processes.
- Alcohols and tinctures must be naturally produced using natural fermentation processes and must be from certified organic sources where commercially available.
- Hydrogenation of fats and oils is prohibited (except where it is consistent with the standards).
- Testing of products or ingredients on animals is prohibited.
- Synthetic colouring agents, fragrances and perfumes, silicons, paraffin and other petroleum products are prohibited.
- Ethoxylation, sulphonation, sulfuration and sulfation are prohibited.
- The solvents benzene, hexane, propylene glycol, butylene glycol, mineral oils and petroleum-derived products are prohibited.

Negatives

- Petrochemicals may be used as catalysts during the processing of ingredients.
- Floral waters may be certified organic.

National Association for Sustainable Agriculture, Australia (NASAA)

The National Association for Sustainable Agriculture, Australia (www.nasaa.com.au) was formed in 1986 and has accreditation with Australian Quarantine and Inspection Service (AQIS), International Federation of Organic Agriculture Movements (IFOAM), Japanese Agricultural Standard (JAS) and the United States Department of Agriculture (USDA). Their certification service covers the entire organic supply chain, from input manufacturers to producers to retailers. In 2005 NASAA developed draft health and beauty standards, which have now been incorporated into their organic standard.

Labelling

- Products labelled as '100 per cent organic' must contain 100 per cent raw or processed agricultural products that meet certain production and handling/processing requirements.
- Products labelled as 'certified organic' must contain a minimum of 95 per cent organic ingredients (excluding salt and water). The remaining 5 per cent of ingredients must be of agricultural origin and it must be demonstrated to NASAA that these are not available in sufficient quantities as certified organic ingredients.
- Where more than 5 per cent of the ingredients are from a producer in the process of converting to organic, the product must be labelled as 'In conversion to organic'.
- Products containing a minimum of 70 per cent certified organic ingredients may make reference to the organic ingredients on the label. The NASAA logo cannot be used on the product.
- Products containing less than 70 per cent certified organic ingredients may not make a reference on labelling to certification or certified ingredients.[20,21]

Positives

- Products labelled as 'certified organic' must contain at least 95 per cent organic ingredients.
- The use of genetically modified organisms or their derivatives is prohibited.
- Testing products on animals is prohibited.
- The use of synthetic colours, flavours and fragrances is prohibited.

- Parabens, synthetic vitamins, talc, sodium lauryl sulphate, padimate O (PABA) and silicones are prohibited.
- The solvents mineral oil, benzene, hexane, propylene glycol, butylene glycol, paraffin and petroleum-derived solvents are prohibited.
- Sulphonation, ethoxylation and propoxylation are prohibited.
- Non-organic grapefruit seed extract is prohibited.
- If the product contains more than 70 per cent water, the percentage of organic ingredients are calculated on the basis of the total volume of the product.

Negatives

- Fats, oils and waxes, lecithin, lanolin, monosaccharides, oligosaccharides and polysaccharides, proteins and lipoproteins may undergo hydrogenation, esterification and transesterification, for use as emulsifying agents and/or surfactants.

Other organizations

- **Biodynamic Agricultural Association (BDAA)** – certify to Demeter standards and offer own certification to EU organic standards (EU 2092/91). www.biodynamic.org.uk.
- **California Certified Organic Farmers (CCOF)** – certify to USDA–NOP standard. www.ccof.org
- **Cosmebio** – Cosmebio charter certifies to Ecocert standard. www.cosmebio.org
- **Ecogarantie** – standards are an amalgamation of those developed by Ecocert France, Cosmebio, BDIH and the Soil Association. www.ecogarantie.be
- **Guaranteed Organic Certification Agency (GOCA)** – certify to USDA–NOP standard. www.goca.ws
- **Naturland** – certify to BDIH standards with additional provisions. www.naturland.de
- **Oregon Tilth** – certify to USDA–NOP standards. www.tilth.org
- **Organic Crop Improvement Association (OCIA)** – certify to various standards including USDA–NOP, CAAQ, JAS-Japan. www.ocia.org
- **Organic Food Chain (OFC)** – certify to own standards, USDA–NOP standards, JAS-Japan standards and AQIS (Australian government). www.organicfoodchain.com.au.
- **Organic Growers of Australia (OGA)** – certify to BFA's ACO standards. www.organicgrowers.org.au
- **Quality Assurance Institute (QAI)** – certify to USDA–NOP standards. www.qaiworldwide.org

PART 2
Resources

Alternative beauty brands

Originally, when collating brands to feature in this section I was planning to call it 'Natural brands', but disturbingly in the course of my research I discovered that many companies were misleadingly using the terms 'natural' and 'organic' for products that contained a number of synthetic ingredients and sometimes predominantly synthetic ingredients with only one or two organic components. Many brands label their products as '100 per cent natural', '100 per cent organic', 'contains natural ingredients' and 'derived from natural ingredients', but unless an ingredient is certified organic, it may contain residues of pesticides, have undergone intense chemical processes that involve the use of petrochemicals or other synthetic compounds, metal catalysts and goodness knows what else. As a result I have renamed this section 'Alternative beauty brands', because there are a handful of genuinely 100 per cent organic brands currently in existence. It is hoped that this will change in the future.

The ten brands featured at the top of the list produce the most natural products. Some of them are 100 per cent organic. The rest generally contain fewer ingredients and synthetic substances than most conventional brands. Many of them claim to be 'natural' or 'organic', but don't necessarily carry certification, or some of their products are certified but not others, or the products may contain a blend of organic, synthetic and other non-organic ingredients.

Top 10 certified organic product ranges

Brand	Country of origin	Are the products certified organic?
Terressentials (www.terressentials.com)	USA	Yes. USDA certified 100% organic products
Beyond Organic Skincare (www.beyondskincare.co.uk)	UK	Yes. BDAA certified 100% organic products to EU organic standards (EU 2092/91)
Eselle (www.eselle.co.uk)	UK	Yes. SA certified 100% organic products
Spiezia (www.spieziaorganics.com)	UK	Yes. SA certified 100% organic products
Balm Balm (www.balmbalm.com)	UK	Yes. SA certified 100% organic products
Dr Bronner's (www.drbronner.com)	USA	Yes. Oregon Tilth/USDA certified organic
Nui (www.nuicoconut.com)	Australia	Yes. Products certified by ACO
Organic Blessings (www.organic-blessings.com)	USA	Yes. Pennsylvania Certified Organic (to USDA standards)
Nature's Paradise (www.naturesparadiseorganics.com)	USA	Yes. USDA certified organic
Sensibility Soaps (www.sensibilitysoaps.com)	USA	Yes. USDA certified 95–100% organic products

Other product ranges

Note: These brands are organized in alphabetical order according to country and brand name. Many of these brands use synthetic and/or other non-organic ingredients in their products unless otherwise indicated.

Brand	Are the products certified organic?
Australia	
Aura Natural Skin Care (www.auraskincare.com.au)	No

Ayurda (www.ayurda.com.au)	No
Botani (www.botani.com.au)	No
Desert Pea (www.desertpea.com.au)	No
Earthy Essences (www.earthyessences.com.au)	No. Mineral make-up
Elemental (www.elemental.com.au)	Some products are NASAA certified
Elly B Organic Skincare (www.ellyb.com.au)	No
Emma Cool (www.organicformulations.com.au)	No
Haven Scent (www.havenscent.com.au)	No
Hemp Hemp Hooray (www.hemphemphooray.com.au)	No
Hip Lilly (www.hiplilly.com)	No
Inika (www.inika.com.au)	No. Mineral make-up
Invoke Natural Skincare (www.invokenaturalskincare.com)	No
JOI pure (www.joipure.com)	No
MiEssence (www.mionegroup.com)	Some products USDA and ACO certified (but use some synthetic ingredients)
Mineral Makeup (www.mineralmakeup.com.au)	No. Mineral make-up
Mokosh (www.mokosh.com.au)	No
Mukti Botanicals (www.muktibotanicals.com.au)	OFC certified products (but use some synthetic ingredients such as coco betaine)
Nancy Evans (www.rosehipskincare.com)	Most products certified by OFC
Nvey Make-up (www.nveymakeup.com/ eco.html; www.nveyeco.co.uk)	Products certified organic by OFC and Australian government (but use some synthetic ingredients)
Organic Selections (www.organicformulations.com.au)	No
Pure and Natural Botanika (www.pureandnaturalbotanika.com.au)	No
Purestuf (www.purestuf.com.au)	No

Riddells Creek (www.organicformulations.com.au)	Yes. Products ACO certified
Soaps by Trance (www.trancesoaps.com.au)	No
Stem Organics (www.stemorganics.com)	No

Brazil

Surya Cosmetics (www.suryacosmetics.com)	No

Canada

Bare Organics (www.bareorganics.ca)	No
Dimpleskin Naturals (www.dimpleskinsnaturals.com)	No
Le Savon Populaire (www.savonpopulaire.ca)	No
Moom (www.moom.com)	Yes. CCOF certified
Simply By Amanda (www.simplybyamanda.com)	No
Suncoat (www.suncoat.ca; www.suncoatproducts.com)	No

Denmark

Urtekram (www.urtekram.dk)	Products are Ecocert certified (use some synthetic ingredients)

Germany

Martina Gebhardt (www.martina-gebhardt-naturkosmetik.de)	Products Demeter certified

Greece

Oliva (www.abea.gr)	No

Fiji

Pure Fiji (www.purefiji.com)	No

Philippines

Cocovida (www.cocovida.com)	No

Spain

Andalucia Soap Company (www.andalucia-naturalsoap.com)	No

UK

Akamuti (www.akamuti.co.uk)	No
Alvin Connor Natural Balance (www.alvinconnor.com)	No
Balance Me (www.balanceme.co.uk)	No
Circaroma (www.circaroma.com)	SA certification for 13 products (use some synthetic ingredients)
Earthbound Organics (www.earthbound.co.uk)	No
Essential Care (www.essential-care.co.uk)	Most products SA certified (use some synthetic ingredients)
Great Elm Physick Garden (www.greatelmphysickgarden.co.uk)	No
Hedgerow Herbals (www.hedgerowherbals.com)	No
House of Mistry (www.houseofmistry.com)	No
Innocent Oils (www.innocentoils.com)	No
Jane Scrivner (www.janescrivner.com)	No
Kristen Bailey Organic Collection (www.kristenbailey.co.uk)	Yes. SA certified products (use some synthetic ingredients)
Lily Lolo (www.lilylolo.co.uk)	No. Mineral make-up
Littlecote Soap (www.littlecotesoap.co.uk)	No
Mother Earth (www.motherearth.co.uk)	No
Nacherel (www.nacherel.co.uk)	No
NHR Organic Oils (www.nhrorganicoils.com)	Most of the essential oils are SA certified (use some synthetic ingredients)
Nothing Nasty (www.nothingnasty.com)	No
Organicarian (www.organicarian.co.uk)	No
Pai Skincare (www.paiskincare.com)	Products certified by SA (use some synthetic ingredients)
Peachy Keen Organics (www.peachykeenorganics.co.uk)	No
PitRok (www.pitrok.co.uk)	No
Pur Skincare (www.purskincare.co.uk)	Some products are SA certified (use some synthetic ingredients)

Pure Nuff Stuff (www.purenuffstuff.co.uk)	No
Pure Potions (www.purepotions.co.uk)	No
Raw Gaia (www.rawgaia.com)	No
Simply Soaps (www.simplysoaps.com)	No
Super Natural Skincare (www.supernatural-skincare.co.uk)	No
The Organic Pharmacy (www.theorganicpharmacy.com)	Most products certified by SA (use some synthetic ingredients)
Trevarno (www.trevarnoskincare.co.uk)	Most of the range is certified by OF&G
Vital Touch (www.vitaltouch.com)	No
Willow Beauty Products (www.willowbeautyproducts.co.uk)	Some products certified by SA

USA

A Wild Soap Bar (www.awildsoapbar.com)	No
Affordable Mineral Makeup (www.affordablemineralmakeup.com)	No. Mineral make-up
Afterglow Mineral Cosmetics (www.afterglowcosmetics.com)	No. Mineral make-up
Alima Pure (www.alimapure.com)	No. Mineral make-up
Aubrey Organics (www.aubrey-organics.com)	Some products are certified by QAI
Babybearshop (www.babybearshop.com)	All the Better to Kiss You lip balm bears, USDA seal and certified organic by NMOCC
Biologika (www.biologikaorganic.com)	No
Blissful Organics (www.blissfulorganics.com)	No
Brown Bag Botanicals (www.brownbagbotanicals.com)	No
Bubble & Bee (www.bubbleandbee.com)	Yes. By the Utah State Department of Agriculture
Buddha Nose (www.buddhanose.com)	One product (lip balm) is USDA certified organic
Crazy Rumors (www.crazyrumors.com)	No

Earth Mama Angel Baby (www.earthmamaangelbaby.com; www.babylosscomfort.com)	Personal care products in process of being certified by Oregon Tilth (to USDA standards)
Erba Organics (www.erbaorganics.com)	Some products carrying the USDA seal (certifier SCS)
Evan Healy (www.evanhealy.com)	No
From the Meadows (www.fromthemeadows.com)	No
Grateful Body Organic Skincare (www.gratefulbody.com)	No
Hemper Shop (www.hempershop.com)	No
Herbaria Soap (www.herbariasoap.com)	No
Isabella's Dream (www.isabellasdream.com)	No
JASCO (www.jascoorganics.com)	No
John Masters (www.johnmasters.com)	No
Joia Botanicals (www.joiabotanicals.com)	No
Ka Nani Essentials (www.kananiessentials.com)	No
Khushi Spa Products (www.khushispa.com)	No
Klecka Naturals (www.kleckanaturals.com)	Happy Spray Scent and Oils are not certified organic. The rest of the line is certified by NCCIA to USDA standards
Light Mountain Hair Colour (www.light-moutain-hair-colour.com)	No
Lulu Organics (www.luluorganicsnyc.com)	No
Luxe Essentials (www.luxeessentials.com)	No
Mambino Organics (www.mambinoorganics.com)	No
Msingi Organics (www.msingi.com)	No
Perfect Organics (www.perfectorganics.com)	No
Pure Beginnings (www.purebeginnings.com; www.babecology.com)	No
Sanre Organic Skin Food (www.sanreorganic.com)	No
Skinnyskinny Soaps (www.skinnyskinnysoaps.com)	No
Suki (www.sukipure.com; www.sukicolor.com)	No

Trillium Organics (www.trilliumorganics.com)	Products OCIA International certified
Tsi~La (www.tsilaorganics.com)	No

West Indies

Caribbean Blue (www.gocaribbeanblue.com)	No

Organic certifiers

AB – Agriculture Biologique
SA – Soil Association
BDAA – Biodynamic Agricultural Association
OF&G – Organic Farmers & Growers
ACO – Australian Certified Organic
USDA – United States Department of Agriculture
NASAA – National Association for Sustainable Agriculture, Australia
OFC – Organic Food Chain
OCIA – Organic Crop Improvement Association
CCOF – California Certified Organic Farmers
NMOCC – New Mexico Organic Commodity Commission
NCCIA – North Carolina Crop Improvement Association
SCS – Stellar Certification Services

A–Z
Common chemical ingredients

Acetaldehyde (acetic aldehyde, ethanal, ethyl aldehyde)
Found in Fragrances, nail products.
Purpose Manufactured by the oxidation of ethyl alcohol and the hydration of acetylene and used in resins, dyes, disinfectants, cosmetics (as a fragrance ingredient), pesticides, varnishes, explosives, some fuel compounds, foods (in flavourings) and pharmaceuticals. It occurs naturally in coffee, ripe fruit, broccoli, mushrooms, onions and fresh bread; also as a result of forest fires, in animal wastes and in insects.
Adverse reactions Acetaldehyde has been linked to asthma, mild irritation of the skin, eyes and respiratory tract in humans, as well as gene mutation, developmental and reproductive abnormalities in experimental animals. It is cited as a possible human carcinogen by the US Environmental Protection Agency and the International Agency for Research on Cancer. A toxicity study on rats conducted by the Chemicals Evaluation and Research Institute, Japan, using inhaled doses of acetaldehyde, induced increased heart rate and blood pressure, pulmonary oedema and a central nervous system response. Acetaldehyde causes gene mutations in bacteria and DNA damage in cultured mammalian cells and mice. Symptoms of exposure to acetaldehyde include nausea, vomiting, headache, dermatitis and fluid in the lungs. It has a narcotic effect and can cause drowsiness, hallucinations and loss of intelligence.

Acetamide MEA (acetylethanolamine, N-(2-hydroxyethyl), N-acetyl-2-aminoethanol)

Found in Shampoo, conditioner, hairspray, hair relaxer, hair colour/bleach, antiperspirant/deodorant, styling gel/cream.

Purpose An amide produced from acetamide and monoethanolamine (MEA) used as a skin and hair conditioning agent, surfactant and humectant in cosmetics.

Adverse reactions Acetamide MEA has been identified as a mild skin irritant in one rabbit study and caused liver cancer when given orally in high doses to experimental animals. Acute exposure has been linked to depression of the central nervous system, lung irritation and hepatic, renal and lung injury along with skin irritation and burns. Acetamide MEA can become contaminated, forming carcinogenic *nitrosamines* in the presence of nitrosating agents.

Acetic acid (ethanoic acid, glacial acetic acid)

Found in Conditioner, moisturizer, hair colour/bleach, shaving cream, styling gel/cream, nail treatment, tanning cream/lotion.

Purpose A carboxylic acid used in various topical medical formulations as an antibacterial and antifungal (for instance in products intended to destroy warts and in ear drops); in the manufacture of numerous chemical compounds, pharmaceuticals, plastics, dyes, insecticides, photographic chemicals, vitamins, antibiotics and cosmetics (as a fragrance, pH adjuster and solvent), as well as in textile printing, foods (as a preservative) and as a solvent for gums, resins and oils. Acetic acid occurs naturally in apples, cheese, cocoa, coffee, vinegar and a variety of other food products.

Adverse reactions Acetic acid can cause allergic reactions. There is evidence that it is a respiratory toxicant. Inhaling concentrated vapours can damage the lining of the nose, throat and lungs. In Europe it is classified by the European Commission as a flammable and corrosive substance that can cause severe burns. Direct contact with the skin causes redness, pain and blisters. Asthma has been caused by glacial acetic acid (concentrated or water-free acetic acid). Repeated exposure to its vapour can cause eye, nose and respiratory irritation. Less than 5 per cent acetic acid solution can cause mild skin irritation. Just 1 ml (¼ teaspoon) glacial acetic acid has caused perforation of the oesophagus. Ingestion can cause corrosion of the mucous membranes in the mouth, throat and oesophagus, accompanied by vomiting, diarrhoea, circulatory collapse and death. When administered to mice orally or via injection acetic acid has caused cancer.

Acetone (propanone, dimethyl ketone)

Found in Nail polish remover, nail polish, facial cleanser, moisturizer, exfoliant, hairspray, acne treatment.

Purpose An organic solvent, used as a denaturant, solvent and fragrance ingredient in nail polish removers and perfumes, and present in vehicle exhaust, tobacco smoke and landfill sites. It is also used to make plastic, fibres, drugs and other chemicals. Acetone is present naturally in plants, trees, volcanic gases, as a result of forest fires and in small amounts in the human body (formed when the body uses fat instead of glucose for energy).

Adverse reactions According to the Agency for Toxic Substances and Disease Registry, brief exposure via inhalation to medium to high levels of acetone can cause eye, nose, throat and lung irritation, headaches, arrhythmia (palpitations), an elevated pulse rate, nausea, vomiting, drowsiness and menstrual abnormalities in women. Extreme doses can lead to unconsciousness and death. If acetone comes into contact with the skin, it may cause irritation and skin dryness and cracking. In animal studies, acetone has instigated kidney, liver, spleen and nerve damage, red blood cell alterations and reproductive abnormalities, such as reduced sperm motility. Contact with the eyes can cause permanent eye damage. Swallowing acetone can damage the mucous membranes in the mouth.

Acrylates

Found in Hair colour/bleach, hairspray, mascara, lipstick, body wash, moisturizer, nail polish, sunscreen, lip gloss, exfoliant, styling gel/cream, foundation, concealer, face powder, eyeshadow.

Purpose Acrylates are film-formers, emulsifiers and surfactants. They are added to cosmetic and personal care products to adhere to the skin, hair or nails and generate a continuous film, as well as increasing the product's spreadability.

Adverse reactions Acrylates used for artificial nail building have been linked to allergic contact dermatitis and have been identified in some studies as occupational sensitizers and skin irritants. Certain acrylates, when inhaled, have been shown to cause occupational asthma and rhinitis. Common acrylates include acrylates copolymer, C10–30 alkyl acrylate crosspolymer and polymethyl methacrylate.

Alcohol (ethanol, ethyl alcohol, grain alcohol)

Found in Mouthwash, moisturizer, fragrance, facial cleanser, acne treatment, body spray, hand sanitizer.

Purpose The word 'alcohol' usually denotes ethanol, a volatile liquid obtained by the fermentation of sugars, starches and other carbohydrates. Ethanol is actually a primary alcohol. We are most familiar with its use in alcoholic beverages, but it is also used for numerous medical and industrial applications as a solvent, and in cosmetics as a solvent, astringent, fragrance ingredient and viscosity-decreasing agent.

Adverse reactions Ethanol can cause skin and eye irritation. Ingestion can cause nausea, vomiting and inebriation. Chronic ingestion can potentially cause liver damage. In animal studies, reactions to ethanol have included reproductive effects, mutation, endocrine disruption and skin irritation. Alcohol is a penetration enhancer (able to modify the structure of the skin, enhancing the absorption of other chemicals). Within the body, ethanol is converted into acetaldehyde (associated with cirrhosis of the liver and cancer) and acetic acid.

Alcohol denat (denatured alcohol, SD 40)
Found in Fragrance, acne treatment, hairspray, aftershave, hair colour/bleach, moisturizer, antiperspirant/deodorant, sunscreen.
Purpose Denatured alcohol is ethanol mixed with small amounts of foul-tasting chemicals such as methanol (methyl alcohol) and isopropanol to make the mixture toxic and unfit for consumption. It is commonly used in the production of artificial flavourings, perfumes, varnishes, inks, and in cosmetics and pharmaceutical preparations.
Adverse reactions If denatured alcohol comes into contact with the skin it can cause frostbite. High concentrations can cause central nervous system depression and aggravation of bronchitis. It is also a penetration enhancer (able to modify the structure of the skin, enhancing the absorption of other chemicals) and can cause skin irritation and dryness at low doses. (*See also* Alcohol)

Alkylphenols
Found in Facial cleanser, toner/astringent, hair colour/bleach, shaving cream, body wash, face mask.
Purpose Synthetic chemicals mainly used to produce alkylphenol ethoxylates (APEs), which are non-ionic surfactants that were widely used in household and industrial detergents to make them clean effectively.
Adverse reactions Alkylphenols (such as nonylphenol and octylphenol) are toxic to aquatic organisms and oestrogenic to fish. They can cause skin irritation in humans (which usually clears up once use of the product stops), skin reddening, contact dermatitis and photosensitivity. Nonylphenol has been detected in water and sediment downstream from sewage treatment plants and other industrial facilities. Alkylphenols can leak from plastic water pipes into drinking water supplies. Low levels have been detected in drinking water in the UK and USA. Alkylphenol metabolites accumulate in organisms, with bioconcentration factors ranging from ten to several thousand.

Alpha hydroxy acids (AHAs)
Found in Moisturizer, facial cleanser, toner/astringent, hand cream, around-eye cream, acne treatment, exfoliant, skin lightener, sunscreen, face mask.

Purpose A group of acids originating from a range of sources, including fruit and milk sugars, which are used in cosmetic products as exfoliants to remove the outer layer of skin. Some AHAs are also used as pH adjusters and emollients. AHAs are used in much higher concentrations by dermatologists and cosmetic surgeons to reduce the signs of ageing and treat skin disorders, in the form of chemical or facial peels.

Adverse reactions Alpha hydroxy acids can increase sensitivity to sunlight because of their ability to remove the protective outer layer of skin when applied topically. In one study the AHA glycolic acid doubled the sensitivity of human skin to sunburn in some individuals. Key AHAs incorporated into cosmetic products are: glycolic acid, lactic acid, malic acid, tartaric acid, citric acid, ammonium glycolate, ammonium alpha-hydroxyethanoate, alpha-hydroxyethanoic acid, among others. AHAs used in peels include: trichloroacetic acid, phenol, resorcinol and salicylic acid. The AHAs used in cosmetics are artificially produced. AHAs have been shown to cause skin irritation and stinging in high concentrations. According to the Australian government's Department of Health and Ageing, in experimental animals glycolic acid can be harmful in small ingested doses and large inhaled doses.

Alpha-terpineol

Found in Fragrance, deodorant stick, hairspray, shampoo, body bar.

Purpose A volatile component of essential oils, used as a fragrance (in a range of consumer products), antioxidant and flavouring ingredient. It is found in fruits such as grapes, guavas, apricots, plums and nectarines, and manufactured from alpha-pinene.

Adverse reactions Alpha-terpineol mist or vapour is irritating to the eyes, skin and mucous membranes. When ingested it causes chronic gastritis. If inhaled, Alpha-terpineol can lead to depression of the central nervous system, hypothermia and respiratory failure. In rabbit studies alpha-terpineol was shown to be moderately irritating to the skin. In rats subject to repeated oral doses, liver effects were witnessed. Using the Ames test it has been shown to be mutagenic in various strains of the bacterium *Salmonella typhimurium*. It has not been safety tested by the Cosmetic Ingredient Review Expert Panel.

Alum

Found in Antiperspirant/deodorant, toner/astringent, moisturizer, aftershave, acne treatment.

Purpose Alums are used as astringents, fire retardants, antibacterial agents in deodorants, food additives and in the production of foamite (used in fire extinguishers for chemical and oil fires). Examples include potassium alum, aluminium sulphate, sodium alum and ammonium alum, which are used in cosmetics for various purposes depending on the compound and as oral care drugs.

Adverse reactions In 1992 the US Food and Drug Administration proposed a ban on 415 ingredients from seven categories of non-prescription drugs because they had not been shown to be safe and effective for their stated use. The list included potassium alum (banned from topical antifungal drug products, skin protectorant drug products and astringent drug products) and ammonium alum (banned from skin protectorant drug products). There is a lack of safety data for alum.

Alumina (aluminium oxide)

Found in Moisturizer, foundation, concealer, sunscreen, toothpaste, exfoliant.

Purpose Naturally present in emery, topaz, amethyst, ruby, sapphire and emerald. It is commercially extracted from ores such as bauxite, cryolite and clays and is used to produce aluminium. It is also used as an abrasive, catalyst, absorbent (in the petroleum industry), filler for coatings, food additive, and in ceramics, glass, electrical insulators and resistors and dental cements. In cosmetics it is used as an abrasive, anti-caking agent, bulking agent and opacifying agent.

Adverse reactions High concentrations of inhaled alumina dust may irritate the respiratory tract. It is also toxic by inhalation. The dry powder can cause skin and mucous membrane inflammation and corrosion. Ingestion can cause gastrointestinal irritation and corrosion, nausea, vomiting, stomach pain and diarrhoea. Occupational exposure can cause lung diseases. (*See also* Aluminium)

Aluminium

Found in Eyeshadow, nail polish, eye liner, mascara, glitter, bronzer/highlighter, blush, lipstick, concealer. Aluminium salts are used in antiperspirants.

Purpose Aluminium is a silvery-white ductile metal used as a structural material in construction, in automobiles and aircraft, and in the production of metal alloys. Aluminium compounds are used in the production of glass, ceramics, rubber, wood preservatives, pharmaceuticals and waterproofing textiles. They are also used in packaging (foils and cans), water treatment, cooking utensils and a variety of other products. Aluminium powder (made up of fine aluminium particles) is used as a colour additive in face powders, eyeshadow, mascara, blusher, lip gloss, nail polish, facial moisturizers and hair colourings. Aluminium salts are used in antiperspirants. Aluminium is a common element in the earth's crust and found naturally in soil, air, plants, animal tissues and water.

Adverse reactions Aluminium can cause contact dermatitis. Human exposure to aluminium in the environment (other than occupational exposure) mainly occurs through the ingestion of food and water. Researchers have found that aluminium binds to oestrogen receptors in the breast, mimicking the effects of oestrogens. There is a substantial amount of evidence suggesting that aluminium is neurotoxic in experimental animals, and aluminium compounds can be neurotoxic in humans. Aluminium and its salts have been implicated in dialysis dementia (a neurological condition that occurs in some long-term dialysis patients), a type of anaemia known as hypochromic microcytic anaemia, renal osteodystrophy (a bone disease occurring as a result of failure of the kidneys to maintain correct levels of calcium and phosphorous in the blood) and Alzheimer's disease in some scientific studies. Occupational exposure has also resulted in asthma and lung diseases, as well as impairment of cognitive function where workers were exposed to aluminium fumes. If aluminium particles enter the eye they can damage the cornea. It has caused chromosomal aberrations (abnormalities in the normal structure of chromosomes that can lead to genetic conditions such as Down's syndrome) in the bone marrow cells of mice and rats. Aluminium has also demonstrated a toxic effect on male and female reproduction and is toxic to aquatic organisms. It can cause reduced skeletal mineralization in pre-term infants and infants with growth retardation. Prolonged used of antiperspirants and deodorants based on aluminium zirconium and zirconium has been linked to the development of underarm granulomas (nodular tissue inflammation). Aluminium is ubiquitous in the environment.

Aluminium acetate (*see* Aluminium)

Aluminium behenate (*see* Aluminium)

Aluminium chlorohydrate (*see* Aluminium)

Aluminium diacetate (*see* Aluminium)

Aluminium glycinate (*see* Aluminium)

Aluminium phenosulphate (*see* Aluminium)

Aluminium zirconium tetrachlorohydrex gly (*see* Aluminium)

Aminomethyl propanol (2-amino-2-methylpropranol)
Found in Facial cleanser, moisturizer, styling gel/cream, hairspray, sunscreen, hair colour/bleach, mascara, styling mousse.
Purpose An alkanolamine used as an emulsifier, buffering agent and pH

adjuster in personal care products. In hairsprays it regulates the water solubility of the resin film and helps it resist humidity.

Adverse reactions Aminomethyl propanol has caused mild irritation of the eyes and skin in animal studies. Prolonged exposure can irritate the skin. In its pure form aminomethyl propanol is irritating due to its high level of alkalinity, but the Cosmetic Ingredient Review state that it is buffered when used in cosmetics and therefore safe. It is classified in the EU as irritating to the eyes and skin and harmful to aquatic organisms and may be contaminated with carcinogenic *nitrosamines*.

4-amino-2-nitrophenol

Found in Hair colour.

Purpose Used as an oxidizing base in permanent and semi-permanent hair-dye formulations.

Adverse reactions 4-amino-2-nitrophenol caused dose-dependent bladder tumours in male rats and several female rats, and demonstrated DNA-damaging potential in bacterial and mammalian cells. It has also induced tumours of the urinary bladder in male mice. It is banned for use in cosmetics and hair dyes in the EU and in Canada.

Aminophenols

Found in Hair colour.

Purpose Aminophenols are phenol derivatives used as intermediates in orange-red and mid-brown hair dyes, and also dyes for furs, developers in photography and intermediates in pharmaceutical preparations. Examples include *m*-aminophenol, *o*-aminophenol, *p*-aminophenol, 2-methyl-5-hydroxyethylaminophenol, 3-methyl-4-aminophenol, 2-amino-4-nitro-phenol and 2-amino-5-nitrophenol (banned for use in cosmetics in the European Union and Canada) and 2-amino-6-chloro-4-nitrophenol.

Adverse reactions Aminophenols are toxic and can be fatal if swallowed, inhaled or absorbed through the skin. They can cause skin irritation, rashes and sensitization. *m*-aminophenol, *o*-aminophenol and *p*-aminophenol are used in oxidative hair dyes at concentrations of up to 5 per cent. Aminophenols can be metabolized into compounds capable of causing damage to DNA when the body has low levels of glutathione. *o*-aminophenol is a known human immune system toxicant and it is likely to be a skin toxicant. It has caused occupational exposure due to dust inhalation and can cause contact dermatitis. In mice it damaged sperm and in hamsters *o*-aminophenol has caused damage to unborn fetuses. It has also been shown to be toxic to some species of algae. *p*-aminophenol has been shown to be mutagenic in six out of eight mutagenicity tests, and both *m*-aminophenol and *o*-aminophenol have also proved to be mutagenic in some studies.

Most aminophenols have shown limited evidence of carcinogenicity in animal studies.

Ammonia

Found in Hair colour/bleach, moisturizer.

Purpose A colourless alkaline gas made up of nitrogen and hydrogen. Approximately 80 per cent of ammonia manufactured is used in fertilizers. In addition, it is used as a refrigerant gas, a fragrance ingredient and pH adjuster in hair colourants and cosmetics, and in the manufacture of plastics, explosives, pesticides, detergents and other chemicals. Ammonia is also a naturally occurring compound required for protein synthesis by the majority of organisms and a waste product of animal, fish and microbial metabolism.

Adverse reactions Ammonia is a suspected neurotoxicant, gastrointestinal or liver toxicant, reproductive toxicant, respiratory toxicant and skin or sense organic toxicant. People with asthma may be more sensitive to ammonia. The liquid can cause severe burns to the skin, mouth, throat, lungs and eyes after short exposure. Both ammonia gas and liquid are corrosive to the skin and can cause contact urticaria. Its vapours cause irritation of the eyes, skin and respiratory tract, even in low concentrations. High concentrations can cause conjunctivitis, laryngitis, fluid accumulation in the lungs and inflammation of the lung tissue. Ingestion of ammonia can cause blood in the stools, burns of the oesophagus and stomach, severe abdominal pain and vomiting. Ammonia is released into the environment by many industries. When it enters the atmosphere it undergoes a variety of reactions, producing compounds such as ammonium sulphate and ammonium nitrate (which in high concentrations is toxic to fish). At certain levels ammonia is acutely toxic to fish and can cause increased breathing rate, cardiac output and oxygen uptake and even convulsions, coma and death. At lower concentrations it causes other changes in fish such as a reduction in egg hatching, growth rate and changes in the tissues of the gills, liver and kidney. Anhydrous ammonia can draw water from the eye (the eye is comprised of 80 per cent water), rapidly destroying eye cells and tissue. Ammonium hydroxide can cause similar adverse reactions and environmental effects as ammonia. According to the Australian Society of Cosmetic Chemists, ammonia-based surfactants and emulsifiers in cosmetic products can be sources of *nitrosamines*.

Ammonium hydroxide (*see* Ammonia)

Ammonium laureth sulphate (ALES)

Found in Shampoo, conditioner, bubble bath, bath oil, body wash, cleanser, liquid hand soap, hair relaxer, exfoliant, acne treatment, dandruff treatment.

Purpose Used as an anionic surfactant, stabilizer, solubilizer and emulsifier.

Adverse reactions Ammonium laureth sulphate is considered to be less of an irritant than ammonium lauryl sulphate, although in some studies on experimental animals and humans it has produced eye and skin irritation. The level of irritation may depend on the concentration used.

Ammonium lauryl sulphate (ALS, ammonium dodecyl sulphate)

Found in Shampoo, conditioner, bubble bath, body wash, facial cleanser, liquid hand soap, hair relaxer, exfoliant, acne treatment, dandruff treatment.

Purpose An alkyl sulphate used in personal care products as a surfactant and emulsifier.

Adverse reactions Ammonium lauryl sulphate can cause respiratory tract irritation, skin irritation and dryness and irritation of the eyes. Ingesting large amounts can cause gastrointestinal irritation, nausea and diarrhoea. In animal studies, it induced skin corrosion and severe irritation at high concentrations.

Ammonium thioglycolate

Found in Hair perm, hair relaxer, depilatory.

Purpose The ammonium salt of thioglycolic acid is used as a hair-straightening agent, antioxidant and depilatory. It is the same reducing agent that is used in permanent waving. Thioglycolates weaken the keratin structure of the hair.

Adverse reactions Inhalation of ammonium thioglycolate has been shown to cause asthmatic breathing, coughing and blocked nasal passages in people with asthma. It is a skin and lung irritant, a skin sensitizer and is known to produce contact dermatitis in hairdressers and their clients. It can also cause severe burns and blistering of the skin.

Amyl acetate

Found in Nail treatment, nail polish, sunscreen, moisturizer, aftersun.

Purpose Used as a flavouring agent, a solvent for surface coatings, photographic film, nail polish, printing ink, paint, lacquer and fabric finishes, and in the preparation of penicillin. It is also used as a dry cleaning agent and insecticide.

Adverse reactions Amyl acetate is a suspected neurotoxicant, respiratory toxicant and skin or organ toxicant. It can cause irritation of the skin, eyes and mucous membranes as well as skin dryness and redness. Excessive inhalation can cause coughing, dizziness, weakness, drowsiness, headache, sore throat and possibly unconsciousness. Ingestion can cause gastrointestinal irritation, nausea, vomiting and diarrhoea. High exposures can cause heart failure. Overexposure in animals has caused liver abnormalities, lung, spleen and kidney damage.

Aromatic hydrocarbons

Found in Nail polish, nail treatment, cuticle treatment, shampoo, conditioner, dandruff treatment.

Purpose A class of petroleum-derived chemicals with molecular structures known as benzene rings (named after the simplest aromatic hydrocarbon, benzene). Hydrocarbons are chemical compounds composed of only hydrogen and carbon. Aromatic hydrocarbons can contain impurities. Examples of aromatic hydrocarbons include benzene, *toluene*, naphthalene, phenanthrene, xylene, *coal tar* and styrene.

Adverse reactions Many aromatic hydrocarbons are toxic, neurotoxic and carcinogenic given certain concentrations and exposure times. (*See also* Polycyclic aromatic hydrocarbons)

Avobenzone (butyl methoxydibenzoylmethane, Parsol 1789)

Found in Sunscreen, moisturizer, fragrance, tanning cream/lotion, hand cream.

Purpose A dibenzoylmethane derivative used in sunscreen products as a UVA light absorber.

Adverse reactions Avobenzone can cause allergic reactions. It is photo-unstable, meaning it rapidly breaks down with ultraviolet (UV) exposure, thus diminishing its UV protection capabilities. Concerns have also been highlighted over avobenzone's ability to degrade other sunscreen ingredients. Sometimes other substances are added to counteract this instability, but studies have shown that sunscreens with the combination of avobenzone and ethylhexyl methoxycinnamate are photo-unstable, regardless of what other ingredients are incorporated. One study has linked avobenzone to in vitro DNA damage (strand breaks), due to its ability to produce carbon-centred radicals under UV light in combination with dibenzoylmethane (a UV absorber).

Azo dyes

Found in Hair colour, temporary tattoos.

Purpose A large class of synthetic colours containing two nitrogen atoms connected by a double bond (-N=N-) used in cosmetics, clothing, food and other consumer items. They are commonly used in non-permanent hair rinses and tints.

Adverse reactions Azo dyes have been linked with contact allergies and attention deficit hyperactivity disorder (ADHD). People who are sensitive to permanent hair dyes containing *phenylenediamine* also develop a cross-sensitivity to azo dyes. Some azo dyes are broken down by the body into carcinogenic aromatic amines, which are also genotoxic (capable of damaging DNA). A number of azo dyes have proven to be carcinogenic in animal studies and many others are considered to be potentially carcinogenic. Azo dyes may be toxic to aquatic organisms and accumulate in water sediments and soil. Some azo dyes that can break down to release aromatic amines under certain conditions have been banned from consumer goods in the EU.

Azulene (cyclopentacycloheptene)

Found in Facial cleanser, moisturizer, antiperspirant/deodorant, face mask, toner/astringent, hair removal waxes, acne treatment, aftershave, toothpaste.

Purpose Azulene is a hydrocarbon that is present in the essential oil of German chamomile. It is used as a colour additive and skin-conditioning agent in cosmetic products and hair dyes.

Adverse reactions Azulene acts as an anti-inflammatory agent but in some in vitro cell studies it has been shown to be genotoxic (capable of damaging DNA) under visible and UV light. It can also cause skin, eye and respiratory tract irritation. Ingestion can cause gastrointestinal irritation with nausea, vomiting and diarrhoea. Its toxicology has not been comprehensively investigated. The Cosmetic Ingredient Review Expert Panel has concluded that there are insufficient data to support the safety of this chemical.

Benzaldehyde (artificial almond oil, benzenecarbonal, benzenecarboxaldehyde)

Found in Shaving cream, baby lotion, body wash, body bar, bath oil, body oil.

Purpose An aromatic aldehyde used in perfumes as a denaturant and fragrance. Benzaldehyde is also used as a food additive and in the synthesis of other organic compounds, pharmaceuticals, aniline dyes and plastics. It is the main component of bitter almond extract oil.

Adverse reactions Benzaldehydes have been linked to contact dermatitis and, at high doses, depression of the central nervous system and respiratory failure. Benzaldehyde vapours can irritate the eyes, mucous membranes, respiratory system, nose and throat and cause headache, loss of concentration and dizziness. Chronic exposure may lead to nausea and vomiting. Benzaldehyde has been shown to be carcinogenic and a cause of gastrointestinal, brain, kidney, liver and endocrine system damage in some animal studies conducted by the US Department of Health and Human Services, National Toxicology Program.

Benzalkonium chloride (alkyl benzyl dimethylammonium chloride, alkyl dimethyl benzyl ammonium chloride)

Found in Moisturizer, eye drops, sunscreen, facial cleanser, baby lotion, acne treatment.

Purpose A mixture of chloride salts used as an antimicrobial disinfectant, surfactant, preservative, fungicide and deodorant, used in rinse-off hair products, disinfecting hand soaps, hand, face and eye washes, mouthwashes, spermicides and aftershave lotions, as well as household cleaners, disinfectants and dishwashing detergents.

Adverse reactions Benzalkonium chloride, a quaternary ammonium compound and cationic surfactant, is a known primary skin irritant and has been proven at certain concentrations to be a severe eye irritant in human studies. It can cause allergic conjunctivitis when incorporated into eye washes. It is highly irritating to the skin in concentrations of 10 per cent, and in some cases less, and irritating to the eyes and mucous membranes in concentrations as low as 0.1–0.5 per cent. In high concentrations benzalkonium chloride can burn the skin. When used in spermicides it can cause vaginal burning and irritation. It is poisonous and corrosive if ingested. In animal studies it has caused drowsiness, central nervous system depression, nausea, vomiting, respiratory problems, dermatitis and reproductive abnormalities. Benzalkonium chloride is very toxic to aquatic organisms.

Benzene
Found in Nail polish remover, fragrance.

Purpose Benzene is an aromatic hydrocarbon derived from petroleum and *coal tar* that is used in nail polish remover and perfumes, industrially as a fuel, as well as varnishes, modelling glue and lacquers. It is also used in the manufacture of many other products, including: plastics, synthetic fibres, dyes, nylon, detergents, drugs, artificial leather and pesticides, and as a solvent for fats, waxes, resins, inks, paints, rubber and oils. Benzene is naturally present in crude oil, cigarette smoke, and fumes from volcanoes and forest fires.

Adverse reactions A known carcinogen, benzene has been shown to be a moderate skin and eye irritant in animal studies, as well as causing tumours, muscle weakness, shortness of breath, seizures, debilitating brain effects, reproductive abnormalities, respiratory depression, liver problems, endocrine system disruption and a damaged immune response. In human studies, where the substance was inhaled, it had a damaging effect on the blood, bone marrow, immune system and body temperature and caused gastrointestinal and skin problems. Short-term exposure via inhalation causes depression of the central nervous system, drowsiness, light-headedness, nausea, loss of coordination, confusion and unconsciousness. It can also cause sensitivity to light and nose and throat irritation. In mammalian cell studies it caused chromosomal abnormalities. Prolonged or repeated skin contact with the substance can cause redness, drying and dermatitis. Chronic exposure in occupational environments has caused blood disorders, damaged bone marrow, aplastic anaemia, DNA damage and leukaemia. The International Agency for Research on Cancer has concluded that there is sufficient evidence that benzene is carcinogenic to humans. Benzene is a banned ingredient in cosmetics in the EU and

Canada. It cannot be used in any cosmetic product manufactured in or imported into the UK or the other member states of the EU.

Benzoates

Found in Facial cleanser, moisturizer, fragrance, hair colour/bleach, hairspray, hair relaxer, styling gel/cream, body wash, sunscreen, baby lotion.

Purpose Salts or esters of benzoic acid are primarily used as antibacterial preservatives in foods, cosmetics and pharmaceuticals. They are naturally present in foods such as cranberries, prunes, tea and cinnamon and can also be synthetically produced. Examples include benzoic acid, benzyl benzoate, ammonium benzoate, stearyl benzoate and sodium benzoate.

Adverse reactions Benzoates have been associated with asthma, urticaria (hives or nettle rash), eye irritation and angioedema (spontaneous swelling of areas of the skin or the mucous membranes). In oral toxicity studies in animals, benzoic acid and sodium benzoate caused toxic effects at concentrations of less than 1 per cent. In Europe, benzyl benzoate is classified as harmful.

Benzoic acid (benzenecarboxylic acid, carboxybenzene, phenylformic acid)

Found in Facial cleanser, moisturizer, body wash, sunscreen, foundation, shampoo, lipstick, mouthwash, exfoliant.

Purpose The simplest aromatic carboxylic acid used as a perfume, food preservative and in the production of a large number of chemicals, dyes and plastics. It is also used in antiseptic ointments for the treatment of fungal infections, in insect repellants and as a pH adjuster in cosmetics.

Adverse reactions Benzoic acid is a mild skin irritant and can cause allergic reactions, including aggravation of asthma. Ingestion can cause gastric irritation. A report by the International Programme on Chemical Safety stated that following either dermal, oral or inhalation exposure to the substance, cases of asthma, urticaria, rhinitis or anaphylactic shock have been reported. Skin reactions to benzoic acid among the general public are uncommon. Inhalation of high concentrations can cause coughing. In animal studies, benzoic acid caused eye and skin irritation. It has been shown to be genotoxic (capable of damaging DNA) in some animal studies and other effects have been demonstrated on the respiratory system, brain, nervous system and sense organs.

Benzophenones

Found in Fragrance, sunscreens, moisturizer, lip balm, lipstick, styling gel/cream, body wash, conditioner, shampoo, hairspray, liquid hand soap, exfoliant.

Purpose A group of aromatic ketones used as perfume fixatives and sunscreen agents. Examples include benzophenone-3, oxybenzone, dixoxybenzone and sulisobenzone. Benzophenone is also used in the manufacture of dyes, pesticides and drugs.

Adverse reactions Benzophenones are probably one of the most common causes of photocontact allergy. They have also been reported to cause immediate and delayed hypersensitivity, hives, contact urticaria and anaphylaxis. Benzophenone-3 (oxybenzone) has been detected in human urine and human milk. Concerns about its potential oestrogenicity have been raised. Benzophenone-3 produces free radicals under UV light, which can potentially damage DNA. It is also a photoallergen and may cause skin sensitization. Benzophenones are also penetration enhancers (able to modify the structure of the skin, enhancing the absorption of other chemicals).

Benzoyl peroxide (dibenzoyl peroxide, peroxide)
Found in Facial cleanser, moisturizer, acne treatment, body bar, shaving cream, face mask, toner/astringent, dental products, artificial nail products.
Purpose Peroxide derivative used as an anti-acne, bleaching and drying agent in acne medications, and in hair, artificial nail and dental products.
Adverse reactions Benzoyl peroxide can cause skin irritation, respiratory tract irritation and contact dermatitis. It is a skin sensitizer and there is some evidence to suggest that it can promote skin tumours. When administered onto the skin in some animal studies it caused mild eye irritation. In a study on various strains of mice it promoted skin tumours. Benzoyl peroxide has caused DNA damage in mammalian cell studies. It is toxic to aquatic organisms. In Europe benzoyl peroxide is classified as irritating to eyes, explosive and a possible skin sensitizer.

Benzyl acetate
Found in Fragrance, moisturizer, dandruff treatment, tanning cream/lotion, sunscreen.
Purpose The ester of benzyl alcohol and acetic acid is used as a synthetic fragrance in soaps, perfumes and air fresheners, as a flavouring agent in foods, as a solvent for cellulose acetate and nitrate and is also used in varnish removers, lacquers and polishes.
Adverse reactions Benzyl acetate can cause skin, eye and respiratory tract irritation and chronic exposure at certain ambient concentrations can cause kidney damage. Ingestion of benzyl acetate can cause gastrointestinal irritation, accompanied by vomiting and diarrhoea. It was found to increase the incidences of pancreatic tumours in male rats, as well as increasing the incidences of liver cancer and forestomach tumours in male and female mice when administered via gavage (force feeding through a tube in the stomach).

Benzyl alcohol (benzenemethanol, benzylic alcohol, phenylmethanol)

Found in Facial cleanser, moisturizer, sunscreen, shampoo, conditioner, fragrance, hair colour/bleach.

Purpose A volatile flammable liquid obtained by fermentation of sugars and starches that is used as a solvent, pH adjuster, preservative, viscosity-decreasing agent and fragrance in perfume, air fresheners, food and a variety of household products. It is also used as a solvent in inks, paints, lacquers, explosives, pharmaceutical preparations and epoxy resin coatings. Benzyl alcohol occurs naturally in some plants.

Adverse reactions Benzyl alcohol is a skin irritant and severe eye irritant. It has been linked with contact dermatitis and contact urticaria. It is classified as a well-recognized consumer allergen by the Scientific Committee on Cosmetic Products and Non-food Products Intended for Consumers (SCCNFP). In animal studies, it caused lethargy, respiratory and gastrointestinal problems, haemorrhage, liver, kidney and endocrine system disruption, reproductive abnormalities and DNA damage. Its vapours can irritate the nose and throat and in high concentrations can potentially cause headache, nausea, light-headedness and drowsiness. It is thought that human ingestion of benzyl alcohol can cause central nervous system depression, similar effects to alcohol intoxication and unconsciousness.

Benzyl butyl phthalate (*see* Phthalates)

Benzyl cinnamate (*see* Cinnamates)

Benzyl salicylate (*see* Salicylates)

Beta hydroxy acids (BHAs)

Found in Facial cleanser, moisturizer, toner/astringent, acne treatment, exfoliant, dandruff treatment, concealer, face mask.

Purpose Beta hydroxy acids (generally referring to salicylic acid for cosmetic purposes) are lipid (oil)-soluble organic acids, whereas alpha hydroxy *acids* are water-soluble only. They are believed to be better for oily skin because they penetrate the sebum-containing pores of the skin and remove the dead skin cells that have accumulated inside the pore.

Adverse reactions Beta hydroxy acids are believed to cause less irritation than alpha hydroxy acids and, when applied topically, are said to be able to reduce fine lines and wrinkles in the skin. According to the US Food and Drug Administration, BHAs may be listed as salicylic acid (or related substances—salicylate, sodium salicylate and willow extract), beta hydroxybutanoic acid, tropic acid and trethocanic acid. Salicylic acid (a metabolite of aspirin) can penetrate the skin and approximately 10 per cent of applied salicylates can remain in the skin. It is irritating to the skin, mucous membranes and epithelial cells. In animal studies, exposure of parents to salicylic acid caused reproductive and developmental toxicity in offspring. Salicylic acid also strips away the horny outer layer of the skin, prompting concerns that repeated use could increase the risk of damage from UV radiation by 50 per cent. Those who have allergic skin reactions to aspirin may also react to topically applied salicylic acid.

Bisabolol
Found in Facial cleanser, moisturizer, sunscreen, around-eye cream, aftershave, lipstick, concealer, acne treatment.
Purpose An unsaturated monocyclic terpene alcohol used in cosmetics as a skin-conditioning agent and fragrance ingredient. It is derived from German chamomile.
Adverse reactions Short-term oral exposure to bisabolol in rats caused inflammatory alterations in the liver, trachea, spleen, thymus and stomach. It can also cause skin irritation and is a penetration enhancer (able to modify the structure of the skin, enhancing the absorption of other chemicals).

Bisulphites
Found in Facial cleanser, moisturizer, face mask, skin lightener, hair colour/bleach, tanning cream/lotion, hairspray.
Purpose Inorganic salts used as preservatives in cosmetics and reducing agents in oxidative hair-dye products, hair waving/straightening products, self-tanning products. Sulphites, bisulphites and metabisulphites liberate sulphur dioxide under certain conditions.
Adverse reactions At high concentrations sulphur dioxide irritates the upper airways and can cause bronchitis. In human lymphocytes it caused chromosomal abnormalities. Oral ingestion of bisulphites can induce asthmatic symptoms.

Boric acid (boracic acid, boron trihydroxide, orthoboric acid)
Found in Facial cleanser, moisturizer, eye make-up remover, styling gel/cream, eye drops, contact lens cleaner, around-eye cream.
Purpose A weak acid derived from boron (a naturally occurring element present in rocks, soil and water) used as an antimicrobial, antiseptic, buffer, emulsifier, preservative, water softener and pH adjuster, in baby powders, eye creams, mouthwashes, aftershave lotions, soaps, skin fresheners and other cosmetics. It is also used as an insecticide, pesticide, antiseptic, and in nuclear power plants to restrain the fission rate of uranium.

Adverse reactions Boric acid can irritate the skin and eyes and is absorbed quite readily through broken or otherwise damaged skin. Human reactions following ingestion have included nausea, vomiting, dermatitis, cardiac effects, renal failure and effects on the sense organs and bladder. Poisonings have occurred after topical application to broken skin, and in cases of chronic exposure hair loss has been reported. In human infants and children, when administered on the skin, boric acid has in some instances caused convulsions, gastrointestinal problems, dermatitis, eye irritation and respiratory depression. Chronic toxicity in children is often a result of treatment with a nappy rash formulation containing boric acid. It has also been linked to fetal abnormalities. Boric acid is banned for use in cosmetic products in Japan.

Bronopol (2–bromo–2–nitropropane–1,3–diol)
Found in Facial cleanser, moisturizer, shampoo, conditioner, baby wipes, body wash, make-up remover, exfoliant.
Purpose An antimicrobial chemical used as a preservative and antiseptic in cosmetics, toiletries and topical medications.
Adverse reactions Bronopol can be a skin sensitizer and has been linked with contact dermatitis and urticaria. This substance has been shown to cause phototoxic (damage caused by light) effects in vitro. At concentrations of 1 per cent and above it is a severe irritant. In some animal studies it has led to blood, respiratory, endocrine, nervous system and gastrointestinal alterations and skin irritation. One of bronopol's degradation products is *formaldehyde*, which can react with secondary amides and amines in personal care products to form carcinogenic *nitrosamines* or nitrosamides.

1,3-butadiene
Found in May be an impurity in antiperspirant/deodorants, styling mousse, shaving cream, hairspray, body spray, mascara, fragrance, lip gloss.
Purpose Plasticizer produced from the processing of petroleum, primarily used in the production of synthetic rubber and plastics. Food and cosmetics containers can contain this chemical as a contaminant. It is not deliberately added to cosmetic products but can be present as an impurity in butane – a propellant added to aerosol personal care products. In the EU, 1,3-butadiene is banned for use in cosmetic products.
Adverse reactions In low concentrations, 1,3-butadiene is a central nervous system depressant. It is a multiple-organ carcinogen in rats and mice and is classified as a probable human carcinogen by the International Agency for Research on Cancer and as a known human carcinogen by bodies such as the National Toxicology Program and the US Environmental Protection Agency. Occupational exposure is associated with leukaemia. There is also some evidence that it is genotoxic (capable of damaging DNA) in humans and

it has caused liver and kidney disease and damaged lungs in animals exposed to low levels over a year. Long-term exposure to 1,3-butadiene caused shrinking of the ovaries in female mice and shrinking of the testes in male mice. It also causes adverse effects to the bone marrow and blood of mice. High-level exposure to 1,3-butadiene can cause eye, nose and throat irritation, drowsiness, decrease blood pressure and pulse rate, blurred vision, nausea, vertigo, unconsciousness and even death at high concentrations. It is also irritating to the skin and mucous membranes.

Butane (N-butane)

Found in Shaving cream, spray-on tanning products, styling mousse, fragrance, antiperspirant/deodorant, hair colour/bleach, body spray.

Purpose An unbranched alkane used as a propellant in cosmetics, foods and household sprays. It is a gaseous component of natural gas and can be extracted from crude oil. Butane is also used for refrigeration, heating and fuel for cigarette lighters.

Adverse reactions At high concentrations butane can cause central nervous system depression, nausea, headaches, dizziness, drowsiness and confusion. When inhaled in high concentrations, such as in cases of substance abuse, butane can cause euphoria, cardiac arrhythmias (an irregular heart beat), asphyxia and sudden death. Direct skin contact with butane can cause frostbite. Butane can become contaminated with *1,3-butadiene*, a known human carcinogen. Butane is a volatile, highly flammable substance. In the EU and its member states butane is not authorized in cosmetic formulations if it contains 0.1 per cent or above of 1,3-butadiene.

Butylated hydroxyanisole (BHA)

Found in Moisturizer, skin lightener, eyeshadow, lipstick, lip gloss, lip liner, eye liner.

Purpose A phenol compound used as an antioxidant and preservative in food, food packaging, animal feed, rubber and petroleum products and cosmetics such as lipsticks and eyeshadow.

Adverse reactions In patch tests butylated hydroxyanisole has been shown to cause allergic contact dermatitis. In animal studies, it caused respiratory problems, blood, brain, nervous and endocrine system, gastrointestinal and liver effects, reproductive abnormalities, cancerous tumours and DNA damage (where it was used in combination with other chemicals). In large doses it can affect liver and kidney function. It has been concluded by the World Heath Organization, the National Toxicology Program of the US Department of Health and Human Services and the International Agency for Research on Cancer, as well as other bodies, that BHA is a possible human carcinogen, based on the evidence of carcinogenicity in experimental animals. In the

European Union and its member states BHA is prohibited from use as a fragrance in cosmetic formulations.

Butylated hydroxytoluene (BHT)

Found in Moisturizer, sunscreen, foundation, concealer, lipstick, fragrance, antiperspirant/deodorant.

Purpose A phenol compound used as an antioxidant and fragrance in cosmetics, foods, drinks, rubber, plastic, petroleum, embalming fluid, oils, paints and waxes.

Adverse reactions Butylated hydroxytoluene is highly corrosive and can cause allergic reactions. Cases of contact dermatitis in humans as a result of BHT have been reported. It is a skin, eye and respiratory tract irritant and may be toxic to the blood, liver and central nervous system. Ingestion of large amounts can cause nausea, vomiting and diarrhoea. In animal studies, reactions to BHT have included weight loss, cancerous tumours, blood, gastrointestinal, respiratory, endocrine system, liver, kidney and lung effects, internal haemorrhaging, skin and eye irritation, DNA damage and reproductive abnormalities. BHT is banned from food products in Japan, Sweden, Romania and Australia.

Butylene glycol (1,3-butanediol)

Found in Facial cleanser, moisturizer, sunscreen, around-eye cream, foundation, acne treatment, exfoliant.

Purpose A petroleum-based compound used as a humectant, solvent and skin-conditioning agent in cosmetics and perfumes.

Adverse reactions Butylene glycol can potentially cause contact dermatitis. In animal studies, reactions to the substance have included mild skin and eye irritation, drowsiness, lack of coordination, endocrine system alterations and reproductive brain and nervous system effects. It can irritate the respiratory tract if inhaled. When ingested, butylene glycol can cause nausea, vomiting and gastrointestinal irritation.

Butylparaben (*see* Parabens)

Butylphenyl methylpropional (Lilial)

Found in Fragrance, hair colour/bleach, moisturizer, shampoo, conditioner, body wash, styling gel/cream.

Purpose Synthetic fragrance used in perfumes and cosmetics.

Adverse reactions Lilial can cause skin and respiratory irritation, sensitization and contact dermatitis. It is a possible immune system toxicant. In animal studies, reactions to this substance have included skin irritation and brain, nervous system, respiratory and reproductive effects.

Calcium benzoate (*see* Benzoates)

Calcium thioglycolate
Found in Hair colour, depilatory, hair removal waxes, hair relaxer, perming, moisturizer.
Purpose Organic compound used in hair-colouring products, permanent wave and hair-straightening products and depilatory products.
Adverse reactions Calcium thioglycolate can cause dermatitis and eye irritation. In Europe thioglycolic acid and its salts and esters are permitted for use in hair-waving or straightening products at a concentration of no more than 8 per cent for general use (with a pH of 7–9.5) and 11 per cent (with a pH of 7–9.5) for professional use. These compounds can also be used in depilatories and other hair products that are removed following application, at no more than 5 per cent (for a pH of 7–9.5). Cautionary statements must also feature on the product packaging highlighting the need to avoid direct skin and eye contact. The same restrictions apply in Canada.

Camphor
Found in Facial cleanser, moisturizer, face mask, facial powder, lip balm, nail polish, nail treatment, acne treatment.
Purpose Camphor is a ketone found in the wood of the camphor tree. It can also be synthetically produced and is used as a moth repellant, plasticizer and chemical intermediate, and as an additive in explosives, foods (as a flavouring) varnishes, household products, lacquers, insecticides, fungicides, pharmaceuticals and cosmetics. In cosmetics it is used as a denaturant, fragrance ingredient and plasticizer.
Adverse reactions Camphor is a central nervous system stimulant. Symptoms from ingestion and skin absorption can include headache, confusion, vertigo, delirium, hallucinations, convulsions and coma. Ingestion can also cause liver and central nervous system damage. It is readily absorbed through the skin and may cause skin irritation. Camphor crosses the placenta and has been implicated in fetal and neonatal death. Exposure through the skin has caused neurotoxicity and hepatotoxicity (chemical-induced liver damage). Exposure to small amounts of camphor-containing products has caused toxic effects in small children. In 1980 the US Food and Drug Administration prohibited products labelled as camphorated oil, camphor oil, camphor liniment and camphorated liniment and restricted the concentration used in consumer products to a maximum of 11 per cent.

Carrageenan (*Chondrus crispus*, chondrus, Irish moss extract)
Found in Moisturizer, around-eye cream, toothpaste, tooth whitening, mouthwash, shampoo, foundation, exfoliant.

Purpose A polysaccharide extracted from red seaweeds that is used in cosmetic products as a fragrance ingredient, thickener and hair-conditioning agent. In processed foods it is used as a texturizer, thickener and stabilizer. It is also used in pharmaceutical products and industrial applications.

Adverse reactions Carrageenan may cause skin sensitization in some individuals. In 1982 the International Agency for Research on Cancer found that degraded carrageenan presented a carcinogenic risk in animals. One animal study found an association between carrageenan exposure and intestinal ulcerations and abnormal tissue growth. Carrageenan in the diet has also caused liver effects in rats and chromosome damage in mice repeatedly fed high doses. Small oral doses can affect the immune system in experimental animals. Consumption of carrageenan may play a part in intestinal inflammation.

Ceteareth compounds

Found in Facial cleanser, moisturizer, face mask, sunscreen, acne treatment, depilatory, shampoo, conditioner, body wash, hair colour/bleach, hair relaxer, exfoliant, antiperspirant/deodorant, hand cream, eye liner, styling gel, styling mousse, nail polish.

Purpose Ceteareths are produced from cetearyl alcohol (a mixture of *cetyl* and stearyl alcohol) and ethylene oxide. Examples include ceteareth-12, ceteareth-20, ceteareth-25 and ceteareth-30. They are usually used as surfactants, emollients, solubilizers, emulsifiers and cleansing ingredients in hair products, hair dyes, body and hand lotions, moisturizers, mud packs and tanning products.

Adverse reactions Ceteareth compounds may be contaminated with the impurities *1,4-dioxane*, a possible human carcinogen and *ethylene oxide*, a known human carcinogen. The Cosmetic Ingredient Review Expert Panel have stated that ceteareths should not be used on damaged skin or under conditions where N-*nitroso compounds* can form. Ceteareth compounds are penetration enhancers (able to modify the structure of the skin, enhancing the absorption of other chemicals). Penetration enhancers are typically used to aid the skin's absorption of patch drugs, enabling them to enter the bloodstream more rapidly. However, many other cosmetic ingredients also have penetration-enhancing attributes.

Cetearyl alcohol

Found in Facial cleanser, moisturizer, hair colour, sunscreen, conditioner, hand cream, styling gel/cream, exfoliant, foundation.

Purpose A mixture of fatty alcohols that is used in cosmetic products as an emollient, opacifying agent, foam booster, viscosity-increasing agent and emulsifier.

Adverse reactions Cetearyl alcohol can cause skin irritation in sensitive individuals. It has not been comprehensively assessed for safety.

Cetrimonium chloride (cetyl trimethyl ammonium chloride, hexadecyltrimethylammonium chloride, *N,N,* *N*-trimethyl-1-hexadecanaminium chloride)

Found in Styling gel, styling mousse, hairspray, detangler, hair colour, shampoo, conditioner, hair relaxer, dandruff treatment.

Purpose A quaternary ammonium compound used as a surfactant, cosmetic biocide, preservative, emulsifier and antistatic agent in cosmetic and hair formulations.

Adverse reactions Cetrimonium chloride can cause allergic reactions. Its vapours cause eye, nose and throat irritation.

Cetyl alcohol

Found in Facial cleanser, moisturizer, sunscreen, around-eye cream, shampoo, conditioner, hair colour/bleach, exfoliant.

Purpose A fatty alcohol that is used in cosmetic products as an emulsion stabilizer, opacifying agent, fragrance ingredient, emulsifier, foam booster and viscosity-increasing agent. It may be derived from spermaceti found in whales and dolphins, or of vegetable origin.

Adverse reactions Cetyl alcohol can cause contact dermatitis in some individuals. It produced mild irritation when applied to the skin of albino rabbits.

Chlorhexidine

Found in Facial cleanser, moisturizer, conditioner, antibacterial soaps, feminine hygiene products, antiseptic mouthwash.

Purpose A potent bactericide used as an antiseptic, antimicrobial and skin-sterilizing chemical.

Adverse reactions Chlorhexidine is a severe eye irritant. It can cause contact dermatitis and irritate the mucous membranes. It has been linked to occupational asthma. People with eczema or leg ulcers are at risk of allergic reactions to chlorhexidine. In animal studies, reactions to this substance have included gastrointestinal ulceration, respiratory, blood, reproductive and immune system effects, convulsions and fluid and swelling in the lungs. Chlorhexidine has caused mutation in non-mammalian microorganisms. When used in oral care products reactions can include discoloured tongue and teeth and hypersensitivity.

Chlorhexidine digluconate (*see* Chlorhexidine)

Chlorobenzene

Found in Fragrance, hair loss treatment.

Purpose A chlorinated benzene used as a solvent in perfumes, pesticides, paints, adhesives, dyes, polishes, waxes; as a dry cleaning agent and an intermediate in the production of other chemicals. In the past it was used in the production of pesticides such as DDT.

Adverse reactions Chlorobenzene can cause irritation of the skin, eyes and respiratory tract (if inhaled). Acute exposure to chlorobenzene via inhalation has caused central nervous system effects such as headaches, drowsiness and unconsciousness. In animal studies, repeated exposure to chlorobenzene caused adverse liver and kidney effects. In some studies on cultured cells chlorobenzene had a mutagenic effect, and it has shown some evidence of carcinogenicity in male rats.

Chlorofluorocarbons (CFCs)

Purpose First developed in 1928, chlorofluorocarbons (such as trichlorofluoromethane and dichlorodifluoromethane) are compounds containing only chlorine, fluorine and carbon. They were once commonly used as coolants in refrigeration and air conditioners, in the manufacturer of plastic foams, in aerosol propellants (for cosmetic products and a variety of other consumer products) and cleaning solvents.

Adverse reactions Chlorofluorocarbons cause stratospheric ozone depletion and are a potent greenhouse gas. Although CFCs have been largely phased out in the developed world as a result of international control agreements, damage to the stratospheric ozone layer continues as CFCs will remain in the troposphere (the lowest layer of the earth's atmosphere) for several decades. In the USA, people who work with CFC and hydrofluorocarbon (*HFC*) gases are required to pass licensing examinations set by the Environmental Protection Agency. The Montreal Protocol on Substances that Deplete the Ozone Layer is an international treaty intended to protect the ozone layer by phasing out several groups of halogenated hydrocarbons that contribute to ozone depletion. Regulation (EC) No. 2037/2000 (replacing Regulation (EC) No. 3093/94 on the phasing out of substances that deplete the ozone layer) bans the sale, use, production and importation of CFCs and other fully halogenated CFCs in the EU, with the exception of 'essential uses' as defined by the 1987 Montreal Protocol. However, according to the Environmental Investigation Agency (EIA) CFCs are still being produced by chemical companies in the EU for export to developing countries, where they are then illegally traded.

4-chlororesorcinol (*see* Resorcinol)

Cinnamates

Found in Sunscreen, moisturizer, fragrance, toothpaste, foundation, lip balm, lipstick, bubble bath, body wash, hand cream, antiperspirant/deodorant.

Purpose Derivatives of cinnamon that are used as sunscreen agents and common ingredients used in a variety of products. Cinnamates are related to balsam of Peru, cinnamon oils, cinnamic acide and aldehyde, so individuals allergic to these substances may also be allergic to cinnamates.

Adverse reactions The best known cinnamate is 2-ethylhexyl-*p*-methoxycinnamate (octyl methoxycinnamate), which has been detected in human milk. In an in vitro study on mouse cells, octyl methoxycinnamate added to an ethyl alcohol was found to kill 50 per cent of the cells (only 10 per cent were killed with ethyl alcohol alone). When the solution was placed underneath a UV lamp additional cell mortality was noted. Octyl methoxycinnamate is also a penetration enhancer (able to modify the structure of the skin, enhancing the absorption of other chemicals). Cinnamates can cause skin irritation and contact allergies. They are also mildly oestrogenic. Other well-known cinnamates are isoamyl-*p*-methoxycinnamate and cinoxate. Octocrylene is chemically related to cinnamates.

Cinnamyl alcohol (cinnamic alcohol)

Found in Moisturizer, bubble bath, bath oil, antiperspirant/deodorant, aftershave, fragrance, hair colour/bleach.

Purpose A fragrance compound found in the bark of cinnamon trees, the leaves of the tea-tree and hyacinth and daffodil flowers that can also be synthetically produced. It is used as a fragrance ingredient and flavouring agent in perfumes and deodorants.

Adverse reactions Cinnamyl alcohol is a common contact allergen and skin irritant. In animal studies, reactions to this substance have included skin irritation, blood effects and reproductive abnormalities.

Cinoxate (*see* Cinnamates)

Citral (3,7-dimethyl-2,6-octadienal)

Found in Fragrance, body bar, facial cleanser, moisturizer, body wash, sunscreen, styling gel/cream, aftershave, exfoliant.

Purpose Lemon-scented fragrance ingredient and flavouring agent used in foods, detergents and household cleaners. Citral is a component of lemongrass oils and various other essential oils.

Adverse reactions Citral is a skin irritant and there is evidence that it is a skin sensitizer. It is classified as a well-recognized consumer allergen by the Scientific Committee on Cosmetic Products and Non-food Products Intended for Consumers (SCCNFP). In animal studies, reactions to this substance have included skin irritation, liver, kidney, endocrine and immune system effects and reproductive abnormalities.

Citric acid (anhydrous citric acid)
Found in Facial cleanser, moisturizer, shampoo, conditioner, body wash, bubble bath, liquid hand soap.

Purpose Derived from citrus fruits, citric acid is an astringent, pH adjuster, flavour enhancer, preservative and antioxidant used in foods, beverages, detergents, household cleaners and polishes and cosmetics. It is used in cosmetics as a preservative and *alpha hydroxy acid*.

Adverse reactions Citric acid is considered to be of low toxicity, although it can cause skin irritation and severe eye irritation. Ingestion of large quantities of this substance can cause nausea, abdominal pain and vomiting. In animal studies, reactions have included skin and eye irritation, gastrointestinal, blood, brain, respiratory and immune system effects. Prolonged exposure to citric acid via ingestion can erode the teeth. The use of citric acid is restricted in Canada, as is the case with all *alpha hydroxy acids*.

Citronellol
Found in Fragrance, facial moisturizer, body wash, hair colour/bleach, sunscreen, conditioner, styling gel/cream.

Purpose A fragrance compound that occurs naturally in many plant oils and certain fruits and beverages. It is used in perfumes and cosmetics, and as an artificial flavouring in foods and pesticides.

Adverse reactions Citronellol can irritate the skin. In animal studies, reactions to this substance have included skin and eye irritation and sense organ, brain and nervous system effects.

Coal tar
Found in Shampoo, dandruff treatment, conditioner, bath oil, eczema treatment.

Purpose Brown or black liquid derived from bituminous coal used in adhesives, insecticides, creosotes, food and in medicated anti-dandruff, seborrhoeic dermatitis, eczema and psoriasis products and soaps. Coal tar dyes (produced from coal tar hydrocarbons or derivatives) are used to make colours in cosmetics and hair dyes. Coal tar contains many components, including aniline, benzene, naphthalene, xylene, quinoline and phenol.

Adverse reactions Coal tar has been classified as a known human carcinogen based on evidence produced by various groups, including the US National Toxicology Program, the US Environmental Protection Agency and the International Agency for Research on Cancer. In animal studies, reactions to this substance have included skin irritation, cancerous tumours and DNA damage. Extracts of coal tar shampoos were mutagenic in studies on *Salmonella typhimurium* bacteria. Coal tar can cause allergic and phototoxic reactions, as well as polluting the air. Crude and refined coal tars are banned in EU and Canadian cosmetics. In Canada most coal tar dyes, bases or intermediates are prohibited for use in cosmetics intended for the eye area. They are permitted in hair dyes providing a cautionary statement is placed on the packet. The Cosmetic Ingredient Review Expert Panel state there is insufficient data to support the safety of coal tar, but it is permitted for use in cosmetic formulations (apart from over-the-counter drug products) as long as the concentration used does not induce a biological effect.

Cocamide DEA (cocamide diethanolamine)
Found in Shampoo, bubble bath, body wash, facial cleanser, liquid hand soap, dandruff treatment, bath oil, hair colour/bleach, hair relaxer, exfoliant.
Purpose Derived from fatty acids of coconut oil, cocamide DEA is a surfactant, viscosity builder and foam booster used in a variety of cosmetics and dishwashing liquids.
Adverse reactions Cocamide DEA can cause mild skin irritation and sensitization. In individuals with other skin allergies it may cause contact dermatitis. In animal studies, reactions to this substance have included skin irritation, kidney, bladder and respiratory system effects and cancerous tumours. Acute exposure to cocamide DEA can cause nausea, breathing difficulties, vomiting and diarrhoea. Occupational asthma has been reported after prolonged contact with this chemical. Cocamide DEA can become contaminated with carcinogenic *nitrosamines* formed in the presence of nitrosating agents.

Cocamide MEA (*see* Cocamide DEA)

Cocamidopropyl betaine
Found in Shampoo, facial cleanser, body wash, hair colour/bleach, bubble bath, liquid hand soap, conditioner, toothpaste.
Purpose Derived from coconut oil or petrochemical origin, cocamidopropyl betaine is a surfactant, detergent, foam booster and viscosity builder used in various cosmetic formulations.
Adverse reactions Cocamidopropyl betaine can cause allergic reactions, most commonly allergic dermatitis of the head and neck. It can also become contaminated, forming carcinogenic *nitrosamines* in the presence of nitrosating agents. Cocamidopropyl betaine is said to be less of an irritant than other surfactants such as *sodium lauryl sulphate*. Hairdressers can develop contact dermatitis from hair products containing this ingredient.

Cocoyl sarcosine

Found in Shampoo, conditioner, body bar, foundation, acne treatment, hair relaxer, facial cleanser, dandruff treatment.

Purpose Formed from caffeine through degradation with barium hydroxide, cocoyl sarcosine is a surfactant, cleansing and conditioning agent used in a variety of cosmetic formulations.

Adverse reactions Cocoyl sarcosine is a penetration enhancer (able to modify the structure of the skin, enhancing the absorption of other chemicals). It can also become contaminated with carcinogenic *nitrosamines* formed in the presence of nitrosating agents.

Coumarin

Found in Fragrance, deodorant, body bar, hair colour, moisturizer, sunscreen, body wash, hand cream, tanning creams/lotions.

Purpose A fragrance ingredient, emollient and solvent used in cosmetic formulations and in industrial and household products. It is a chemical compound found in some plants that can also be obtained by chemical synthesis.

Adverse reactions Coumarin can cause skin irritation, allergic reactions and photosensitivity. It is classified as a well-recognized consumer allergen by the Scientific Committee on Cosmetic Products and Non-food Products Intended for Consumers (SCCNFP). In animal studies, reactions to this substance have included cancerous tumours, blood, liver, brain, nervous, endocrine and respiratory system effects and reproductive abnormalities. Cancer was triggered in rats and mice when high levels of coumarin were administered over a long period of time. Fairly small amounts can damage the liver in sensitive individuals.

Cyclohexasiloxane (*see* Silicones)

Cyclomethicone (*see* Silicones)

Cyclopentasiloxane (*see* Silicones)

DEA-cetyl phosphate (*see* Diethanolamine)

Diaminobenzenes

Found in Hair colour.

Purpose Colourless crystalline compounds primarily used for the manufacture of pigments and dyes. In hair dyes they are used as colour developers.

Adverse reactions Diaminobenzenes are poisonous, dangerous for the environment and can cause cyanosis (blue coloration of the skin and mucous membranes caused by a lack of oxygen in the blood) and liver damage if absorbed. Diaminobenzenes can cause allergic reactions and are also associated with skin sensitization and mutations when tested on mammalian and non-mammalian cells. Those who are allergic to one diaminobenzene may be cross-sensitized to others. (*See also* Phenylenediamines)

Diaminotoluenes

Found in Hair colour.

Purpose Synthetic aromatic amines used as intermediates in the production of dyes used for furs, leathers, textiles, spirit varnishes, wood stains and pigments.

Adverse reactions Diaminotoluenes are dangerous for the environment, toxic to aquatic organisms, carcinogenic for animals and reproductive toxicants. At high levels they are toxic for the central nervous system, causing headaches, tremors, weakness, nausea, dizziness, vomiting and even death. Diaminotoluenes have been found to be mutagenic in vitro. There is limited evidence that they may reduce fertility in males and adversely affect developing fetuses. In humans they are irritating to the eyes, skin and respiratory tract. They were widely used in hair dyes, but 2,4-diaminotoluene was removed in a number of countries after it was found to be capable of causing liver cancer in rats.

Diazolidinyl urea

Found in Facial cleanser, moisturizer, sunscreen, styling gel/cream, conditioner, around-eye cream, acne treatment, shampoo.

Purpose Diazolidinyl urea is formed by reacting allantoin with formaldehyde in the presence of sodium hydroxide solution and heat and is used as a preservative and antiseptic in cosmetics. It is also used in the textile industry.

Adverse reactions In a safety assessment, diazolidinyl urea was found to be a mild skin irritant in humans at concentrations of up to 0.4 per cent. It can cause contact dermatitis. In animal studies, reactions to this substance have included skin sensitization and gastrointestinal, brain, nervous system and endocrine effects. Diazolidinyl urea caused DNA damage in tests on mammalian cells. It is also a *formaldehyde* releaser, having an easily detached formaldehyde group in its structure that is released under specific conditions.

Dibutyl phthalate (*see* Phthalates)

Diethanolamine (DEA, 2,2'-Iminodiethanol)

Found in Facial cleanser, moisturizer, sunscreen, foundation, acne treatment, hair colour/bleach, hand cream, shampoo, body wash, liquid hand soap, bubble bath.

Purpose Derived from fatty acids of soybeans or coconut oil, DEA is a solvent, detergent, humectant, emulsifier, pH adjuster, emollient and viscosity builder used in cosmetic formulations, such as creams, shampoos and lotions. It is not commonly used in isolation as a cosmetic ingredient, but DEA-containing compounds prevalent in cosmetic products include cocamide DEA, DEA oleth-3 phosphate, DEA lauryl sulphate, lauramide DEA, linoleamide DEA, myristamide DEA, oleamide DEA, stearamide MEA and *triethanolamine* (TEA).

Adverse reactions Diethanolamine can irritate the skin and mucous membranes due to its high pH. It is a severe eye irritant. Its vapours can also irritate the eyes, nose, throat and respiratory tract. In experimental studies on rats and mice, exposure via ingestion and topical application in fairly low doses resulted in dose-related anaemia and toxicity to the liver, kidney and central nervous system. It can also become contaminated, reacting with amines in cosmetic preparations to form the carcinogen N-nitrosodiethanolamine (NDELA), a common and acutely toxic *nitrosamine* impurity that is easily absorbed by the skin and accumulates in organs such as the stomach, liver and bladder, where it results in chronic toxicity.

Diethyl phthalate (*see* Phthalates)

Diethylhexyl adipate (adipic acid, dioctyl adipate)
Found in Moisturizer, lip gloss, foundation, eyeshadow, concealer, antiperspirant/deodorant, nail polish remover, fragrance, bath oil, tanning cream/lotion.

Purpose The ester of diethylhexyl alcohol and adipic acid, it is used as a plasticizer, emollient and solvent in cosmetic formulations. It is also used in producing plastics, aircraft lubricants and meat wrapping operations.

Adverse reactions Diethylhexyl adipate can irritate the skin, eyes (applied dermally) and respiratory tract (if inhaled). In animal studies, reactions to this substance have included gastrointestinal and reproductive effects. It has been labelled as a possible human carcinogen by the US Environmental Protection Agency. Diethylhexyl adipate is classified as very toxic to aquatic organisms by the Danish Environmental Protection Agency.

Diethylhexyl phthalate (*see* Phthalates)

Dihydroxyacetone (DHA)
Found in Moisturizer, sunscreen, tanning cream/lotion, bronzer/highlighter, skin lightener.

Purpose A colourless sugar derivative that is a self-tanning agent, colourant, emulsifier, humectant and UV protector.

Adverse reactions Dihydroxyacetone can cause contact allergies. It caused DNA damage to human skin cells in vitro.

Dimethicone (see Silicones)

Dimethicone copolyol (see Silicones)

Dimethyl ether
Found in Hairspray, styling mousse, hair colour/bleach, sunscreen.
Purpose A flammable gas used as a solvent, aerosol propellant, refrigerant, extraction agent and chemical intermediate. It is also used as a viscosity decreasing agent in hairsprays and styling mousse. Dimethyl ether can be produced from biomass, coal or natural gas.
Adverse reactions Concentrations of 5–10 per cent dimethyl ether in the ambient air can cause central nervous system effects in humans. It is readily absorbed through the skin and the vapour is irritating to the eyes, nose and throat.

Dimethyl phthalate (see Phthalates)

1,4-dioxane (dioxane)
Found in May be an impurity in moisturizer, shampoo, hair colour/bleach, facial cleanser, body wash, styling gel/cream, exfoliants, foundation, acne treatment, lipstick, face mask, eyeshadow, tanning lotions/creams, hairspray, shaving cream, body bar, bubble bath, liquid hand soap, blush, face powder, lip gloss, make-up remover, depilatory, baby wipes, bronzer/highlighter, fragrance, aftersun, mouthwash, body spray, nail treatment, sunscreen.
Purpose 1,4-dioxane is not used as a cosmetic ingredient. It is an accidental by-product of the ethoxylation process used during the manufacture of certain ethoxylated cosmetic ingredients. According to the US Food and Drug Administration, these ingredients are identifiable by the prefix or descriptors, 'PEG', 'polyethylene', 'polyethylene glycol', 'polyoxyethylene', '-eth' or '-oxynol'.
Adverse reactions In studies on rats, mice and guinea pigs, orally administered dioxane resulted in an increased incidence of hepatocellular adenomas and carcinomas in mice, tumours of the nasal cavity, liver, subcutaneous tissues and mammary gland and peritoneal mesotheliomas in rats, and tumours of the liver and gall-bladder in guinea pigs. 1,4-dioxane has been classified as possibly carcinogenic to humans by the International Association for Research on Cancer and the US Environmental Protection Agency based on its carcinogenicity in studies on experimental animals. It is readily absorbed by the skin. Acute inhalation of 1,4-dioxane can cause vertigo and eye, nose, throat, skin and lung irritation.

Disodium cocoamphodipropionate

Found in Facial cleanser, foundation, acne treatment, shampoo, hair relaxer, styling gel/cream, styling mousse, hair colour/bleach, exfoliant.

Purpose An amphoteric organic compound used in cosmetic products as a hair-conditioning agent, surfactant, cleansing agent and foam booster.

Adverse reactions Disodium cocoamphodipropionate can cause contact allergies. It can become contaminated, forming carcinogenic *nitrosamines* in the presence of nitrosating agents.

Disodium EDTA (disodium ethylenediaminetetraacetate, edetate disodium)

Found in Facial cleanser, moisturizer, around-eye cream, sunscreen, shampoo, conditioner, body wash, hair colour/bleach.

Purpose A salt of EDTA used as a chelating agent (chemicals used to prevent metal ions from bonding with other ingredients and affecting the product's stability, odour or appearance), preservative and antioxidant in foods, cosmetics and household cleaning products.

Adverse reactions Disodium EDTA can irritate the skin, eyes and respiratory tract. It is a penetration enhancer (able to modify the structure of the skin, enhancing the absorption of other chemicals). In animal studies, reactions to this substance have included seizures, gastrointestinal, liver, brain, kidney and endocrine system effects and reproductive abnormalities. It has also been shown to be a weak mutagen in microbial systems. In a number of studies conducted on mammalian cells in vitro, disodium EDTA inhibited DNA synthesis.

DMDM hydantoin (diemethylol dimethyl hydantoin)

Found in Shampoo, conditioner, body wash, styling gel/cream, moisturizer, sunscreen, facial cleanser, liquid hand soap.

Purpose Preservative and biocide used in shampoos, other hair products and cosmetic products.

Adverse reactions DMDM hydantoin can cause skin irritation, contact allergies and skin sensitization. It has been associated with allergic contact dermatitis in hairdressers. DMDM hydantoin is a *formaldehyde* releaser, having an easily detached formaldehyde group in its structure that is released under specific conditions. In animal studies, reactions to this substance have included skin irritation, gastrointestinal, liver and kidney effects. In products where *diethanolamine* or diethanolamine-containing compounds are present, the carcinogenic chemical N-nitrosodiethanolamine (NDELA) may be generated.

Ethanolamine (2-aminoethanol, monoethanolamine)

Found in Shampoo, conditioner, hair colour, hair relaxer, body wash, bubble bath, moisturizer, hairspray.

Purpose An amino alcohol produced by reacting ethylene oxide with ammonia that is used in the production of surfactants, hair-waving agents, agricultural chemicals and antibiotics. It is also used as an ingredient in cosmetics, polishes, soaps, paints, concrete, photographic chemicals, biocides, cutting oils and textile processing, in sweetening natural gas and coal gas, in the production of ethylene amines and to remove acidic gases from atmospheres. Ethanolamine is often called monoethanolamine (MEA) to distinguish it from *diethanolamine* (DEA) and *triethanolamine* (TEA). In cosmetics the amino alcohols DEA, MEA and TEA are used as alkalizing agents, detergents, emulsifiers, thickeners and wetting agents.

Adverse reactions Ethanolamine is a skin, eye and respiratory irritant in humans, easily absorbed by the skin and can cause allergic contact dermatitis. It has caused occupational asthma in hairdressers and was toxic to the liver in animal studies. Excessive exposure to the vapour, dust or mist can worsen existing respiratory conditions such as asthma and bronchitis, as well as aggravating existing kidney or liver disease. Ethanolamines are corrosive and produce toxic gases when heated, including nitrogen oxides. Rats exposed repeatedly to ethanolamine via inhalation developed lesions on the lungs, liver, kidneys, spleen and testes. Ethanolamine is more toxic by inhalation than ingestion. Undiluted ethanolamine applied to the skin of rabbits caused skin effects such as severe irritation and corrosion. In tests on human lymphocyte cells it caused chromosome breaks. It has also caused reproductive toxicity in animal studies. At concentrations as low as 5 per cent, ethanolamine resulted in severe injury to rabbit eyes. Doses above 5 per cent can cause systemic effects. Ethanolamines may be contaminated with the carcinogen N-nitrosodiethanolamine (NDELA) in the presence of nitrosating agents. Long-term application of ethanolamines to animals caused hepatic and liver damage.

Ethoxylated surfactants
Found in Shampoo, body wash, bubble bath, facial cleanser, liquid hand soap, hair colour/bleach, exfoliant.

Purpose Used in industrial detergents, household cleaners, topical pharmaceuticals, cosmetics and laundry products. Ethoxylation is a chemical process whereby ethylene oxide is added to fatty acids to make them more water soluble, for instance sodium dodecyl sulphate is ethoxylated to produce *sodium laureth sulphate*. Ethoxylated surfactants are widely used in household and industrial cleaners, topical pharmaceuticals, cosmetics and laundry products as foaming agents, emulsifiers and humectants.

Adverse reactions Ethoxylated surfactants can contain the probable carcinogens *1,4-dioxane* and *ethylene oxide*. Ethoxylated surfactants are also susceptible to oxidation, making them more likely to cause skin irritation and contact sensitization.

Ethyl acetate

Found in Nail polish, nail treatment, nail polish remover, nail glue, cuticle treatment, fragrance, facial cleanser, moisturizer.

Purpose Ethyl acetate is the ester derived from ethanol and acetic acid and is used as a fragrance in cosmetics, solvent for nail enamels and polishes, varnishes, lacquers, resins and as a plastics and food additive.

Adverse reactions Ethyl acetate is a mild skin, throat and eye irritant. Inhalation irritates the nose and throat. Chronic exposure via inhalation can cause central nervous system depression, such as headache, drowsiness and light-headedness and may damage the liver, heart and kidneys. High concentrations have a narcotic effect. In animal studies, reactions to this substance have included respiratory, gastrointestinal, sense organ, liver and metabolic effects.

Ethyl acrylate (2-propenoic acid, ethyl ester)

Found in Mascara.

Purpose A monomer used to produce polymers. Ethyl acrylate is used as a solvent and flavouring agent. It is also used in the manufacture of water-based latex paints and adhesives, textile and paper coatings, leather finish resins and in the production of acrylic fibres.

Adverse reactions Ethyl acrylate can cause contact allergic reactions and is a severe eye irritant, a skin irritant and skin sensitizer. It is extremely toxic when inhaled, and reactions can include severe irritation of the nose, throat and upper respiratory system, drowsiness, nausea and headache. The International Agency for Research on Cancer has classified this substance as possibly carcinogenic to humans, based on its carcinogenicity in experimental animals. Human studies on occupational exposure to ethyl acrylate have linked exposure to this chemical with colorectal cancer. However, the US government removed ethyl acrylate from its list of potential cancer-causing agents in 2000 because, although it causes cancer in animals, it only does this when the chemical is administered orally at very high concentrations that cause ongoing injury to the stomach. The government felt it unlikely that humans would be exposed orally to comparably high concentrations. Ethyl acrylate is suspected to have effects on the gastrointestinal tract, immune system, kidneys, nervous system, respiratory system and skin or sense organs. In animal studies, reactions to this substance have included severe skin irritation and corrosion, swelling and congestion of the gastrointestinal system, lungs, heart, liver and kidneys, swelling of the brain, cancerous tumours and reproductive abnormalities. The EU has banned ethyl acrylate as a fragrance ingredient in cosmetics, as has the International Fragrance Association, but it is not banned for other purposes.

Ethyl alcohol (ethanol) (*see* **Alcohol**)

Ethyl dihydroxypropyl PABA (*see* **PABA**)

Ethyl linalool (*see* **Linalool**)

Ethylene oxide
Found in May be an impurity in most cosmetics.
Purpose A volatile chemical predominantly used as a chemical intermediate in the production of ethylene glycol, along with other industrial chemicals. It is also used as a sterilizing agent, disinfectant, fumigant or insecticide. Non-ionic surfactants used in dishwashing products, detergents and industrial applications are produced from ethylene oxide. It is also used to produce ethanolamines (on reaction with ammonia) used in soaps, detergents and textile chemicals.
Adverse reactions Ethylene oxide is likely to be a human skin, immune system, cardiovascular, reproductive, nervous system and respiratory toxicant. It is also a skin irritant, known human carcinogen and possible neurotoxicant that is banned from cosmetic products in the EU and Canada. It is classified by the European Commission as a substance that is flammable, toxic by inhalation, irritating to the eyes, respiratory system and skin and which may cause cancer and genetic damage. Cosmetic products that can contain ethylene oxide as a contaminant may be those with ethoxylated ingredients that, according to the US Food and Drug Administration, are identifiable by the prefix 'PEG' or the words 'polyethylene', 'polyethylene glycol', 'polyoxyethylene', '-eth', or 'oxynol'.

Ethylhexyl methoxycinnamate (*see* **Cinnamates**)

Ethylhexyl salicylate (octyl salicylate) (*see* **Salicylates**)

Ethylparaben (*see* **Parabens**)

Eugenol (eugenic acid, caryophyllic acid)
Found in Facial cleanser, moisturizer, sunscreen, body wash, exfoliant, fragrance, hair colour/bleach.
Purpose Derived from clove oil, eugenol is a denaturant and fragrance ingredient used in cosmetics, over-the-counter drugs, toothpastes and foods.
Adverse reactions Eugenol is a known skin irritant and contact allergen. It is classified as a well-recognized consumer allergen by the Scientific Committee on Cosmetic Products and Non-food Products Intended for

Consumers (SCCNFP). Ingestion of eugenol may cause gastroenteritis. In animal studies, reactions to this substance have included skin irritation, liver tumours and brain, endocrine, nervous and respiratory system effects. In some studies on strains of bacteria in vitro, eugenol damaged DNA. The International Agency for Research on Cancer determined that there is limited evidence for the carcinogenicity of eugenol to experimental animals.

Farnesol
Found in Facial cleanser, moisturizer, fragrance, antiperspirant/deodorant, acne treatment, sunscreen, exfoliant.
Purpose A sesquiterpene alcohol used as a flavouring agent, perfume and pesticide. It is naturally present in various essential oils, including citronella, neroli, lemongrass and balsam.
Adverse reactions Farnesol has caused central nervous system depression in animal studies and DNA inhibition in vitro. It can cause allergic reactions in some individuals.

Fluoride
Found in Toothpaste, tooth whitening, mouthwash, breath freshener.
Purpose A fluorine-containing compound added to toothpaste and water to prevent tooth decay. Sodium fluoride is used as a preservative and antimicrobial in cosmetics.
Adverse reactions Fluoride and sodium fluoride are severe skin irritants and may be corrosive and extremely irritating to the eyes. In hypersensitive individuals fluoride can result in skin eruptions, upset stomach, headache and weakness. In animal studies, reactions to these substances have included convulsions, lung, liver and kidney effects, degenerative brain alterations, osteoporosis and dental fluorosis (damaged enamel appearance and structure). In humans, large doses of ingested fluoride and sodium fluoride can cause abdominal pain, diarrhoea, muscle weakness, tremors, convulsions, central nervous system depression, a weak pulse, shock, cardiac arrhythmias and death, usually as a result of cardiac or respiratory failure. In studies on human cells, fluoride and sodium fluoride have led to chromosomal aberrations (abnormalities in the normal structure of chromosomes, which can lead to genetic conditions such as Down's syndrome).

Formaldehyde (formalin, formic aldehyde, oxomethane)
Found in Nail treatment, hair colour/bleach, styling gel/cream, sunscreen.
Purpose A colourless gas used as a disinfectant, germicide, fungicide, denaturant and preservative in nail polishes and hardeners, soaps and other cosmetic products. It is also used in household products such as furniture polishes and detergents, and in particle board, glues, permanent press fabrics, paper product

coatings and plywood. Formaldehyde is commonly used as an industrial fungicide, germicide and disinfectant.

Adverse reactions Formaldehyde is a suspected carcinogen, common skin and eye irritant and a skin sensitizer. It is very toxic by inhalation, ingestion and through skin absorption, and is readily absorbed through the skin. The International Agency for Research on Cancer has concluded that there is adequate evidence that formaldehyde causes nasopharyngeal cancer in humans and strong but not sufficient evidence for leukaemia. Occupational exposure to this substance has been linked with higher rates of miscarriage in women. It is also a common contact allergen and can cause skin sensitization. Inhalation of higher concentrations can cause extreme irritation of the respiratory tract, coughing, choking, vomiting, inflammation of the lung, chest pain and delayed symptoms of shortness of breath, depending on the level of formaldehyde inhaled. In studies on human and animal cells in vitro, formaldehyde caused DNA damage and gene mutation. Some ingredients used in cosmetics and other products degrade into formaldehyde. These include *diazolidinyl urea*, *imidazolidinyl urea*, *DMDM hydantoin*, *quaternium-15*, *2-bromo-2-nitropropane-1,3-diol*, sodium hydroxymethylglycinate and benzylhemiformal. Formaldehyde is banned for use in cosmetic products in Sweden and Japan.

Geraniol
Found in Fragrance, moisturizer, body oil, bubble bath, body bar, hair colour/bleach, body wash, sunscreen, styling gel/cream, exfoliant.

Purpose A monoterpene alcohol used as a fragrance ingredient in cosmetics and air fresheners. It is also used as a food additive. It is the main component of volatile oils such as oil-of-rose, palmarosa oil and citronella oil and is present in geranium, lemon, lime, ginger and various other essential oils.

Adverse reactions Geraniol can cause allergic reactions and skin sensitization. It is classified as a well-recognized consumer allergen by the Scientific Committee on Cosmetic Products and Non-food Products Intended for Consumers (SCCNFP). In animal studies, reactions to this substance have included severe skin irritation, central nervous system depression and liver, brain and sense organ effects.

Glycerides
Found in Facial cleanser, moisturizer, sunscreen, around-eye cream, lipstick, lip liner, foundation, face powder, concealer, blush, body firming lotion, shaving cream.

Purpose Natural or synthetic esters formed when glycerol reacts with one or more fatty acids. Soaps are manufactured by reacting glycerides with sodium hydroxide. Glycerides are used in soaps, detergents and various cosmetic products as emulsifiers, emollients and skin-conditioning agents.

Adverse reactions Glycerides lack safety data. Some glycerides used in cosmetic products are derived from animals, such as tallow glycerides and fish glycerides.

Glycerin (glycerine, glycerol, glycyl alcohol)

Found in Facial cleanser, moisturizer, sunscreen, shampoo, conditioner, body wash, hair colour/bleach, toothpaste.

Purpose A sugar alcohol that is a component of all animal and vegetable fats and oils. It can also be synthesized. Glycerin is used as a humectant, solvent, fragrance, viscosity-reducing agent and emollient in cosmetics. It is also used in toothpaste, mouthwashes, tobacco, pharmaceutical preparations, food and drink.

Adverse reactions Glycerin is generally considered to be of low toxicity, although it can cause mild skin and eye irritation. Repeated contact with the skin can cause skin dehydration. In high concentrations it can irritate the mucous membranes. In animal studies, reactions to this substance have included mild skin irritation, tumours, gastrointestinal problems, muscle weakness, renal failure, kidney, bladder, blood, endocrine system and repro-ductive effects. Ingestion of large amounts of glycerin can cause headache, dizziness, nausea, vomiting, thirst and diarrhoea.

Glyceryl PABA (see PABA)

Glycol ethers

Found in Fragrance, liquid hand soap, nail polish, nail polish remover, lipstick, moisturizer, lip gloss.

Purpose A large group of chemicals commonly used as industrial solvents and in paints, varnishes, dyes, stains, inks, cleaners, jet fuel de-icing additives, hydraulic fluids, perfumes and cosmetics. A few common glycol ethers include diethylene glycol dimethyl ether, ethylene glycol dibutyl ether, ethylene glycol monoacetate, dipropylene glycol, propylene glycol monomethyl ether and triethylene glycol.

Adverse reactions Glycol ethers can be absorbed from skin contact with the liquid or through inhalation of the vapour. Most glycol ethers are readily absorbed through the skin and can dissolve the skin's protective oils. Some of them can evaporate rapidly, reaching hazardous levels in the air. Overexposure to glycol ethers can cause anaemia (a reduced number of red blood cells), intoxication, nausea and irritation of the skin, respiratory tract and eyes. Acute, short-term exposure can cause fluid accumulation in the lungs and severe liver and kidney damage. In experimental animals, exposure to certain glycol ethers at low concentrations causes birth defects, infertility in males, testicular damage, maternal toxicity and delayed development. Glycol ethers have been shown to induce spontaneous abortion, and occupational exposure could possibly affect a woman's ability to deliver a live birth. Most glycol ethers can damage red blood cells or the bone marrow. Occupational exposures in men have been associated with reduced sperm counts. Products labelled with the terms EGPE, EGME, EGEE, DEGBE, PGME, DPGME and 'methyl' should be avoided.

Glycolic acid (*see* Alpha hydroxy acids)

Glycols
Found in Facial cleanser, moisturizer, sunscreen, shampoo, conditioner, body wash, acne treatment, hair colour/bleach, hair perm, styling gel.

Purpose Glycols are aliphatic organic compounds. Examples include propylene glycol, butylene glycol, ethylene glycol and carbitol. Ethylene glycol is commonly used as anti-freeze in automobile radiators. Propylene and butylene glycol are widely used as humectants in cosmetics and as food additives. Various glycols are used in polymer production.

Adverse reactions Glycols can cause skin and eye irritation and are known to produce adverse impacts on aquatic organisms. When glycols degrade, ammonia gas is released into the environment. Ethylene glycol is poisonous by ingestion. Propylene glycol can cause skin irritation and sensitization in concentrations of 2 per cent or even less, although it is permitted for use in cosmetics at much higher concentrations.

Hexylcinnamaldehyde (*see* Cinnamates)

Hexylene glycol
Found in Facial cleanser, moisturizer, sunscreen, acne treatment, eye make-up remover, hair colour/bleach, shampoo.

Purpose A glycol that is used as a humectant, fragrance, emulsifier, plasticizer and solvent in cosmetics.

Adverse reactions Hexylene glycol is generally considered to be of low toxicity, although it can cause mild skin and eye irritation and contact dermatitis with repeated and prolonged dermal contact. It is not classified as a skin sensitizer, although some cases of skin sensitization have been reported. In animal studies, reactions to this substance have included kidney, sense organs, endocrine system and liver effects.

Homosalate (*see* Salicylates)

Hydrated silica (*see* Silica)

Hydrochlorofluorocarbons (HCFCs)

Found in Some cosmetic aerosol products.

Purpose Haloalkane compounds composed of hydrogen, chlorine, fluorine and carbon atoms. They are one of the substitutes for CFCs as a refrigerant and propellant in aerosol cans.

Adverse reactions Hydrochlorofluorocarbons do have some ozone-depleting effects, although not as much as *chlorofluorocarbons*, and they contribute to the accumulation of greenhouse gases. In Europe, Regulation (EC) No. 3093/94 banned the use of HCFCs as solvents in open systems from 1 January 1996, and the subsequent Regulation (EC) No. 2037/2000 on substances that deplete the ozone layer banned the use of HCFCs from January 2002 in all solvents (with a few exceptions) and set out a timeline for a phased restriction on the use, sale, production and importation of HCFCs. The final deadline for the complete phasing out of the use, sale and importation of HCFCs is December 2009 and the deadline for ending the production of HCFCs is December 2025.

Hydrofluorocarbons (HFCs)

Found in Hairspray, styling mousse, antiperspirant/deodorants.

Purpose One of the main substitutes for *chlorofluorocarbons* (CFCs) and *hydrochlorofluorocarbons* (HCFCs), which are being phased out as a result of their contribution to stratospheric ozone depletion. They are now predominantly used in refrigeration and air conditioning systems. Consumer products containing HFCs include aerosol cosmetic products, spray paints, household products and automotive products.

Adverse reactions Hydrofluorocarbons do not affect the ozone layer, but they are powerful greenhouse gases. The HFC fluoroethane has a global warming potential 1,200 times greater than that of carbon dioxide. According to the Environmental Investigation Agency, HFCs and hydrochlorofluorocarbons (HCFCs) will add the equivalent to an estimated 3 billion tonnes of carbon dioxide to the atmosphere by 2015. They are included as one of the six key greenhouse gases in the Kyoto Protocol. The UK's target under the Kyoto Protocol is to reduce the emissions of HFCs and perfluorocarbons (PFCs) by 12.5 per cent based on 1995 levels by 2008–2012.

Hydrogen peroxide

Found in Mouthwash, toothpaste, hair colour/bleach, nail treatment, ear drops, acne treatment, hair perm.

Purpose A clear colourless liquid used as an antimicrobial, bleaching agent, disinfectant, detergent, antiseptic and oxidizing agent in oral, nail and hair products, household cleaners, fabric stain removers and contact lens disinfectants. For industrial purposes hydrogen peroxide is used as a bleach for textiles and paper; as a component of rocket fuels and for producing foam rubber. Small amounts of hydrogen peroxide gas are naturally present in the air.

Adverse reactions Hydrogen peroxide is toxic in high concentrations. If inhaled, hydrogen peroxide can irritate the nose, throat and respiratory tract. It can whiten or bleach the skin. Ingestion of hydrogen peroxide can cause gastrointestinal irritation, foaming at the mouth, vomiting, temporary unconsciousness, fever and potentially internal bleeding, because of the formation of significant amounts of oxygen gas. When used in concentrations of 3–5 per cent for household disinfectant purposes, it can be mildly irritating to the skin and mucous membranes. It is strongly irritating and potentially corrosive to the eyes and skin at concentrations of 10 per cent, which can be found in some hair-bleaching products. Repeated use of hydrogen peroxide as a mouthwash can irritate the tongue and buccal mucous membrane. In studies on human and animal cells in vitro hydrogen peroxide has caused DNA damage at concentrations of less than 1 per cent. It is banned for use in cosmetic formulations in Japan.

Hydroquinone (1,4-benzenediol, 4-hydroxyphenol, p-hydroxyphenol)

Found in Skin lightener, moisturizer, hair colour/bleach, sunscreen, concealer.

Purpose A white crystalline substance obtained by the reduction of quinone that is used as an antioxidant, fragrance, hair colourant, reducing agent and skin-bleaching ingredient in hair dyes, skin-lightening products and other cosmetic formulations.

Adverse reactions Hydroquinone is a mild skin irritant and an eye irritant. It can cause allergic reactions in some individuals after repeated or prolonged contact, leading to discoloration of the nails and hair. Hydroquinone is also a skin sensitizer. Ingestion can cause tremors, convulsions, nausea, vomiting, tinnitus, abdominal pain, a sense of suffocation, increased heart rate, delirium, coma and death. Some of the aforementioned symptoms can be induced by a dose of just 1 g (less in children). In animal studies, reactions to this substance have included skin and eye irritation, skin sensitization, discoloration of the corneas, tremors, convulsions, leukaemia, tumours, reproductive abnormalities and kidney, liver, blood, gastrointestinal, brain and nervous system effects. In studies on human and animal cells in vitro, hydroquinone has caused DNA damage. Hydroquinone is a possible carcinogen and is very toxic to aquatic organisms.

Hydroxycaprilic acid (see Alpha hydroxy acids)

Imidazolidinyl urea

Found in Facial cleanser, moisturizer, around-eye cream, mascara, eyeshadow, face powder, foundation, sunscreen, shampoo, body wash.

Purpose Imidazolidinyl urea is formed by the condensation of allantoin and formaldehyde and is used as an antimicrobial agent and preservative in many cosmetic formulations. It is the second most commonly used preservative after *parabens*.

Adverse reactions Imidazolidinyl urea can cause allergic contact dermatitis and skin sensitization. It is also a *formaldehyde* releaser. Formaldehyde is classified as a probable human carcinogen by the International Agency for Research on Cancer.

Iodopropynyl butylcarbamate

Found in Facial cleanser, moisturizer, sunscreen, shampoo, conditioner, body wash, baby wipes, styling gel/cream.

Purpose A whitish crystalline powder containing iodine that is used as a preservative in a range of cosmetic products.

Adverse reactions Iodopropynyl butylcarbamate can cause skin irritation and contact allergies. In studies on animals, reactions to this substance have included mild skin irritation, eye irritation, increased liver weights, emphysema and stomach lesions.

Isobutane (1,1–dimethylethane, 2–methylpropane, trimethylmethane)

Found in Styling mousse, antiperspirant/deodorant, shaving mousse, hairspray, body spray.

Purpose An alkane derived from petroleum and natural gas that is used as a propellant in cosmetics, household sprays and foods. It is also used in cigarette lighters and camp stoves as a fuel, and as a refrigerant.

Adverse reactions At high concentrations butane can cause central nervous system depression, nausea, headaches, dizziness, drowsiness and confusion. High inhaled concentrations of isobutane, such as in cases of substance abuse, can cause loss of consciousness, cardiac arrhythmia, convulsions and asphyxiation. In animal studies, reactions to this substance have included central nervous system depression, anaesthesia and cardiac sensitization. Isobutane is a volatile, highly flammable substance. It can become contaminated with *1,3-butadiene*, a known human carcinogen. In the EU and its member states, butane is not authorized in cosmetic formulations if it contains 0.1 per cent or above of 1,3-butadiene.

Isobutylparaben (*see* Parabens)

Isoeugenol (*see* Eugenol)

Isopropyl alcohol (isopropanol, 2-propanol, rubbing alcohol)

Found in Moisturizer, hair colour, nail polish, nail polish remover, nail treatment, mascara, hairspray, conditioner.

Purpose Isopropyl alcohol is produced by combining water and propylene and is used as an antibacterial, denaturant, fragrance ingredient and solvent used for oils, resins, cosmetics, hair colourants and household products. It is also used as a petrol additive.

Adverse reactions Isopropyl alcohol can irritate the eyes and mucous membranes. Repeated use can dry out the skin and cause flaking. Prolonged skin contact can cause corrosion. Ingestion of isopropyl alcohol can cause abdominal pain, shortness of breath, vomiting, nausea, hallucinations, unconsciousness and death. Acute inhalation can cause coughing, dizziness, headache and sore throat, along with the above symptoms. It is also a central nervous system depressant and in high concentrations can cause cardiovascular depression. Isopropyl alcohol is approximately twice as toxic as ethanol and 250 ml (8 fl oz) is a fatal dose by ingestion. In animal studies, reactions to this substance have included hind leg paralysis, respiratory depression, stupor, and reproductive, brain and liver effects.

Isopropyl palmitate (palmitic acid, isopropyl ester palmitic acid, isopropyl *n*-hexadecanoate)

Found in Moisturizer, lipstick, sunscreen, concealer, lip gloss, foundation, eyeshadow.

Purpose Palm oil-based compound used as a binder, fragrance ingredient, skin-conditioning agent and emollient in cosmetic formulations.

Adverse reactions Isopropyl palmitate can cause skin irritation and clog pores.

Kathon CG (methychloroisothiazolinone/ methylisothiazolinone)

Found in Facial cleanser, moisturizer, sunscreen, body wash, shampoo, conditioner, bubble bath, hair colour/bleach, dandruff treatment, styling gel/cream.

Purpose A mixture of methychloroisothiazolinone and methylisothiazolinone used in cosmetic products as a preservative.

Adverse reactions Kathon CG can cause skin irritation, is a potent skin sensitizer and frequent cause of contact dermatitis in Europe. A 1992 safety assessment of methylisothiazolinone and methychloroisothiazolinone found them to be highly toxic to rats when administered orally and moderately toxic when topically applied. Methylisothiazolinone has been linked to neuron cell death in a study on rodent brain cells.

Lactic acid (*see* Alpha hydroxy acids)

Lanolin
Found in Moisturizer, lip gloss, lipstick, lip balm, foundation, styling gel/cream.

Purpose Derived from sheep wool fat. Cosmetic-grade lanolin contains a mixture of esters of alcohols and fatty acids. Lanolin is used as an antistatic agent, lubricant, emollient and emulsifier in a variety of cosmetic formulations.

Adverse reactions Lanolin can cause allergic contact dermatitis and promote acne. There are higher incidences of lanolin allergies among people with eczema. It can also cause contact sensitization. Cosmetic-grade lanolin is sometimes contaminated with small amounts of pesticides, which can be absorbed by the skin and enter the bloodstream.

Lauramide DEA (*see* Diethanolamine)

Laureth compounds
Found in Moisturizer, sunscreen, around-eye cream, foundation, concealer, blush, body wash, body firming lotion, hair colour/bleach, shaving cream, styling mousse, conditioner, hair perm, antiperspirant/deodorant.

Purpose Ethoxylated alcohols commonly used in cosmetic products as cleansing agents, solubilizing agents and emulsifiers. Examples include laureth-4, laureth-7, laureth-10, laureth-12, and laureth-23.

Adverse reactions Laureth compounds are sometimes contaminated with the probable carcinogen *1,4-dioxane*. Ingredients such as laureth-4, laureth-7, laureth-10, laureth-12 and laureth-23 are commonly used as emulsifiers in cosmetic products. These compounds are known as ethoxylated alcohols and many of them can cause skin irritation.

Lead acetate
Found in Hair colour.

Purpose A poisonous soluble lead salt used as a progressive colour additive in hair dyes to gradually alter hair colour. It is also used in textile printing and dyeing and paints and varnishes, and in the preparation of other lead compounds.

Adverse reactions Lead acetate is a suspected human carcinogen and known animal carcinogen. It has been evaluated as possibly carcinogenic to humans by the International Agency for Research on Cancer and is considered to be a known carcinogen and reproductive toxicant by the State of California Environmental Protection Agency (Proposition 65 List of Carcinogens). Lead acetate can cause skin and eye irritation and blood and central nervous system effects. It is toxic by ingestion, inhalation and skin absorption. Lead acetate is dangerous for the environment and very toxic to aquatic organisms. It presents a possible risk of impaired fertility and harm to unborn children. Lead acetate is banned from cosmetic products in Canada and the EU and its member states due to its potential carcinogenicity and reproductive toxicity.

Limonene (D-limonene, DL-limonene, dipentene)
Found in Facial cleanser, moisturizer, hair colour/bleach, fragrance, sunscreen, styling gel/cream.
Purpose A synthetic citrus flavouring and fragrance ingredient that occurs naturally in certain trees and bushes. It is used in food, household cleaning products, cosmetic formulations and perfume. It is also used as a pesticide in flea control products.
Adverse reactions Limonene is a known skin irritant, eye irritant and skin sensitizer. Ingestion of limonene in certain doses can cause gastrointestinal irritation. In animal studies, reactions to this substance have included skin and eye irritation, kidney damage, renal tumours, liver, brain and reproductive effects. It is dangerous to the environment and toxic to aquatic organisms.

Linalool
Found in Moisturizer, sunscreen, fragrance, body wash, hair colour/bleach, conditioner, styling gel/cream.
Purpose Fragrance substance that occurs naturally in many essential oils.
Adverse reactions Linalool is a possible immune system toxicant. It can cause skin irritation, skin sensitization and allergic reactions. Inhalation exposure in mice and humans caused a mild sedative effect. In animal studies, reactions to this substance have included brain and nervous system effects, broad systemic toxicity and skin irritation.

Lye (*see* Sodium hydroxide)

Malic acid (*see* Alpha hydroxy acids)

Mercury
Found in May be an impurity in moisturizer, lip liner, eye liner, brow liner, lip gloss, lipstick, eyeshadow, mascara, nail treatment.
Purpose A naturally occurring metal that exists in various forms. Mercury salts are sometimes used in skin-lightening creams, antiseptic creams and

ointments. Mercury is used in the electrical industry, in control instruments, in the home and in laboratory and medical instruments. The US Food and Drug Authority prohibited the use of mercury in the majority of cosmetic products in 1974. It is now only permitted in trace amounts in particular products intended for the eye area, where no safe and effective alternative is available. Some cosmetic products can contain mercury as an impurity.

Adverse reactions The general public is mainly exposed to mercury through the diet and dental amalgams. It is highly toxic and can cause allergic reactions, skin irritation and neurotoxicity. Inhalation can cause liver, kidney and central nervous system damage. Methylmercury and metallic mercury vapours are more dangerous than other forms because a larger amount of the mercury reaches the brain. Short-term exposure to high levels of metallic mercury vapours can cause lung damage, nausea, vomiting, diarrhoea, increases in heart rate or blood pressure, skin rashes and eye irritation. Methylmercury has caused kidney tumours in male mice and both mercuric chloride and methylmercury are classified as possible human carcinogens by the US Environmental Protection Agency. Mercury can cross the placenta to reach the fetus, causing harmful effects to the unborn child including brain damage, mental retardation, blindness, seizures and inability to speak. It can also be passed on to a nursing infant through breast milk. Children affected by mercury poisoning can develop kidney damage. Mercury is persistent and bioaccumulative in wildlife and humans. Mercury and its compounds are banned for use in cosmetic products in Japan and Canada and restricted in the USA to specific concentrations in cosmetics intended for the eye area. Mecury compounds are only to be included in cases where no other effective and safe preservative is available for use.

Methychloroisothiazolinone (*see* Kathon CG)

Methylisothiazolinone (*see* Kathon CG)

Methylparaben (*see* Parabens)

Microban (*see* Triclosan)

Mineral oil (*see* Paraffinum liquidum)

Myristamide DEA (*see* Diethanolamine)

***N*-butane (*see* Butane)**

2-nitro-*p*-phenylenediamine (*see* Phenylenediamines)

Nitrophenylenediamine (*see* Phenylenediamines)

Nitrosamines
Purpose A class of chemical compounds formed from the reaction of two nitrogen-containing substances: an amine and a nitrosating agent. Nitrosamines can be found in cured bacon, beer, tobacco products, gastric juices, rubber products, pesticides and cosmetics. Cosmetic products containing amines such as monoethanolamine (MEA) (*ethanolamine*), *diethanolamine* (DEA) and *triethanolamine* (TEA) or amino derivatives may be contaminated with nitrosamines, if nitrosating agents such as *bronopol*, are present.
Adverse reactions Around 90 per cent of nitrosamines tested have been found to be carcinogens in a wide variety of experimental animals and they can readily penetrate the skin. There is some evidence that nitrosamines in the diet or environment play a role in human cancer.

N-nitroso compounds (*see* Nitrosamines)

Octocrylene (*see* Cinnamates)

Octyl methoxycinnamate (*see* Cinnamates)

Octyl salicylate (*see* Salicylates)

Oleamide DEA (*see* Diethanolamine)

Oleic acid
Found in Moisturizer, baby lotion, hair colour/bleach, shampoo, conditioner, mascara, hairspray, antiperspirant/deodorant, styling gel/cream.
Purpose A fatty acid derived from a range of animal and vegetable fats and oils. It is used in foods and many cosmetic products.
Adverse reactions Oleic acid can cause skin and eye irritation and clog pores. In animal studies, reactions to this substance have included skin irritation and brain, nervous system and respiratory effects. Oleic acid can induce lung injury when injected into experimental animals. It also damaged reproductive capacity in female rats given 15 per cent oleic acid in feed for 10–16 weeks.

Oleth compounds
Found in Facial cleanser, moisturizer, sunscreen, shampoo, conditioner, body wash, styling gel/cream, styling mousse, shaving cream, hair relaxer, hand cream, eyeshadow.

Purpose Predominantly used in cosmetic products as surfactants, emulsifiers, cleansing and solubilizing agents. Examples include oleth-2, oleth-3, oleth-5, oleth-10, oleth-15, oleth-20 and oleth-30.

Adverse reactions Oleth compounds are made by ethoxylating oleyl alcohol with ethylene oxide and are known as the *polyethylene glycol (PEG) ethers* of oleyl alcohol. The chain length of the PEG is determined by the number of moles of ethylene oxide. Oleth compounds can cause skin irritation and allergic reactions. Oleth-10 was found to be a cumulative skin irritant in experimental animals. Polyethylene glycols can cause skin irritation and sensitization and have shown some evidence of kidney toxicity. Carcinogenic impurities such as *1,4-dioxane* and *ethylene oxide* may be present.

Oxybenzone (*see* Benzophenones)

PABA (para–aminobenzoic acid)

Found in Facial cleanser, moisturizer, shampoo, conditioner, body wash, hair-loss treatment, exfoliant, hairspray, styling gel/cream, sunscreen.

Purpose An organic compound used in sun protection and cosmetic products as a sunscreen agent.

Adverse reactions PABA used to be a very popular sunscreen ingredient but its use has declined due to problems with allergic dermatitis and photosensitivity. It is prohibited from sunscreen products in Canada. It has been found to increase the formation of potentially mutagenic thymine dimers, damaging DNA strands in human cells that some people lack the mechanism to repair, and therefore increasing their risk of skin cancer. PABA has also been found to be weakly oestrogenic in breast cancer cells. Compounds related to PABA include ethyl dihydroxylpropyl PABA, padimate O, padimate A and glyceryl PABA. People sensitive to artificial sweeteners (e.g. saccharin), ester-type anaesthetics (e.g. benzocaine, procaine, tetracaine), para-amino type azo dyes (e.g. paraphenylenediamine, aniline), sulphonamide antibiotics or thiazide diuretics may also be sensitive to sunscreen agents containing PABA or its derivatives.

Padimate A (amyl dimethylaminobenzoate) (*see* PABA)

Padimate O (octyl dimethyl PABA) (*see* PABA)

Palmitic acid

Found in Facial cleanser, moisturizer, sunscreen, shaving cream, shampoo, eyeshadow.

Purpose A fatty acid used as a surfactant, fragrance ingredient and opacifying agent in numerous cosmetic products.

Adverse reactions Palmitic acid may cause mild skin irritation and contact dermatitis in some individuals but is generally considered to be of low toxicity.

Para-aminobenzoic acid (*see* PABA)

Para-aminophenol (*p*-aminophenol) (*see* Aminophenols)

Parabens

Found in Facial cleanser, moisturizer, shampoo, conditioner, styling gel/cream, styling mousse, toothpaste, tooth whitening, bath oil, exfoliant, foundation, face powder, eyeshadow, mascara, lipstick, lip gloss, lip liner, eye liner, sunscreen, hair colour/bleach.

Purpose Parabens are esters of para-hydroxybenzoic acid commonly used as preservatives in foods, cosmetics and pharmaceuticals. Examples include methylparaben, butylparaben, ethylparaben, propylparaben and isobutylparaben.

Adverse reactions A number of studies have shown parabens to be oestrogenic. Certain parabens have been detected intact in the breast tissue of women diagnosed with breast cancer. Studies have found that parabens can be absorbed by the skin and methyl and *n*-propyl parabens have been detected in over 96 per cent of human urine samples assessed in research conducted in the USA. All parabens can cause contact allergies and skin sensitization.

Paraffinum liquidum (mineral oil)

Found in Baby oil, baby lotion, facial cleanser, moisturizer, around-eye cream, foundation, lipstick, lip gloss, concealer, face powder, hair colour/bleach, styling gel/cream.

Purpose A mixture of hydrocarbons obtained from petroleum that is used in cosmetic products as an emollient and film-former. Mineral oil also has many other applications, such as cooling electric components, being used as a cleaner and solvent for inks in fine art printmaking, as a lubricant and fuel. It can be used in foods (particularly sweets) as a glazing agent.

Adverse reactions Untreated and mildly treated mineral oils are known carcinogens according to the US National Toxicology Program. Paraffinum liquidum is said to cause photosensitivity, increasing the risk of skin damage upon exposure to the sun. It is also said to trap dirt and toxicants under the skin, which can promote acne. Repeated exposure to paraffinum liquidum can cause contact dermatitis. Derivatives are sometimes contaminated with carcinogenic *polycyclic aromatic hydrocarbons* (PAHS).

Paraphenylenediamine (*p*-phenylenediamine, PPD)

Found in Hair colour.

Purpose A colourless aromatic amine commonly used as a permanent hair dye. It is also used in textile or fur dyes, temporary tattoos, photographic developer, photocopying and printing inks, black rubber, oils greases and petrol.

Adverse reactions Paraphenylenediamine is a potent contact allergen and for that reason it is banned for use in hair dye products in France, Germany and Sweden. It can also cause respiratory irritation, bronchial asthma, sensitization and, in rare cases, death. People sensitized to paraphenylenediamine may develop a cross-sensitivity to other dye products including aniline dyes and ballpoint pen inks, the pharmaceutical drugs benzocaine and procaine and *PABA* (used in sunscreens). Paraphenylenediamine is toxic by inhalation, skin contact and ingestion, dangerous for the environment and toxic to aquatic organisms. It has also proven to be mutagenic in cell cultures, genotoxic (capable of damaging DNA) in human lymphocytes when combined with *hydrogen peroxide*, and neurotoxic and carcinogenic in animal studies. (*See also* Phenylenediamines)

Para-toluenediamine (*p*-toluenediamine) (*see* Diaminotoluenes)

Parfum (perfume, fragrance)
Found in Most cosmetic products.

Purpose 'Parfum', 'aroma' and 'fragrance' are all terms used to refer to over 100 different fragrance materials added to cosmetics, household products, pesticides, air fresheners, cigarettes and foods. Perfumes are mixtures of essential oils, aroma compounds, fixatives and solvents.

Adverse reactions Parfums are common skin and cosmetic allergens. Some of them (such as synthetic musks) can cause endocrine disruption. Other reactions include headaches, nausea, dizziness, fatigue and difficulty breathing. Several fragrance ingredients are classified as hazardous waste by the US Environmental Protection Agency. Certain perfumes are carcinogens or suspected carcinogens. Perfumes can exacerbate asthma and some of them are penetration enhancers. A number are neurotoxic. Synthetic musk fragrances have been detected in human tissue, blood plasma and breast milk. They can also bioaccumulate in the environment.

Pentasodium EDTA (*see* Disodium EDTA)

Pentasodium triphosphate (sodium tripolyphosphate)
Found in Toothpaste, tooth whitening, mouthwash, bath oil, shampoo, mascara, eye liner.

Purpose The sodium salt of triphosphoric acid used as a chelating agent and pH adjuster. In soaps and detergents it is used as a builder. Pentasodium triphosphate is used as a preservative in various foodstuffs and is also found in toothpastes, household cleaners and laundry detergents.

Adverse reactions Pentasodium triphosphate can cause irritation due to its alkalinity. In animal studies, reactions to this substance have included brain and nervous system effects, endocrine disruption at high doses and skin irritation. In humans it can cause skin and mucous membrane irritation. Ingestion of large amounts can cause nausea, vomiting and diarrhoea.

Petrolatum (petroleum jelly, Vaseline)

Found in Moisturizer, depilatory, baby lotion, lipstick, lip balm, lip gloss, sunscreen, hair relaxer, styling gel/cream.

Purpose A translucent jelly-like mixture of semi-solid hydrocarbons derived from petroleum. It is used in cosmetic products as an emollient.

Adverse reactions Petrolatum can cause allergic reactions on damaged skin. If it is regularly used it can damage the skin's natural oils, causing dryness and cracking. Petrolatum is only permitted for use in cosmetic products in the EU if the full refining history is known and it can be shown that the substance from which it is produced is not a carcinogen.

Petroleum distillates

Found in Fragrance, mascara, concealer, lip balm, lipstick, foundation, eye liner, eyeshadow, moisturizer.

Purpose A group of hydrocarbon-based chemicals extracted by distillation during the refining of crude oil and used in a range of products and applications as solvents. Examples include gasoline, naphtha, mineral spirits, kerosene, paraffin wax and tar. They are used as the main ingredient in consumer products such as furniture polishes, adhesives, paint solvents, motor oil and cosmetic products.

Adverse reactions Occupational exposure to petroleum distillates has been found to increase the risk of undifferentiated connective tissue disease. This is a condition that presents with symptoms similar to those of several chronic inflammatory autoimmune disorders that affect connective tissues, such as systemic lupus erythematosus, rheumatoid arthritis, scleroderma, fibromyalgia, polymyositis and dermatomyositis, but not enough to be characterized as those disorders. Petroleum distillates are suspected cardivascular and blood toxicants, neurotoxicants and respiratory toxicants. Inhaling small amounts of petroleum distillates and other hydrocarbons can cause chemical pneumonia, pulmonary damage and even death. They can also cause skin irritation and sensitivity to light. Petroleum distillates can cause anaesthesia and dermatitis. Many petroleum-based products have been linked to cancer, and petroleum distillates are sometimes contaminated with butadiene, a known carcinogen. In the EU a number of petroleum distillates are banned for use in cosmetic products, with others being permitted provided certain impurity limits are not exceeded. In some cases particular distillates are permitted if it can be shown that the substance from which they were produced is not carcinogenic.

Phenol
Found in Lipstick, lip balm, shaving cream, hand lotion.

Purpose A carbolic acid derived from *coal tar* that is used in the production of phenolic resins, bisphenol A, caprolactum, chlorophenols and various alkylphenols and xylenols. It is also used as an antiseptic in various cosmetics and in disinfectants.

Adverse reactions Phenol is a toxic agent that can adversely affect the central nervous system. It was used by the Nazis as a means of rapid individual execution during the Second World War. It is neurotoxic and nephrotoxic (toxic to the kidneys), poisonous by ingestion, toxic by skin contact and a severe skin and eye irritant. Some individuals can experience adverse reactions at very low doses. Prolonged skin contact with diluted solutions of 1–2 per cent phenol can cause severe burns. Skin absorption of phenol can result in systemic effects. Chronic skin exposure to phenol can cause necrosis. Because phenol damages the skin, it can increase the penetration of other toxic substances. Ingestion can corrode the mucous membrane of the mouth, burn the throat and cause gastrointestinal necrosis. Humans have experienced kidney inflammation after skin exposure to phenol. Acute exposure may cause shock, coma, dark urine, cardiac arrhythmias and death. Phenol may be a skin tumour promoter in certain strains of mice. When administered orally to male rats in one study, a higher risk of leukaemia was reported in rats exposed to low doses. It has also caused oxidative DNA damage in mice. A study of Finnish workers discovered that those exposed to phenol, especially in the short term, had a high risk of lung cancer. Phenol is banned for use in cosmetic products in the EU and Canada.

Phenoxyethanol
Found in Facial cleanser, moisturizer, around-eye cream, sunscreen, body wash, exfoliant, foundation.

Purpose An aromatic ether used as a fragrance ingredient and preservative in a variety of cosmetic formulations.

Adverse reactions Phenoxyethanol can cause skin and respiratory irritation. In animal studies, reactions to this substance have included reduced body weight, increased kidney, liver and thyroid weights, developmental toxicity, brain and nervous system effects and endocrine disruption at high doses. Occupational exposure to phenoxyethanol has resulted in damage to the nervous system in several cases. It is classified by the European Commission as harmful if swallowed and irritating to the eyes. Phenoxyethanol caused slight irritation to rabbit skin at 2.2 per cent.

Phenoxyisopropanol

Found in Facial cleanser, moisturizer, around-eye cream, acne treatment, shampoo, face mask, exfoliant, antiperspirant/deodorant.

Purpose Used in cosmetic products, particularly acne treatments and facial cleansers, as a preservative, antiseptic and solvent.

Adverse reactions Phenoxyisopropanol can cause skin and eye irritation and can be absorbed through the skin. Breathing the vapour can cause respiratory tract irritation.

Phenylenediamines

Found in Hair colour.

Purpose Dye intermediates used in permanent and semi-permanent hair colourants. They are also used in textile and fur dyes, photographic developer, printing and photocopying inks, black rubber and gasoline.

Adverse reactions Phenylenediamines have caused skin and eye irritation, sensitization and degenerative changes in the liver and kidneys in animal studies. Occupational exposures have caused similar adverse effects in humans. They have been found to damage DNA in mammalian cells and cause chromosome breakages in human lymphocyte cultures. p-phenylenediamine is a common allergen. In early studies on hair dyes, chronic liver, kidney and nervous system damage was reported as a result of intoxication in humans caused by hair dyes. Occupational exposure to hair dyes has been associated with increased incidences of certain types of cancer. Phenylenediamines are mutagenic in cell-based studies, dangerous for the environment, and toxic to aquatic organisms. Various phenylenediamines are prohibited or restricted for use in cosmetic products.

Phenyl mercuric acetate

Found in Mascara, eye make-up remover, eye ointments, eye drops.

Purpose Mercury-containing preservative used in cosmetics that has also been used in contraceptive gels, biocide paints, ink, adhesives, eyewashes, as a fungicide for crops and as a herbicide, among other things.

Adverse reactions There is evidence to suggest that phenyl mercuric acetate is neurotoxic. In animal studies, reactions to this substance have included systemic effects, reproductive effects, endocrine disruption and skin irritation. It is classified by the European Commission as toxic if swallowed, can cause burns, toxic, able to cause serious damage to health following prolonged skin contact or if swallowed, very toxic to aquatic organisms and dangerous for the environment. It is banned for use in cosmetics in Canada. (*See also* Mercury)

Phenyl-*p*-phenylenediamine (*see* Phenylenediamines)

Phthalates

Found in Fragrance, nail polish, nail treatment, cuticle treatment, lipstick, lip gloss, eyeshadow, eye liner, glitter, blush, bronzer/highlighter, facial cleanser, conditioner.

Purpose Used as plasticizers in a wide variety of products such as polyvinyl chloride flooring, detergents, plastic clothing, lubricating oils, pharmaceuticals, blood bags and tubing, children's toys and cosmetics. The primary phthalates used in cosmetics are dibutyl phthalate (DBP) and diethyl phthalate (DEP). Phthalates are also present in our diet through food production processes and packaging, often migrating from plastic wrappers into food products.

Adverse reactions Dibutyl phthalate and diethylhexyl phthalate are classified as toxic for reproduction in the EU due to an amendment to the European Commission Cosmetics Directive and are thus banned from cosmetic products sold in the EU and its member states. Manufacturers who produce for both US and EU markets commonly make cosmetic products for the US with these phthalates, even though they are prohibited from their products available on the EU market. When phthalates are used as fragrance carriers they do not have to feature on cosmetic ingredients labels. Certain phthalates have demonstrated oestrogenic activity, along with mutagenic and carcinogenic potential. A group of male reproductive disorders referred to collectively as testicular dysgenesis have been linked with exposure to phthalates and the term phthalate syndrome describes certain reproductive abnormalities in male babies. Phthalate exposure has also been linked to diabetes.

Polycyclic aromatic hydrocarbons (PAHs)

Found in May be impurities in facial cleanser, moisturizer, hand cream, around-eye cream, baby lotion, sunscreen, lip balm, lip gloss, lipstick, petroleum jelly, styling gel/cream, hair relaxer, body wash, concealer, body bar, conditioner, foundation, eye liner, eyeshadow, antiperspirant/deodorant.

Purpose Widespread environmental contaminants found in a variety of consumer products, including plastics, medicines, dyes, pesticides and wood preservatives. They are present in tobacco smoke and are common impurities in *petrolatum*, also known as petroleum jelly.

Adverse reactions Some individuals who have been chronically exposed to PAHs via inhalation or skin contact have developed cancer. Occupational exposure to PAHs has been linked with an elevated risk of prostate cancer, lung cancer, bladder cancer and breast cancer. The US National Toxicology Program has listed 15 PAHs reasonably anticipated to be human carcinogens.

Polyethylene

Found in Facial cleanser, sunscreen, exfoliant, foundation, face powder, lipstick, lip gloss, eyeshadow, eye liner, eye make-up remover, mascara, blush, antiperspirant/deodorant, shaving cream, shaving gel.

Purpose An ethylene polymer produced from petroleum gas or the dehydration of alcohol that is used in cosmetics as an abrasive, bulking agent, viscosity-increasing agent, oral care agent, emulsion stabilizer and film-former. It is also used in wire and cable coatings and insulation, pipe fittings, packaging film, paper coating, lining for drums, toys, refuse bags and petrol containers.

Adverse reactions There is limited evidence of polyethylene having a carcinogenic effect in animal studies, causing liver and kidney damage and brain and nervous system effects, and some evidence of immune system toxicity. It may be a human immune system toxicant. Ethylene can contain impurities such as propylene, carbon dioxide, carbon monoxide, sulphur, hydrogen and acetylene, although these are said by the Cosmetic Ingredient Review to be of a concentration too low to warrant concerns about potential toxicity.

Polyethylene glycol (PEG) compounds

Found in Facial cleanser, moisturizer, face mask, around-eye cream, sunscreen, toner/astringent, shampoo, conditioner, bubble bath, bath oil, body wash, body bar, liquid hand soap, shaving cream, aftershave, styling gel/cream, styling mousse, hair colour/bleach, hair relaxer, foundation, concealer, face powder, eyeshadow, eye liner, lipstick, lip gloss, mascara, blush, toothpaste.

Purpose A group of polymers of ethylene oxide. They are used in cosmetics as surfactants, solvents, cleansing agents, skin-conditioning agents and humectants. PEG is also a plasticizer and used as an ingredient in laxatives, sexual lubricants, as a thickening agent in hydraulic fluids, as an oligomer in polyurethanes, as a packing material for foods (at high molecular weights), and for numerous other purposes. PEGs are usually listed on ingredients labels followed by a number (such as PEG-14), which indicates their average molecular weights.

Adverse reactions Polyethylene glycol compounds can become contaminated with the probable carcinogen *1,4-dioxane*, along with other toxic impurities such as *ethylene oxide, polycyclic aromatic hydrocarbons* (PAHs) and heavy metals, including lead, iron, cobalt, nickel, cadmium and arsenic. They are readily absorbed through damaged skin. Ethylene glycol is a reproductive and developmental toxicant. Sensitization, contact dermatitis and systemic toxicity were reported in burn patients treated with a PEG-based cream. The lower molecular weight PEGs seem to be more toxic than the higher molecular weight PEGs when administered orally, because they are absorbed by the digestive tract. Lower molecular weight PEGs (such as PEG 200 and PEG 400) have caused chromosomal aberrations (changes in the normal structure of chromosomes) in mammalian cells in vitro. Low molecular weight PEG stearates (e.g. PEG 2 stearate and PEG 9 stearate) were able to damage the skin barrier at a concentration of 5 per cent in a water/mineral oil mixture.

Polysorbates (polyoxyethylene sorbitan esters)

Found in Facial cleanser, moisturizer, around-eye cream, shampoo, conditioner, body wash, exfoliant, acne treatment, styling gel/cream, hair colour/bleach, sunscreen, tanning cream/lotion, foundation, mouthwash, toothpaste, baby wipes, eye liner.

Purpose Polysorbates are produced by reacting ethylene oxide with sorbitan esters (sorbitol derivatives). They are used as surfactants and emulsifiers in foods, cosmetics and pharmaceuticals. Polysorbates are usually listed on ingredients labels followed by a number (such as polysorbate 20), which bears relation to their formulas.

Adverse reactions Polysorbates can cause hypersensitivity following topical application. Polysorbate 20, 60 and 80 enhance the skin absorption of fat-soluble substances. Polysorbates can contain residual amounts of the probable carcinogen *1,4-dioxane* and the known carcinogen *ethylene oxide*.

Polystyrene

Found in Facial cleanser, acne treatment, styling gel/cream, shaving cream.

Purpose A thermoplastic substance used as a building material and in the production of cosmetic resins. Also found in foam cartons, meat trays, coffee cups, salad boxes, plastic cutlery, plastic model assembly kits, etc. Styrofoam (or expanded polystyrene – EPS) is a type of foam polystyrene packaging. It is commonly used to make cosmetic compacts. Polystyrene is also used as a film-former and viscosity-increasing agent in styling gels, facial cleansers and other cosmetic products.

Adverse reactions We are more familiar with the use of polystyrene for packaging than as a cosmetic ingredient. Acute short-term exposure to styrene used in the production of polystyrene plastics and resins can cause mucous membrane and eye irritation. Long-term exposure to styrene can affect the central nervous system, causing headaches, fatigue, weakness and central nervous system dysfunction, It can also have slight effects on certain kidney enzyme functions, plus blood and gastrointestinal effects, along with hearing loss. Styrene is classified by the International Agency for Research on Cancer as possibly carcinogenic to humans. *Benzene*, used in the production of polystyrene, is a human carcinogen. Polystyrene may cause eye and respiratory tract irritation. Styrofoam is not easy to recycle and decomposes very slowly in the environment.

Polytetrafluoroethylene (*see* Teflon)

Polyvinylpyrrolidone (PVP, povidone)

Found in Moisturizer, shaving cream, shaving gel, styling gel/cream, styling mousse, shampoo, conditioner, hairspray, mascara, eye liner.

Purpose PVP is a water-soluble polymer used as a binder, emulsion stabilizer, film-former, hair fixative and suspending agent in cosmetic products. It is often used as a binder in pharmaceutical tablets and can also be found in some adhesives that require moistening, foods, batteries, ink and inkjet paper.

Adverse reactions Polyvinylpyrrolidone has caused endocrine disruption in experimental animals at high doses. Ingestion may cause loosening of the stools, flatulence and faecal impaction or damage to lungs and kidneys. Concentrated exposure to PVP in hairsprays may cause a lung disease known as thesaurosis (a condition arising out of the body storing excessive amounts of a normal or foreign substance) in some individuals. It has caused cancer of the connective tissues in mice, and cancer in rats when administered intraperitoneally.

Potassium alum (*see* Alum)

Potassium benzoate (*see* Benzoates)

Potassium hydroxide (caustic potash, potassium lye)

Found in Facial cleanser, moisturizer, around-eye cream, cuticle treatment, acne treatment, exfoliant, body wash, hairspray, depilatory, antibacterial cleanser.

Purpose Used as a pH adjuster, emulsifier and cuticle softener. It is also used in varnish removers, paint and drain cleaners.

Adverse reactions Potassium hydroxide may cause skin irritation. It is corrosive to the skin, eyes and mucous membranes in solutions containing above 2 per cent potassium hydroxide and can cause irritation at concentrations as low as 0.5 per cent. Ingestion can cause pain, vomiting, diarrhoea, bleeding, collapse and death. Exposure to dust or mist can cause eye, nose and throat irritation. Moderate doses repeatedly applied to the skin of mice caused skin cancer. There is some evidence that it instigated chromosomal damage in mammalian cells in culture. It may cause skin rash and burning. Concentrations above 5 per cent may damage fingernails.

PPG-14 butyl ether

Found in Facial cleanser, moisturizer, toner/astringent, make-up remover, conditioner, scalp treatment, styling gel/cream, antiperspirant/deodorant, eye liner.

Purpose A poly ether alcohol used in cosmetics as a hair and skin conditioning agent, imparting smoothness to the skin. It is a petroleum product derived from propylene oxide. It is also used as an insecticide.

Adverse reactions PPG-14 butyl ether may cause skin irritation and has resulted in brain and nervous system effects and endocrine disruption at high doses in animal studies.

Propane

Found in Styling mousse, antiperspirant/deodorant, shaving cream, hairspray, body spray, conditioner.

Purpose Compressed gas used as an aerosol propellant, fuel, solvent and refrigerant.

Adverse reactions High doses of this volatile organic compound (VOC) can cause central nervous system depression, eye, nose and throat irritation, asthma exacerbation, headaches, nausea, dizziness and drowsiness. Inhalation following acute exposures can cause cardiac arrhythmias (irregular heart beat) and, in some instances, sudden death. Direct contact of the liquid with the skin causes burns and frostbite.

Propylene glycol (PG)

Found in Facial cleanser, moisturizer, astringent/toner, shampoo, conditioner, body wash, styling gel/cream, hair colour/bleach, antiperspirant/deodorant, aftershave, eye liner, mascara, concealer, foundation, liquid hand wash, antibacterial washcloths, toothpaste.

Purpose Used in anti-freeze and de-icing solutions for cars, boats and aircraft. Also used in food and cosmetics as a humectant, fragrance ingredient, viscosity-decreasing agent, solvent and wetting agent.

Adverse reactions Propylene glycol can cause skin irritation, eye irritation and contact allergies. It is a penetration enhancer (able to modify the structure of the skin, enhancing the absorption of other chemicals) and weak skin sensitizer in humans. If ingested it may cause irritation of the gastrointestinal tract. It may be absorbed through the skin and cause similar effects to exposure by ingestion. Propylene glycol can de-fat the skin, removing its natural protective sebum. There is some evidence that it may be toxic to the central nervous system and a respiratory toxicant. High oral doses in children have caused central nervous system depression and high doses administered to animals have caused brain, nervous system and reproductive effects. Occupational exposures to propylene glycol can result in the aggravation of pre-existing kidney disorders. It may be mutagenic in humans and cause reproductive effects and birth defects based on animal test data.

PVP (*see* Polyvinylpyrrolidone)

Quaternary ammonium compounds

Found in Facial cleanser, moisturizer, around-eye cream, acne treatment, sunscreen, feminine deodorant, baby wipes, exfoliant, shampoo, conditioner, body wash, bubble bath, liquid hand soap, shaving cream, styling gel/cream, styling mousse, hairspray, hair relaxer, dandruff treatment, hair colour/bleach, hair perm, mascara, face powder, foundation, concealer, lipstick, lip gloss, lip balm, lip liner, antiperspirant/deodorant.

Purpose Synthetic derivatives of ammonium chloride used as disinfectants and sanitizers for homes, farms, hospitals and offices; algaecides for swimming pools, industrial water reservoirs and farm ponds; antiseptics for cleaning wounds; surfactants, fabric softeners and antistatic agents in shampoos; surfactants and preservatives in a range of cosmetic products; softeners for textiles and paper products; in inhalers and nasal sprays as preservatives and wetting agents. Examples include benzalkonium chloride, benzethonium chloride, cetalkonium chloride, cetrimide, stearalkonium chloride, cetrimonium, cetrimonium bromide, quaternium-15 and quaternium-18.

Adverse reactions Quaternary ammonium compounds can cause toxic effects by all routes of exposure. Diluted solutions can cause skin irritation. Concentrated solutions are corrosive and can burn the skin and mucous membranes. Quaternary ammonium compounds can cause skin sensitization and allergic reactions. Clinical effects of exposure include nausea, abdominal pain, vomiting, burning sensation, diarrhoea, restlessness, coma and convulsions. Ingestion of concentrated solutions can cause death. Repeated occupational exposures have been known to cause sensitization and asthma. They can cause irritant contact dermatitis and some of them are very toxic to aquatic organisms.

Resorcinol (1,3-benzediol)

Found in Hair colour, acne treatment, shampoo, facial cleanser, moisturizer, toner/astringent.

Purpose A simple aromatic chemical derived from various resins that is used as a preservative, antiseptic, anti-acne agent, fragrance ingredient, antifungal and astringent. It serves as a coupler in hair dyes and is also used in tanning, photography, tyre building, dyes, pharmaceuticals and adhesives, and in the production of diazo dyes and plasticizers.

Adverse reactions Resorcinol can cause skin redness, itching and dermatitis and corrosion in concentrations above 3 per cent. It is used in hair dye formulations at concentrations of up to 5 per cent. Resorcinol is also irritating to the eyes and mucous membranes. Absorption can cause convulsions and death. In animal studies, reactions to this substance have included skin irritation, thyroid dysfunction, endocrine disruption, central nervous system effects, tumours and changes in adrenal gland weights. Exposure to resorcinol has been linked with central nervous system and thyroid effects and red blood cell alterations in humans. Resorcinol may pose a risk for aquatic organisms in areas where hair dyes are produced and from rubber production plants.

Retinoic acid (tretinoin)

Found in Acne treatment, skin lightener.

Purpose A metabolite of vitamin A used to treat acne and other skin disorders. It is also touted as an 'anti-ageing' ingredient.

Adverse reactions Retinoic acid can cause chronic skin irritation, redness, alopecia (hair loss), scaling, scarring when topically applied and headaches, nausea, fatigue, ulcers, pancreatitis, liver toxicity, respiratory distress and altered vision when ingested. In animal studies, reactions to this substance have included reproductive effects at low doses, blood, brain and nervous system effects and skin irritation. Retinoic acid produced malformations in the developing systems of embryonic mice. Fetal malformations have been reported in humans and animals after the use of tretinoin during the early stages of pregnancy. It is banned for use in cosmetic products in the EU and Canada.

Salicylates

Found in Sunscreen, tanning creams/lotions, moisturizer, body wash, conditioner, shaving cream, depilatory, lip balm, foundation, fragrance, styling gel/cream, styling mousse, hair colour/bleach, nail treatment, toothpaste, tooth whitening, mouthwash, breath freshener.

Purpose Salts or esters of salicylic acid that occur naturally in many plants (such as strawberries, almonds and tomatoes) and were originally derived from willow bark. Now they are often synthetically manufactured. Salicylates are a group of painkilling drugs (the best known is aspirin). They perform diverse functions in cosmetic products. Examples of salicylates include potassium salicylate, sodium salicylate, TEA salicylate, tridecyl salicylates, benzyl salicylate and homomenthyl salicylate (homosalate).

Adverse reactions Salicylates are absorbed readily through the skin. The level of absorption depends on the concentration and other ingredients used in the formulation. They can remove the protective outer layer of the skin (stratum corneum) and can cause skin irritation and contact allergies. Those sensitive to aspirin can develop allergic reactions after ingesting salicylates. Salicylates are also penetration enhancers (able to modify the structure of the skin, enhancing the absorption of other chemicals). Some have been found to be weakly oestrogenic.

Salicylic acid

Found in Facial cleanser, moisturizer, toner/astringent, exfoliant, acne treatment, face mask, shampoo, dandruff treatment, foundation, concealer.

Purpose An aromatic acid obtained from the bark of the white willow and wintergreen leaves. It can also be synthesized by heating phenol with carbon dioxide. It is used in cosmetics as a denaturant, hair-conditioning ingredient, exfoliant, skin-conditioning agent, preservative and antimicrobial. It is also used as a fungicide, dyestuff intermediate and in the manufacture of salicylates and resins, and aspirin.

Adverse reactions Salicylic acid can be absorbed through the skin and it is a penetration enhancer (able to modify the structure of the skin, enhancing the absorption of other chemicals). It can cause skin, eye and mucous irritation. In sensitive individuals salicylic acid may cause skin rashes. Absorption of large amounts can cause headaches, dizziness, hearing difficulties, vomiting, abdominal pain, hyperventilation, acidosis, sweating, thirst, mental confusion and skin rashes in some individuals. Salicylic acid can worsen allergic skin reactions.

Sarcosines

Found in Facial cleanser, facial moisturizer, acne treatment, shampoo, conditioner, dandruff treatment, body wash, sunscreen, lipstick, lip balm, lip gloss, foundation, hair relaxer, shaving cream, aftershave, toothpaste.

Purpose Used in cosmetic products as hair-conditioning agents and secondary or tertiary detergents. Examples include *cocoyl sarcosine*, lauroyl sarcosine, myristoyl sarcosine, stearoyl sarcosine, sodium cocoyl sarcosinate and sodium myristoyl sarcosinate.

Adverse reactions Sarcosines are penetration enhancers (able to modify the structure of the skin, enhancing the absorption of other chemicals) and can be nitrosated to form the known animal carcinogen N-nitrososarcosine.

Selenium sulphide (selenium disulphide)

Found in Dandruff treatment, shampoo, conditioner.

Purpose An antifungal agent used in anti-dandruff shampoos.

Adverse reactions Selenium sulphide is classified as a possible human carcinogen by the US Environmental Protection Agency and the National Toxicology Program in its 11th Report on Carcinogens, and is listed as a possible carcinogen in the State of California's Proposition 65, which lists chemicals known to the state to cause cancer or reproductive toxicity. It is toxic by ingestion, may be neurotoxic to humans and is irritating to the skin and eyes. Selenium sulphide can cause discoloration of the hair. In Europe, selenium compounds are classified as toxic by inhalation and ingestion, danger of cumulative effects, dangerous for the environment and very toxic to aquatic organisms. Selenium sulphide is banned for use in cosmetics in Japan and restrictions apply in the EU.

Silica (silicon dioxide)

Found in Moisturizer, sunscreen, foundation, eyeshadow, lipstick, face powder, concealer, antiperspirant/deodorant, toothpaste.

Purpose A fine particulate dust from quartz rock that occurs in several forms, including crystalline and amorphous (hydrated) silica. It is the main component of sand. Amorphous silica is used as an abrasive, absorbent, anti-caking agent, bulking agent and opacifying agent in cosmetics. It is also used as a filler in rubber products, paints, animal feeds, pesticides and insulation materials.

Adverse reactions Amorphous silica is persistent and bioaccumulative in humans and wildlife. It may also be contaminated with crystalline silica–a known carcinogen. When ground down into a fine powder and used in cosmetic powders, silica may cause respiratory problems. Occupational exposure to silica has been linked with lung inflammation, which can progress to silicosis (a type of occupational lung disease) and an elevated risk of lung cancer. Fine silica, mainly used for industrial purposes, can potentially cause a range of problems, such as respiratory toxicity and cardiovascular toxicity. Amorphous silica is irritating to the skin, eyes and respiratory tract.

Silicates

Found in Facial cleanser, moisturizer, sunscreen, exfoliant, acne treatment, concealer, foundation, face powder, lipstick, lip gloss, eyeshadow, eye liner, blush, bronzer/highlighter, hair colour, antiperspirant/deodorant, depilatory, shaving cream, bath oil.

Purpose Salts derived from silica or the silicic acids containing silicon, oxygen and one or more metals. Used in building materials such as cement, concrete, bricks and glass. Examples of silicates commonly used in cosmetics include magnesium aluminium silicate, aluminium silicate, trimethylsiloxysilicate, sodium metasilicate, sodium silicate and sodium magnesium silicate.

Adverse reactions Sodium silicate can cause irritation of the eyes, skin, respiratory tract, mouth, oesophagus and stomach. Sodium metasilicate has been found to cause reproductive effects at low doses in animal studies and is classified in the EU as corrosive, causes burns and irritating to the respiratory system. Some of the other silicates are suspected neurotoxic substances. Potential adverse reactions depend on the silicate in question.

Silicones

Found in Moisturizer, around-eye cream, hand cream, sunscreen, conditioner, styling mousse, styling gel, foundation, face powder, aftershave gel, concealer, eyeshadow, mascara, hair colour/bleach, antiperspirant/deodorant.

Purpose Silicones are polymers of silicon oxide combined with an organic group, such as ethyl and methyl. Depending on the chain length and cross-linking they can be liquid, gel, waxes, rubbers or hard plastics. They are used in cookware, medical applications, sealants, lubricants, insulation and cosmetics. Examples include dimethicone, cyclomethicones, cyclopentasiloxane, trimethylsiloxysilicate and cetearyl methicone.

Adverse reactions Most of the silicones used in cosmetics are considered to be safe, although they have not been widely studied for safety. Cyclopentasiloxane and cyclomethicone are persistent and bioaccumulative in wildlife and may cause skin irritation in some individuals.

Sodium bisulphite

Found in Moisturizer, skin lightener, acne treatment, tanning creams/lotions, around-eye cream, liquid hand soap, sunscreen, hair relaxer, hair perm.

Purpose The monosodium salt of sulphurous acid is used as a food preservative, disinfectant and bleach for textiles, brewing casks, dye vats and paper making. It is used in wines to prevent oxidation and preserve flavour. In cosmetics it is used as a reducing agent, antioxidant and hair-waving/straightening agent. Sodium bisulphite, along with some other bisulphites, releases sulphur dioxide under certain conditions.

Adverse reactions Concentrated solutions of sodium bisulphite are irritating to the skin, eyes and mucous membranes. Sodium bisulphite can cause allergic reactions in sensitive individuals, particularly people with asthma. Up to 5 per cent of people with asthma are sulphite sensitive. In genotoxicity studies (testing for DNA damage) sodium bisulphite has produced both negative and positive results.

Sodium borate (borax, tetraborate)

Found in Facial cleanser, moisturizer, around-eye cream, hand cream, acne treatment, eye drops, styling gel.

Purpose A sodium salt of boric acid, used as a preservative, emulsifier, pH adjuster, water softener, stabilizer, viscosity-increasing agent and mild antiseptic. It is used as a fungicide and in the production of glazes, enamels, soldering fluxes, cleaning compounds and to fireproof textiles and wood.

Adverse reactions Sodium borate and boric acid have caused neurotoxicity, developmental effects on the brain and endocrine disruption at high doses in animal studies. Borax dust can cause skin and respiratory irritation. In mammalian cells borax was found to be cytotoxic (toxic to cells) at high concentrations. When administered to rats via feed borax caused toxic effects on the gonads and it also caused testicular atrophy (shrinking of the testes) in male experimental animals. Borax and boric acid are readily absorbed through abraded skin, therefore the Cosmetic Ingredient Review Panel surmised that boric acid and borax are not safe for use on infant skin or abraded skin. Both borax and boric acid can cause skin dryness and irritation.

Sodium dodecylbenzenesulphonate

Found in Facial cleanser, body bar, exfoliant, acne treatment, sunscreen, dandruff treatment, shampoo, liquid hand soap.

Purpose A linear alkylbenzene sulphonate (LAS) surfactant used in foaming bath products and creams, laundry detergents and wheel shampoos.

Adverse reactions Sodium dodecylbenzenesulphonate can cause skin and eye irritation. Exposure caused mild intestinal necrosis and haemosiderosis (a rare lung condition where iron builds up in the lungs) of the liver, spleen and kidneys. It has caused endocrine disruption at high doses in animal studies.

Sodium fluoride (*see* Fluoride)

Sodium hydroxide (caustic soda, soda lye)

Found in Facial cleanser, moisturizer, soap, acne treatment, sunscreen, body wash, exfoliant, fragrance, aftershave, depilatory, hair relaxer, toothpaste.

Purpose Used to produce soaps, dyestuffs, explosives and paper. Large amounts are used in petroleum refining, rayon production and rubber reclaiming. It is also used in food preparation, processing cotton fabric, laundering, paint stripper, electroplating, cosmetics and commercial oven and drain cleaning products.

Adverse reactions Sodium hydroxide forms a powerful alkaline solution when dissolved in a solvent. The liquid causes burns following brief skin contact. Very low levels can cause eye and skin irritation. Sodium hydroxide is corrosive to all tissues it comes into contact with. A 5 per cent solution of sodium hydroxide, applied to the skin, causes severe necrosis after several hours. Solutions of more than 30 per cent sodium hydroxide are extremely corrosive to the skin. Ingestion can cause difficulty swallowing, burning pain, swelling, copious salivation, vomiting, rapid breathing, collapse, asphyxia and death. Sodium hydroxide can also cause contact dermatitis, serious eye injuries and nail loss. Inhalation of the dust can damage lung tissue, depending on the level of exposure. Sodium hydroxide is listed in a minimum of 49 of the National Priorities List sites, categorized by the US Environmental Protection Agency.

Sodium hydroxymethylglycinate

Found in Facial cleanser, moisturizer, baby wipes, shampoo, conditioner, acne treatment, sunscreen, hair relaxer.

Purpose An antimicrobial derived from glycine or aminoacetic acid (a naturally occurring amino acid) that is used as a preservative in cosmetics and household cleaners.

Adverse reactions Sodium hydroxymethylglycinate is generally considered to be safe, although it is a *formaldehyde*-forming ingredient.

Sodium laureth sulphate (SLES)

Found in Facial cleanser, shampoo, conditioner, body wash, bubble bath, hair colour, liquid hand soap, exfoliant, hair relaxer.

Purpose A detergent and surfactant widely used in personal care products such as shampoo and foaming bath products.

Adverse reactions Sodium laureth sulphate has been shown to cause eye and skin irritation in experimental animals, although it is reported to be milder than *sodium lauryl sulphate* (SLS). It can be contaminated with the probable carcinogen 1,4-dioxane, which is formed when SLS is ethoxylated to produce SLES. .

Sodium lauryl sulphate (SLS)

Found in Shampoo, body wash, liquid hand soap, exfoliant, moisturizer, acne treatment, hair colour/bleach, toothpaste, shaving cream, tooth whitening.

Purpose An anionic surfactant used in a range of household products (such as dishwashing and laundry detergents) and personal care products as a cleaning and foaming agent. It is also used as a food additive (thickener and emulsifer) and dispersing agent in creams, lotions and pharmaceutical preparations and as an emulsifier and penetrant in varnish and paint remover. For industrial applications, SLS is used in floor scrubbing and degreasing solutions.

Adverse reactions Sodium lauryl sulphate is a frequent cause of eye irritation and can cause contact dermatitis. It is an industrial floor cleaner and degreasant that damages the protective outer layer of skin and is a known skin irritant and penetration enhancer (able to modify the structure of the skin, enhancing the absorption of other chemicals). SLS is used as a primary skin irritant in clinical testing on animals or human volunteers, as a point of reference to measure the healing or modifying properties of other substances, or to increase the penetration of other substances. Repeated skin exposure to SLS can cause dermatitis. When it is used in toothpastes SLS can irritate the mucous membranes of the mouth, predisposing individuals to mouth ulcers. Application of 10–20 per cent SLS detergent caused skin corrosion and severe irritation in experimental animals.

Sodium metabisulphite

Found in Facial cleanser, moisturizer, face mask, tanning lotion/cream, sunscreen, hair colour/bleach, hairspray.

Purpose An inorganic salt used as an antimicrobial, reducing agent and antioxidant in cosmetics, as a food additive (E223) and as an antioxidant in photographic film development.

Adverse reactions Sodium metabisulphite is a known immune system toxicant and possible respiratory toxicant. Up to 5 per cent of people with asthma are sensitive to sulphite. Occupational asthma and skin sensitization has been reported as a consequence of workplace exposure to sodium metabisulphite. When used in food and drugs it has been known to cause life-threatening asthma. Acute toxicity can result in nausea, vomiting, diarrhoea, stomach pain and gastric haemorrhage. If it comes into contact with strong acids a poisonous gas is released. It is classified by the European Commission as harmful if swallowed, presents a risk of serious damage to eyes and if it comes into contact with acids toxic gases are liberated. (*See* also Bisulphites)

Sodium monofluorophosphate (*see* Fluoride)

Sorbitol
Found in Toothpaste, tooth whitening, moisturizer, conditioner, hair colour/bleach, sunscreen, body bar, shaving gel, antiperspirant/deodorant, mouthwash.
Purpose A sugar alcohol used as a flavouring agent, fragrance ingredient, humectant, thickener and skin-conditioning agent. It is also used as antifreeze, in toothpastes as a stabilizer, in some cigarettes as a humectant, and in foods as a sweetener.
Adverse reactions If ingested in excess, sorbitol can cause diarrhoea, gastrointestinal disruption and alter the absorption of other drugs, making them less effective or more toxic. Frequent consumption of sorbitol may contribute slightly to dental caries. Some individuals have a sorbitol intolerance that results in abdominal pain, bloating and diarrhoea.

Stearalkonium chloride
Found in Shampoo, conditioner, hair colour/bleach, styling gel/cream, hair perm, facial cleanser, moisturizer, styling mousse, face mask, hairspray.
Purpose A cationic quaternary ammonium salt that is used in hair products as an antistatic agent, neutralizing electrical charges on the hair and making it easier to comb through the hair, and as a conditioning agent.
Adverse reactions Stearalkonium chloride can cause skin and eye irritation. (*See* also Quaternary ammonium compounds)

Stearamide MEA (*see* Ethanolamine)

Steareth compounds
Found in Facial cleanser, moisturizer, toner/astringent, face mask, around-eye cream, acne treatment, skin lightener, hand cream, sunscreen, aftersun, tanning cream/lotion, hair colour/bleach, hair relaxer, shampoo, conditioner, bath oil, liquid hand soap, exfoliant, foundation, eyeshadow, face powder, blush, mascara, antiperspirant/deodorant, styling mousse, fragrance.

Purpose Steareth compounds (such as steareth-2, steareth-10, steareth-15, steareth-20) are waxy solids produced by reacting stearyl alcohol with ethylene oxide and used as emulsifiers in cosmetics. They are ethers of *polyethylene glycol* (PEG).

Adverse reactions Steareth compounds can cause mild eye irritation. They may contain small amounts of the probable carcinogen *1,4-dioxane*, a by-product of ethoxylation, as an impurity.

Stearic acid

Found in Facial cleanser, moisturizer, around-eye cream, hand lotion, sunscreen, foundation, concealer, mascara, body bar, exfoliant, shaving gel, cuticle treatment.

Purpose A saturated fatty acid used as a fragrance ingredient, emulsifier and cleansing agent in cosmetic products. It is also used as an ingredient in the production of candles, soaps, oil pastels, and for softening rubber. Stearic acid is often obtained from fat found in cows, pigs and sheep although stearic acid can be gleaned from vegetable fats, such as coconut.

Adverse reactions Stearic acid can cause skin sensitization in rare cases and skin and eye irritation in its solid form. Stearic acid dust is irritating to the eyes, nose and throat. Ingesting large amounts may cause intestinal obstruction.

Stearyl alcohol

Found in Facial cleanser, moisturizer, around-eye cream, sunscreen, hair colour/bleach, conditioner, antiperspirant/deodorant, shaving cream.

Purpose A mixture of solid alcohols prepared from sperm whale oil or from vegetable sources. It is used in cosmetic products as a fragrance ingredient, emulsion stabilizer, foam booster and viscosity-increasing agent. It is also used in perfumes, lubricants and resins.

Adverse reactions Stearyl alcohol can cause skin irritation and contact dermatitis in some individuals. It is generally considered to be of low toxicity.

Strontium compounds

Found in Toothpaste, depilatory, facial cleanser, toner/astringent, moisturizer, acne treatment.

Purpose Strontium is a naturally occurring earth element found in rock, soil, dust, oil and coal. Strontium compounds (salts) are used in the production of ceramics and glass products, pyrotechnic materials, fluorescent lights, paint pigments and pharmaceutical preparations, and as ingredients in cosmetic products and oral care products (although most now use potassium nitrate instead). Examples of strontium compounds used in cosmetics include strontium chloride, strontium nitrate, strontium hydroxide, strontium peroxide, strontium sulphide and strontium thioglycolate.

Adverse reactions Exposure to low levels of strontium may harm children, with high levels possibly impairing bone growth. Inhaling high levels of radioactive strontium can damage bone marrow and cause anaemia. Exposure may also cause cancer in humans, and has caused leukaemia and cancers of the bone, nose, lung and skin in animals, and birth defects. Strontium compounds can cause skin irritation and hair breakage. Strontium compounds are banned for use in cosmetic products in Japan. Strontium nitrate is banned for use in cosmetic products in the EU.

Sulisobenzone (*see* Benzophenones)

Talc (magnesium silicate)

Found in Baby powder, face powder, foundation, eyeshadow, blush, bronzer/highlighter, concealer, lipstick, foot powder, antiperspirant/deodorant.

Purpose A basic magnesium silicate mineral. In its loose form it is known as talcum powder. It is the primary ingredient in various cosmetics and personal care products. It is also used as a food additive, lubricant, and as a filler in paper manufacture.

Adverse reactions Talc can cause skin, respiratory and eye irritation. Some studies have indicated a risk of developing ovarian cancer in women using talc-based body powder in the genital region. Talc can be contaminated with toxic asbestiform fibres, known to cause a variety of cancers and lung damage by prolonged exposure through inhalation. The cosmetics industry and US Food and Drug Administration consider cosmetic-grade talc to be safe, but in 1993 the National Toxicology Program conducted toxicology and carcino-genicity studies of cosmetic-grade talc (free from asbestiform fibres), and found that rats exposed to this mineral via inhalation developed a spectrum of inflammatory lung disorders, cancer of the lungs and rare adrenal cancers. In mice, inhalation exposure caused chronic inflammation of the lungs. Talcum powder has been reported to cause coughing, chest pain and vomiting when it is accidentally inhaled, particularly by babies. Acute inhalation exposure to talc can cause coughing, sneezing, vomiting, airway obstruction, respiratory distress and pneumoconiosis (a type of lung disease usually associated with occupational inhalation of dust). Talc is restricted for use in baby products in Canada as a result of data indicating potential hazards to infants and children.

TEA laureth sulphate (*see* Triethanolamine)

TEA lauryl sulphate (*see* Triethanolamine)

TEA sodium lauryl sulphate (*see* Triethanolamine)

Teflon (polytetrafluoroethylene/PTFE)

Found in Face powder, eyeshadow, mascara, moisturizer, sunscreen, nail polish, nail treatment.

Purpose Teflon belongs to a group of fluorine-containg chemicals known as perfluorinated compounds (PFCs) used for a variety of applications due to their special attributes such as stain- and stick-resistant properties. These include coatings for cookware, food packaging, computer chips, curling irons, dental floss, hair dryers, luggage, clothing, furnishings, cosmetics, shaving foam and many more items.

Adverse reactions Perfluorooctanoic acid (PFOA), also known as C8 (because it has eight carbons), is used in the manufacture of Teflon and is persistent and bioaccumulative in the environment, wildlife and humans. The US Environmental Protection Agency has found an association between PFOA and various cancers in laboratory animals, as well as birth defects, suggesting a potential risk for humans of developmental and other undesirable effects. Toxicological studies have also discovered that PFOA adversely affects the liver, thyroid gland, immune system and heart in laboratory animals. For male workers at one plant that produced PFOA, ten years of employment were associated with an increase in prostate cancer mortality, compared with those not occupationally exposed to PFOA.

Tetrasodium EDTA (tetrasodium ethylenediamine-tetraacetic acid)

Found in Facial cleanser, moisturizer, around-eye cream, sunscreen, body bar, body wash, shampoo, conditioner, liquid hand soap, styling gel/cream, hair colour/bleach, antiperspirant/deodorant, antibacterial wipes.

Purpose Used as a chelating agent in cosmetics.

Adverse reactions Tetrasodium EDTA is a penetration enhancer (able to modify the structure of the skin, enhancing the absorption of other chemicals). Long-term exposure to EDTA and its edetates in rabbits and rats caused structural changes in the intestines and impeded DNA synthesis in rat intestines. Oral exposure to EDTA in experimental animals caused reproductive and developmental toxicity. EDTA has caused maternal toxicity and malformations in rat offspring, which may have been a result of EDTA causing a zinc deficiency. Small amounts of the impurity nitrilotriacetate, a potential carcinogen in rats at large doses, can sometimes be present in EDTA. (*See also* Disodium EDTA)

Thimerosal (thiomersal)

Found in Mascara, eye drops, contact lens cleaners, vaginal spermicides.

Purpose An ethylmercury derivative that is almost 50 per cent mercury used as an antiseptic and preservative in vaccines, cosmetics and other products.

Adverse reactions Thimerosol was once routinely used in childhood vaccines and has been linked by some scientists and researchers to growing incidences of autism, although many have rejected this hypothesis. Since 2002, childhood vaccines in the US and Europe contain very little or no thimerosal. Exposure to low doses of thimerosal has also been associated with hypersensitivity reactions. Much earlier, in the 1980s, the US Food and Drug Administration began to eliminate thimerosal from pharmaceutical preparations due to toxicity concerns. Mercury derivatives often cause contact allergies and mercurials exert damaging effects on immune, renal and neurological function. They are reported to cause programmed cell death in cultured neurons. Mercury has also been linked with bronchitis, cognitive impairment, hearing loss, immune suppression, menstrual disorders, pneumonia, reduced fertility and fetotoxicity (injury to the fetus from a substance that can cross the placenta and cause death or retardation of growth and development), amongst other things. Ten of 13 infants suffering from a congenital defect known as exomphalos were exposed dermally to a 0.1 per cent thimerosal tincture and died following exposure. Concentrations of mercury were detected in numerous tissues from six of these young children. Thimerosal is also persistent and bioaccumulative in wildlife and humans. It is banned for use in cosmetic products in Canada and restricted in the US and EU.

Titanium dioxide
Found in Sunscreen, eyeshadow, eye liner, foundation, concealer, mascara, lipstick, lip gloss, face powder, blush, moisturizer, body bar, shampoo, dandruff treatment, nail treatment, nail polish, hair colour/bleach, toothpaste.
Purpose A white pigment primarily produced from iron titanate and natural rutile (titanium dioxide) that is used as a colourant, opacifier and UV absorber in cosmetics. It is also commonly used in foods, ceramics, paints, paper and inks.
Adverse reactions Titanium dioxide nanoparticles in aqueous environments generate free radicals, which cause DNA damage in vitro and in human skin cells. The toxicity of titanium dioxide particles is dependent on their size. Titanium dioxide has also been found to cause cell death in cultured neurons at certain concentrations and exposure levels. In high concentrations titanium dioxide dust can damage the lungs and has been found to cause increased incidences of lung tumours in rats and squamous–cell carcinomas (a form of skin cancer) in female rats. Titanium dioxide particles were reported to be photogenotoxic (capable of damaging DNA under UV light) in studies on mouse lymphoma cells. Concentrated titanium dioxide fumes are irritating to the respiratory tract. Titanium dioxide can also cause skin irritation.

Toluene (methylbenzene)
Found in Nail polish, nail treatment, cuticle treatment.

Purpose A volatile, flammable aromatic hydrocarbon liquid produced during the manufacture of petrol and other fuels from crude oil. It is used to produce benzene and in the production of paints, paint thinners, lacquers, rubbers and adhesives. In cosmetics, toluene is used as an antioxidant and solvent. It is used in concentrations of up to 50 per cent in nail polish.

Adverse reactions This lipophilic (fat-loving) agent accumulates in tissues with a high fat content. It can cause skin, eye and respiratory tract irritation, defatting of the skin (potentially leading to skin dryness, fissuring and infection), central nervous system depression, respiratory irritation, cardiac effects and metabolic acidosis (an increase in total body acid), depending on the type and length of exposure. Inhalation of toluene can lead to drowsiness, dizziness, nausea, headaches, tiredness, confusion and, in high doses and exposures, spasms, tremors, impaired speech, hearing, vision, memory, liver and kidney damage, and even death. It is reported to cause asthma in previously healthy individuals. According to the US Environmental Protection Agency, the highest concentrations of toluene occur in indoor air from common household products such as paints, paint thinners, synthetic fragrances and nail polish, as well as cigarette smoke. High levels of toluene can potentially damage the kidneys. In 1991 toluene was added to Proposition 65 in the State of California as toxic to reproduction. Some occupational exposures to toluene have been linked to spontaneous abortion or offspring with birth defects. Toluene can also be contaminated with the carcinogen *benzene*. At low doses toluene targeted the kidneys and testes and at high doses it caused liver and central nervous system effects. Chromosome aberrations (abnormalities in the normal structure of chromosomes that can lead to genetic conditions such as Down's syndrome) have been reported in the lymphocytes of workers exposed to toluene.

Toluene sulphonamide/formaldehyde resin

Found in Nail polish, nail treatment, cuticle treatment.
Purpose Used as a nail hardener and as a film-former and plasticizer.
Adverse reactions Toluene sulphonamide/formaldehyde resin can cause skin, eye and respiratory irritation, skin sensitization and contact dermatitis. It is known to cause occupational allergic contact dermatitis.

2,4-toluenediamine (4-methyl-*m*-phenylenediamine) (*see* Phenylenediamines)

Triclosan (2,4,4'-trichloro-2'-hydroxy diphenyl ether)

Found in Toothpaste, antiperspirant/deodorant, liquid hand soap, body wash, facial cleanser, moisturizer, hand cream, acne treatment, body spray, lipstick.

Purpose An organochlorine widely used as an antimicrobial agent to zap microbes in personal care and cosmetic products. It is also included in plastics, textiles and health care products. When used in plastics and clothing it is marketed under the name Microban(r).

Adverse reactions Organochlorines contain carbon, chlorine and sometimes other constituents and they are characterized by their stability, lipophilicity and ability to bioaccumulate. Triclosan is often detected in wastewater effluent and surface water samples. It is incredibly toxic to aquatic animals and algae. A study on North American bullfrogs found that triclosan disrupted thyroid hormones at very low levels. Triclosan has been detected in human plasma and breast milk. When exposed to sunlight in water triclosan can transform into dichlorodibenzo-*p*-dioxin. Although this particular dioxin is considered to be fairly benign, certain dioxins are suspected carcinogens. Triclosan can cause skin, eye and respiratory irritation, contact dermatitis and photoallergic contact dermatitis. It has also been shown to cause reproductive effects, such as fetal death when administered orally. Triclosan has been identified in breast milk but as of yet, not the breast. It can cause allergic contact dermatitis and is classified by the European Commission as irritating to eyes and skin, very toxic to aquatic organisms and dangerous for the environment. Reportedly, triclosan can combine with free chlorine in tap water to form the probable human carcinogen chloroform gas. Triclosan is chemically similar to dioxins, polychlorinated biphenyls (PCBs) and Agent Orange. Some studies have raised concerns that triclosan may encourage the emergence of bacteria resistant to antibiotics.

Triethanolamine (TEA)

Found in Facial cleanser, moisturizer, around-eye cream, astringent/toner, sunscreen, styling gel, foundation, concealer, mascara, shaving cream, aftershave, styling gel/cream, hair colour/bleach, cuticle treatment.

Purpose A tertiary amine commonly used as an intermediate for surfactants in household cleaning products, textiles, pharmaceutical preparations, agricultural herbicides, and for fuels, waxes, cutting oils, paints, inks, metalworking fluids and cement additives. It is also used as an ingredient in emulsifiers, thickeners, wetting agents, detergents and alkalinizing agents in cosmetic products, and as a solvent for shellac, dyes and resins.

Adverse reactions Triethanolamine has been found to cause irritation, scaliness, inflammation and crustiness of the skin at the area of application in experimental rats. Undiluted application to the skin of rats caused necrosis. Repeated high dose dermal applications of triethanolamine to guinea pigs resulted in liver, kidney and lung lesions. Direct contact can cause skin, eye and mucous membrane irritation in humans. Increased liver and kidney weights were reported in female rats and some of the rats developed benign tumours. Increased malignant tumours were noted in female mice fed triethanolamine in their diet. In the presence of nitrosating agents triethanolamine can be nitrosated to the carcinogen *N*-nitrosodiethanolamine (NDELA). Acute toxicity is usually a result of its alkaline nature. People occupationally exposed to triethanolamine have been known to develop asthma, eczema, skin irritation and allergic contact dermatitis. In cultured human lymphocyte cells triethanolamine caused chromosome aberrations (alterations in the normal number and structure of chromosomes). Triethanolamine caused a dose-related elevation of early deaths in chicken embryos. In some individuals it can cause skin sensitization.

Triethanolamine lauryl sulphate (*see* Triethanolamine)

Trisodium EDTA (*see* Tetrasodium EDTA)

Turpentine
Found in Fragrance.
Purpose A volatile oil derived from the resin of living or dead coniferous trees, predominantly pine trees, used as a solvent for surface coatings, liniments, paints, varnishes and perfumes. It is also used as an intermediate for camphor and menthol. Turpentine is composed of terpenes.
Adverse reactions Turpentine is a common skin sensitizer in painters, and a central nervous system depressant. Its vapour is irritating to the eyes, nose and throat. Inhalation can cause nausea, vomiting, headache, choking, coughing, delirium, difficulty breathing and loss of consciousness. The liquid is irritating to the skin and can cause contact allergies. If ingested it can cause burning pain in the mouth and throat, gastrointestinal irritation and injure the kidneys. If the liquid enters the lungs it causes inflammation of lung tissue. Turpentine oils can also irritate the mucous membranes. Turpentine can penetrate the skin and cause systemic effects. Those particularly at risk of adverse reactions include those with pre-existing skin disorders, liver disease, chronic respiratory disease and kidney disease. According to its European classification, turpentine oil is flammable, harmful by inhalation, skin contact and ingestion (may cause lung damage if swallowed), irritating to eyes and skin, a possible skin sensitizer, toxic to aquatic organisms and dangerous for the environment.

Urea (carbamide)
Found in Facial cleanser, moisturizer, around-eye cream, sunscreen, foundation, depilatory, hair colour/bleach, body wash, shampoo, depilatory.
Purpose A natural product of protein metabolism and a component of mammalian urine. It is used in cosmetics as a buffering agent, humectant, skin-

conditioning agent and antimicrobial. It also has a variety of other uses, for instance as a stabilizer in pesticides, and in paper coating, moist bakery products and to assist the fermentation of wine. Its primary use is as a fertilizer.

Adverse reactions Urea is a penetration enhancer (able to modify the structure of the skin, enhancing the absorption of other chemicals) and is frequently used in scientific studies due to its ability to uncoil DNA molecules. Urea can cause eye and skin irritation. A solution containing 5 per cent urea has been found to be slightly irritating to the skin. Adverse reactions following ingestion of urea can include headache, nausea, vomiting, disorientation and electrolyte depletion. Urea injected into the amniotic sac, where the fetus develops, can cause mid-trimester abortions. At high concentrations urea can damage DNA in vitro.

Vinyl acetate
Found in Mascara, eye liner, nail polish, hairspray.
Purpose Vinyl acetate monomer is used in the production of a variety of polymers in the production of food packaging, paints, paper coatings, foils, films, textile finishes, adhesives, and in some instances as film-formers in cosmetics. It is also used in the production of other industrial chemicals.
Adverse reactions Vinyl acetate is a confirmed animal carcinogen and a suspected human carcinogen. It is quickly transformed into the potential carcinogen acetaldehyde in human blood and animal tissues, according to the International Agency for Research on Cancer. Acetaldehyde and vinyl acetate caused nasal cancer in rats following exposure by inhalation and both of these substances are capable of damaging DNA and inducing DNA cross-links in human cells in vitro, and in vivo in animals. Vinyl acetate administered via inhalation to female rats during pregnancy caused maternal toxicity and inhibited the growth of embryos. When administered via injection it also caused sperm abnormalities in male rats. Vinyl acetate vapours can cause eye and respiratory irritation. The liquid can cause skin irritation. Vinyl acetate is also mildly toxic to fish.

Vinyl polymers
Found in Nail polish, false nails, mascara, eye drops, facial cleanser, moisturizer, around-eye cream, eye liner, shampoo, styling gel/cream.
Purpose Vinyl polymers are the most common type of plastic and are also used in synthetic fibres, surface coatings, and as film-formers in nail products. Examples of vinyl polymers include polyvinyl alcohol, polystyrene, vinyl acetate and vinyl chloride.
Adverse reactions Vinyl polymers can cause respiratory irritation and some show limited evidence of carcinogenicity. Vinyl chloride is prohibited in

aerosol products due to its carcinogenicity in animals and likely hazard to human health. (*See also* Vinyl acetate)

Xylene

Found in Nail polish, nail polish remover, fragrance.

Purpose An aromatic hydrocarbon used as a solvent in the leather, printing and rubber industries, as a cleaner, paint thinner and in varnishes. It is also used as a fragrance ingredient and solvent in cosmetic products and as an ingredient in paper and fabric coatings. Xylene is naturally present in coal tar and petroleum.

Adverse reactions Xylene is a central nervous system depressant. Transient exposure to high levels can cause skin, eye, nose and throat irritation, memory problems, gastrointestinal discomfort and potentially liver and kidney effects. Some people have died from short-term exposure to high levels of xylene. Chronic occupational exposures to xylene have caused headaches, chest pain, dyspnoea (laboured breathing–a symptom of a serious disease of the airways, heart or lungs), fever, confusion and other adverse effects. Reportedly, women occupationally exposed to xylene in concentrations above the exposure limits are at an increased risk of menstrual disorders, miscarriage, haemorrhage during childbirth and infertility. Xylene has been shown to cross the placenta in humans, rats and mice. In one animal study xylene demonstrated hazardous effects on the fetus at the late stages of fetal development, leading the research authors to suggest that pregnant females should avoid coming into contact with xylene.

Zinc acetate

Found in Facial cleanser, moisturizer, acne treatment.

Purpose A salt produced by reacting zinc oxide with acetic acid that is used as a food additive, dietary supplement, in lozenges used to treat colds, in industrial applications such as wood preserving and manufacturing other zinc salts, and in cosmetics as an astringent, biocide and skin protectorant.

Adverse reactions Zinc acetate can cause skin and eye irritation. Prolonged exposure to zinc acetate may damage the kidneys. It may also be mutagenic in humans and cause adverse reproductive effects (in cases of chronic exposures). Ingestion can cause gastrointestinal irritation, stomach cramps, nausea and vomiting. The dust can cause respiratory tract irritation. Zinc acetate is persistent and bioaccumulative in wildlife.

Zinc oxide

Found in Sunscreen, foundation, face powder, concealer, blush, eye liner, moisturizer, baby oil, toothpaste.

Purpose Used in electronic devices, pigments, foods (as a source of dietary zinc), bandages, pharmaceutical ointments, cosmetics and rubber. In cosmetics it is used as a bulking agent, colourant, skin protectant and UV screen.

Adverse reactions Zinc oxide dust can cause respiratory and eye irritation. Micronized zinc oxide (particles reduced to only a few micrometres in diameter) has damaged chromosomes and DNA under UV light, in laboratory tests conducted on in vitro mammalian cells. A study published in 1997, testing the irritant potential of *titanium dioxide* and zinc oxide on rat skin found that neither of these substances caused irritation, but the results indicated that they had penetrated the skin, influenced by other agents in the mixture such as *polyethylene glycol*. Inhalation of nano-sized zinc oxide particles can cause lung damage. Zinc compounds are persistent and bioaccumulative in wildlife. Zinc oxide has adversely affected the lungs and reproductive system in animals, as well as being an experimental mutagen. Chronic exposure to zinc oxide by skin contact can cause pus-filled bumps on the skin. The European classification for zinc oxide states that it is very toxic to aquatic organisms, dangerous for the environment and must be disposed of as hazardous waste.

Zinc pyridinethione

Found in Dandruff treatment, conditioner.

Purpose Zinc pyridinethione is a bactericide and fungicide used in anti-dandruff products and as a preservative in hair conditioner.

Adverse reactions Zinc pyridinethione can cause allergic contact dermatitis and nerve damage. It is also a severe irritant and extremely poisonous to aquatic organisms. Zinc pyridinethione is restricted for cosmetic use in Japan.

Glossary of
chemical and cosmetic terms

Abrasive – Material used for grinding, polishing, shaping, etc. through the action of rubbing. Abrasives are often used in toothpastes and exfoliating scrubs.

Absorbant – Substance used in cosmetics to absorb water or other substances.

Acid – Corrosive organic or inorganic substance with a pH less than 7 that donates hydrogen ions in an aqueous solution. Cosmetics with a low acid level would cause skin irritation.

Alkaline – Having a pH between 7 and 14, with 14 being the most alkaline.

Alkane – An organic molecule consisting only of carbon and hydrogen atoms in straight or branched chains, where the carbon atoms in the chain are linked by single bonds. Alkanes occur naturally in petroleum and natural gas. Examples include butane, hexane, methane, pentane and propane.

Amines – Ammonia derivatives that contain nitrogen.

Amphoteric surfactant – An amphoteric substance can function as an acid or base. Amphoteric surfactants can have different ionization states in solution – anionic, cationic or non-ionic – depending on the water's pH.

Anionic surfactant – In anionic surfactants the water-hating (hydrophobic) part of the molecule carries a negative charge. Anionic surfactants are most widely used for shampoos, dishwashing liquids and laundering. Examples include alkyl sulphates, alkyl ethoxylate sulphates and soap.

Anti–caking agent – Compound used to prevent clumping or caking in a product.

Anti–foaming agent – A substance that reduces the formation of excess foam, both during production and consumer use.

Antimicrobial – Substance added to cosmetic products to prevent or minimize the growth of undesirable microbes on the skin or body.

Antioxidant – A molecule capable of slowing or reducing oxidative damage (damage caused by oxygen), such as the damage caused by free radicals. Antioxidants are usually added to cosmetics to prevent their deterioration by exposure to oxygen in the air.

Antiseptic – See *Antimicrobial*.

Antistatic agent – Substance that prevents the build–up of static charges within cosmetics on human surfaces, for example on skin, hair or clothing.

Astringent – Substance used to constrict the skin thereby producing a tightening sensation.

Binder – Substances added to a product for their adhesive qualities, helping solids bind together, e.g. face powder, eyeshadow.

Biocide – A chemical agent capable of killing living organisms, e.g. fungicides, herbicides and pesticides. Triclosan is often used as biocide in antibacterial hand and body washes to inhibit bacterial development.

Botanical – Ingredients derived from plants to proffer particular attributes, e.g. aloe vera.

Buffering agent – Additive that adjusts the pH of a formulation.

Bulking agent – Substance that increases the volume of a product.

Carbolic acid – A common name for phenol, the simplest of the phenol compounds.

Carbomers – A trade name for synthetic polymers commonly used in cosmetic products as thickeners, emulsion stabilizers and suspending agents.

Carboxylic acid – A group of organic compounds having the carboxyl group (-COOH) as a common feature. A number of compounds of carboxylic acid are used as surfactants, emulsifiers and cleansers in cosmetic products.

Catalyst – Substance used to alter or speed–up a chemical modification in another material, without being consumed or incorporated into the end product.

Cationic surfactant – Chemical in which the hydrophobic (water-hating) portion of the molecule contains a positive charge.

Chelating agent – Chemical used to prevent metal ions from bonding with other ingredients and affecting the products stability, odour or appearance.

Denaturant – Chemical added to alcohol-containing products to make them bitter and therefore unpleasant to the taste.

Detergent – Any of various surfactants used to aid cleaning (see *Surfactant*).

Disinfectant – Agent that prevents infection by inhibiting the growth or activity of microorganisms.

Emollient – Emollient ingredients increase the levels of moisture in the skin by forming an oil barrier to prevent moisture evaporation from the skin's surface, causing the outer layers to swell as they absorb water from the deeper layers.

Emulsifier – A substance used to suspend one liquid in another that normally cannot be mixed together (such as oil and water).

Emulsion – A mixture of two substances that don't readily mix together, where one is dispersed in the other as tiny droplets. Emulsifiers form a film around the droplets, which enables the immiscible (unblendable) substances to mix together.

Emulsion stabilizer – Enhances the stability of an emulsion and increases the shelf-life of a product.

Ester – Reaction product of an acid and an alcohol.

Ether – Any of a group of compounds characterized by a molecular structure where an oxygen atom is interjected between two carbon atoms that are part of hydrocarbon molecules. Common examples of ethers are the anaesthetic diethyl ether (ethoxyethane) and polyethers such as polyethylene glycol (PEG) used in cosmetic products.

Ethoxylation – A chemical process in which ethylene oxide is added to fatty acids to increase their solubility in water.

Exfoliating agent – Substance that removes the skin's outer surface layer (stratum corneum) either chemically (e.g. alpha hydroxy acids) or physically (e.g. oatmeal or apricot kernel powder).

Fatty acids – Organic compounds consisting of a hydrocarbon chain with a carboxyl group at one end. Normally a carboxylic acid with at least four carbon atoms is considered a fatty acid. Fatty acids can be natural or synthesized and are either saturated or unsaturated.

Fatty alcohols – Alcohols primarily derived from natural fats and oils used in cosmetic products as emulsifiers, thickeners and emollients.

Film-former – Substance added to a product to generate a continuous film when applied to a surface (e.g. in face masks, nail varnish and hair styling products).

Fixing agent/fixative – A chemical compound that sets something. Used in hair styling products to maintain the hold and shape of the style.

Foam booster – Substance added to detergents to increase suds or lather.

Foaming agent – Chemical that produces suds or lather.

Free radicals – Atoms with unpaired electrons that attempt to stabilize themselves by 'stealing' electrons from the closest stable atoms. The newly formed unstable atoms become free radicals, initiating a chain reaction that becomes a major problem when they harm vital cellular components such as DNA and cell membranes.

Fungicide – A substance used to destroy or inhibit the growth of fungi.

Germicide – A substance used to destroy or inhibit the growth of germs.

Hydrogenation – A chemical reaction in which hydrogen molecules are added to unsaturated organic compounds such as unsaturated fatty acids, with hydrogen gas under pressure and a temperature of 120–210°C, aided by a metal catalyst.

Hydrolysis – Breaking down a chemical compound by reacting it with water.

Humectant – A substance used to preserve moisture within the product or increase the moisture content in the top layers of the skin.

Hydrocarbons – Chemical compounds composed of only hydrogen and carbon (e.g. benzene, butane, ethane, proprane).

In vitro – An experiment conducted in a controlled environment in a test-tube or other laboratory vessel, rather than within a living organism.

In vivo – Experimentation conducted inside a living organism.

Ketones – A group of organic compounds that have a carbonyl group. Includes the simplest ketone, acetone, commonly used as nail polish remover.

Lubricant – A substance used to reduce friction.

Monomer – A low molecular weight molecule that can combine with other identical or similar molecules to form a polymer.

Oleochemical – Chemical compound derived from animal (e.g. tallow) or plant (e.g. palm and coconut) fats or oils.

Opacifier – Substance added to clear or translucent products to reduce the transparency/translucency. May give a creamy or pearly appearance.

Organic compound (chemistry definition) – Carbon-based chemical compound.

Organochlorine – An organic compound that contains at least one chlorine atom. This group of chemicals includes the pesticide DDT (dichlorodiphenyltrichloroethane).

Oxidation – In simple terms, oxidation occurs when oxygen reacts with another element to form an oxide of that element or when a substance gives up electrons.

Oxidizing agent – A substance that oxidizes another substance. Used to remove hair colorants or stabilize the hair after perming.

Penetration enhancers – These substances modify the structure of the skin, enhancing its absorption of other chemicals, allowing them to enter the bloodstream more rapidly.

Petrochemical – Chemical derived from petroleum or natural gas.

pH – A measure of a solution's acidity or alkalinity, on a scale from 0 to 14, with 7 being neutral, greater than 7 being alkaline or basic and less than 7 more acidic.

pH adjuster – Substance that alters the acidity/alkalinity of a product. The skin's pH is naturally slightly acidic, so manufacturers adjust their products accordingly.

Plasticizer – A substance added to plastics to increase flexibility, reduce brittleness and modify flow properties. Plasticizers are often used in cosmetics such as nail polish to add texture and lustre.

Polymer – A high molecular weight compound comprising repeating linked monomers (e.g. polyethylene, nylon and the naturally occurring polymer, cellulose).

Preservative – Substance that guards a product against the growth of undesirable microorganisms and spoilage, extending its shelf-life and protecting the product against accidental contamination during consumer usage.

Propellant – A compressed gas used to deliver the contents of an aerosol.

Reagent – Starting material in a chemical reaction.

Resin – An organic compound of plant origin that is usually a viscous liquid that dries to become solid. Synthetic resins are commonly used.

Saponification – The process of making soap through the hydrolysis of fatty acid esters using an alkali to form the soap, and glycerin.

Sequestering agent – See *Chelating agent*.

Soap – Substance used for cleansing formed by treating a fat with an alkali.

Solubilizer – Agent used to improve the solubility of product ingredients.

Solvent – A liquid that dissolves other ingredients. Many toiletries use water to dissolve and blend ingredients.

Stabilizer – Substance added to another substance to prevent an undesirable modification of its physical state.

Sulphation – The production of a sulphate ester of a fatty alcohol that is neutralized with an alkali such as sodium hydroxide to create a surfactant.

Sulphonation – The production of a sulphonate ester of a fatty alcohol that is neutralized with an alkali, such as sodium hydroxide, to create a surfactant.

Surfactants (surface active agents) – Substances that lower the surface tension of the liquid in which they are dissolved allowing it to spread more easily across and lift dirt from soiled surfaces such as textiles and the human skin. Types of surfactants include wetting agents, foaming agents, cleansers, emulsifiers and solubilizers.

Terpene – Unsaturated hydrocarbon occurring in plants, particularly conifers. Simple terpenes are present in essential oils and resins of plants.

Transesterification – The reaction of an ester and an alcohol in the presence of an acidic substance.

Viscosity-controlling agent – Substance that controls the thickness of a product.

Viscosity-increasing agent/booster – Additive that increases the thickness of a product.

Wetting agent – Ingredient used to lower the surface tension of a liquid, enabling it to spread more easily across a surface.

Recommended reading

Ashton, K., Salter-Green, E., *The Toxic Consumer*, Bath: Impact Publishing, 2006.

Carson, R., *Silent Spring*, New edition, London: Penguin Classics, 2000.

Colborn, T., Dumanoski, D., Meyers, J.P., *Our Stolen Future: Are We Threatening our Fertility, Intelligence and Survival?*, New York: Plume, 1997.

Epstein, S.S., *Unreasonable Risk*, second edition, Chicago: Environmental Toxicology, 2005.

Epstein, S.S., Steinman D, *The Safe Shopper's Bible*, New Jersey: Wiley Publishing Inc, 1995.

Malkan, S., *Not Just a Pretty Face: The Ugly Side of the Beauty Industry*, British Columbia: New Society Publishers, 2007.

Schapiro, M., *Exposed: The Toxic Chemistry of Everyday Products and What's at Stake for American Power*, Vermont: Chelsea Green Publishing Company, 2007.

Thomas, P., *What's in this Stuff?* London: Rodale International, 2006.

Winter R, *A Consumer's Dictionary of Cosmetic Ingredients*, sixth edition, New York: Three Rivers Press, 2005.

Recommended resources

Agency for Toxic Substances and Disease Registry (ATSDR)
1825 Century Blvd., Atlanta, GA 30345, USA
Tel: +1 (0) 800 232 4636
www.atsdr.cdc.gov/toxpr02.html (toxicological profiles)

Campaign for Safe Cosmetics
www.safecosmetics.org

CHEC's Heal the House – Children's Health Environmental Coalition (CHEC)
12300 Wilshire Blvd. Suite 320, Los Angeles, CA 90025, USA
Tel: +1 (0) 310 820 2030
www.checnet.org/healtheHouse/chemicals/chemicals.asp

Cosmetics INFO
http://cosmeticsinfo.org/ (maintained by the Personal Care
Council – formerly the Cosmetic, Toiletry and Fragrance Association
or CTFA)

Environmental Working Group (EWG)
1436 U Street. N.W., Suite 100, Washington, DC 20009, USA
Tel: +1 (0) 202 667 6982
www.ewg.org
EWG's Skin Deep Cosmetic Safety Database
www.cosmeticsdatabase.com

European Commission – Enterprise and Industry/Cosmetics
Commission Européenne, DG Enterprise and Industry, Unit F3,
Brey 10-173, B-1049 Brussels, Belgium
Tel: +32 (0) 2 299 1111 (switchboard)
http://ec.europa.eu/enterprise/cosmetics/index_en.htm

Health Protection Agency
HPA Central Office, 7th Floor, Holborn Gate, 330 High Holborn,
London WC1V 7PP, UK
Tel: +44 (0) 207 759 2700/2701
http://www.hpa.org.uk/webw/HPAweb&Page&HPAwebContentAreaL
anding/Page/1153386734384?p=1153386734384 (Chemicals and
Poisons)

HERA (Human and Environmental Risk Assessment on Ingredients of Household Cleaning Products)
HERA Secretariat, Avenue Herrmann Debroux 15A, B-1160 Brussels,
Belgium
Tel: +32 (0) 2 679 6260
www.heraproject.com

Household Products Database – National Institutes of Health/National Library of Medicine/Specialised Information Services
householdproducts.nlm.nih.gov/

International Programme on Chemical Safety (IPCS) – INCHEM
www.inchem.org/

Organic Consumers Association (OCA)
6771 South Silver Hill Drive, Finland, MN 55063, USA
Tel: +1 (0) 218 353 7652
www.organicconsumers.org

Our Stolen Future
www.ourstolenfuture.org

Terressentials
2650 Old National Pike, Middletown, MD 21769, USA
Tel: +1 (0) 301 371 7333
www.terressentials.com

The Collaborative on Health and the Environment (CHE)
c/o Commonweal, PO Box 316, CA 94924, USA
http://database.healthandenvironment.org/index.cfm

TOXNET Toxicology Data Network
Specialized Information Services, National Library of
Medicine/National Institutes of Health, 2 Democracy Plaza, Suite 510,
6707 Democracy Blvd. MSC 5467, Bethesda, MD 20892-5467, USA
Tel: +1 (0) 301 480 3537, Toll Free: +1 (0) 888 FINDNLM
http://toxnet.nlm.nih.gov/

US Environmental Protection Agency (EPA)
Ariel Rios Building, 1200 Pennsylvania Avenue, N.W., Washington, DC
20460, USA
www.epa.gov

US Food and Drug Administration (FDA)
Center for Food Safety and Applied Nutrition/Cosmetics, 5600 Fishers
Lane, Rockville, MD 20857, USA
Tel: +1 (0) 888 463 6332 (main FDA phone number)
www.cfsan.fda.gov/~dms/cos-toc.html

Women's Environmental Network (WEN)
PO Box 30626, London E1 1TZ, UK
Tel: +44 (0) 207 481 9004
www.wen.org.uk

References

Introduction

1. *State of the Evidence: The Connection Between Breast Cancer and the Environment*, fifth edition, Breast Cancer Fund, 2008; online at: www.breastcancerfund.org/evidence.
2. Council Directive 93/35/EEC of 14 June 1993 amending for the sixth time Directive 76/768/EEC on the approximation of the laws of the member states relating to cosmetic products, The Council of the European Communities, Brussels, Belgium, 1993, Article 2.

Chapter 1

1. *Annual Report of the Cosmetic, Toiletry and Perfumery Association (CTPA)*, 2005; online at: www.ctpa.org.uk.
2. *Annual Report of the Cosmetic, Toiletry and Perfumery Association (CTPA)* 2006; online at: www.ctpa.org.uk.
3. *Fragrances and Cosmetics – Pan-European Overview: Executive Summary*, Mintel Reports, July 2006.
4. *Cosmetics and Fragrances: Market Report Plus 2007*, Research and Markets, March 2007; online at: www.researchandmarkets.com.
5. Montague-Jones, G., British men sniff out manly fragrances and cosmetics, *Cosmetics Design Europe*, 14 August 2007; online at: www.cosmeticsdesign-europe.com.
6. *Comparative Study on Cosmetics Legislation in the EU and Other Principal Markets with Special Attention to so-called Borderline Products – Final Report*, prepared for European Commission DG Enterprise by Risk and Policy

Analysts Ltd, European Commission, Enterprise and Industry Directorate General, Consumer Goods, Cosmetics, Brussels, Belgium, August 2004; online at http://ec.europa.eu/enterprise/cosmetics.

7. Marketing boosts cosmetic sales, Cosmeticsdesign.com, 23 November 2006; online at: www.cosmeticsdesign.com.

8. Odell, A.M., Toxic Cosmetics Getting Under Skin of Concerned Investors, Social Funds, March 1, 2007; online at: www.socialfunds.com.

9. *Indoor Air Quality: Organic Gases (Volatile Organic Compounds – VOCs)*, US Environmental Protection Agency (EPA), Washington, DC; accessed 10 January 2008; online at: www.epa.gov.

10. Colón, I., et al., Identification of phthalate esters in the serum of young Puerto Rican girls with premature breast development, *Environmental Health Perspectives*, September 2000; 108(9): 895–900.

11. Barrett, J.C. et al., 12th Meeting of the Scientific Group on Methodologies for the Safety Evaluation of Chemicals: Susceptibility to Environmental Hazards, *Environmental Health Perspectives*, June 1997; 105(4): 699.

12. Selevan, S.G., Kimmel, C.A., Mendola, P., Identifying critical windows of exposure for children's health, *Environmental Health Perspectives*, June 2000; 108(3): 451–455.

13. *Intolerable Risk: Pesticides in our Children's Food*, Natural Resources Defense Council, 27 February 1989; online at: www.tobaccodocuments.org.

14. Body burden – the pollution in newborns: a benchmark investigation of industrial chemicals, pollutants and pesticides in umbilical cord blood, Environmental Working Group (EWG), 14 July 2005; online at: www.ewg.org.

15. Davis, D., Oh, to be so innocent! Remembering a more activist FDA conjures up memories of two ingredients that brought about the need for safety testing, *Global Cosmetic Industry*, August 2002.

16. Nayan, D., Pathways for skin penetration, *Cosmetics and Toiletries*, June 2005; 120(6): 67.

17. Elder, R.L., Final report on the safety assessment of sodium lauryl sulfate and ammonium lauryl sulfate, *Journal of the American College of Toxicology*, 1983; 2(7): 127–181.

18. *Chemicals in the European Environment: Low Doses, High Stakes?* European Environment Agency (EEA) and United Nations Environmental Programme (UNEP), 3 October 1998; online at: www.eea.europa.eu.

19. *EPA Statement Regarding Endocrine Disruptor Low-Dose Hypothesis*, US Environmental Protection Agency (EPA), Washington, DC, March 26, 2002; online at www.epa.gov.

20. Vom Saal, F., Hughes, C., An extensive new literature concerning low

dose-effects of bisphenol-A shows the need for a new risk assessment, *Environmental Health Perspectives*, 2005; 113: 926–933.

21. Boatman, N.D., Evidence for the indirect effects of pesticides on farmland birds, *IBIS*, November 2004; 146(2): 131–143.

22. *ENDS Report 349*, Haymarket Media, February 2004, pp. 13–14.

23. Peck, A.M., Hornbuckle, K.C., Synthetic musk fragrances in Lake Michigan, *Environmental Science and Technology*, January 2004; 38: 367–372.

24. *Chain of Contamination: The Food Link (Fact Sheet) Synthetic Musks*, World Wildlife Fund UK (WWF-UK): accessed 5 December 2007; online at: www.wwf.org.uk.

25. Jobling, S. et al., A variety of environmentally persistent chemicals, including some phthalate plasticisers are weakly estrogenic, *Environmental Health Perspectives*, June 1995; 103(6): 582–587.

26. *Down the Drain: Sources of Hormone-Disrupting Chemicals in San Francisco Bay*, Environmental Working Group (EWG), 12 July 2007; online at: www.ewg.org.

27. *Phthalates, Chain of Contamination: The Food Link (Fact Sheet)*, World Wildlife Fund UK (WWF-UK): accessed 5 December 2007; online at: www.wwf.org.uk.

28. Xie, Z., Occurrence and air-exchange of phthalates in the Arctic, *Environmental Science and Technology*, July 2007; 41(13): 4555–4560.

29. Boulanger, B. et al., Mass budget of perflurooctane surfactants in Lake Ontario, *Environmental Science and Technology*, December 2004; 39(1): 74–79.

30. Smithwick, M., Temporal trends of perfluoroalkyl contaminants in polar bears (*Ursus maritimus*) from two locations in the North American Arctic, 1972–2002, *Environmental Science and Technology*, January 2006; 40(4): 1139–1143.

31. *EPA Science Panel Says Teflon Chemical 'Likely' Cause of Cancer*, Environmental Working Group (EWG), 30 January 2006; online at: www.ewg.org.

32. Wolff, M.S., Endocrine disruptors: challenges for environmental research in the 21st century, *Annals of the New York Academy of Sciences*, September 2006; 1076: 228–238.

33. Ying, G., Fate, behaviour and effects of surfactants and their degradation products in the environment, *Environment International*, February 2007; 33(2): 272–273.

34. Cakal Arslan, O., Parlak, H., Embryotoxic effects of nonylphenol and octylphenol in sea urchin *Arbacia lixula*, *Ecotoxicology*, August 2007; 16(6): 439–444.

35. Daughton, C.G., Ternes, T.A., Pharmaceuticals and personal care products in the environment: agents of subtle change? *Environmental*

Health Perspectives, December 1999; 107(6): 907–938.

36. Commission of the European Communities, Commission Staff Working Paper: Impact Assessment Report on Simplification of the 'Cosmetics Directive' – Directive 76/768/EEC (COM(2008)49 final), (SEC(2008)118), Brussels, Belgium, 5 February 2008.

37. Carmichael, H., Making up rules: testing times are ahead for the cosmetics industry, with a spate of regulations in the pipeline aimed at tightening up consumer safety, *Chemistry and Industry*, 9 April 2007, Issue No. 7, p. 19.

38. *Navigating REACH, An Activists Guide to Use and Improving the New EU Chemicals Legislation*, Friends of the Earth (FOE), 29 August 2007; online at: www.foe.co.uk.

39. Regulation (EC) No. 1907/2006 of the European Parliament and of the Council of 18 December 2006 concerning the Registration, Evaluation, Authorisation and Restriction of Chemicals (REACH), *Official Journal of the European Union*, Article 60(4), Brussels, Belgium, 30 December 2006.

40. *FDA Authority over Cosmetics*, US Department of Health and Human Services, US Food and Drug Administration (FDA), Center for Food Safety and Applied Nutrition (CFSAN), Office of Cosmetics and Colors, College Park, MD, 3 March 2005; online at: www.cfsan.fda.gov.

41. *Annual Report of the Cosmetic, Toiletry and Fragrance Association (CTFA)*, 2005; accessed 28 November 2007; online at: www.ctfa.org.

42. Bergfield, W.F. et al., Safety of ingredients used in cosmetics, *Journal of the American Academy of Dermatology*, January 2005; 52(1): 125–132.

43. Cosmetics with banned and unsafe ingredients, Environmental Working Group (EWG), 26 September 2007; online at: www.ewg.org.

Chapter 2

1. Lewis, C., *Clearing Up Cosmetic Confusion*, US Department of Health and Human Services, US Food and Drug Administration (FDA), Center for Food Safety and Applied Nutrition (CFSAN), Office of Cosmetics and Colors, FDA Consumer, College Park, MD, May–June 1998; Revised May 1998 and August 2000; online at: www.cfsan.fda.gov.

2. *What are Cosmetics?* British Association of Dermatologists (BAD); accessed 11 September 2007; online at: www.bad.org.uk.

3. *The Globally Harmonized System of Classification and Labelling of Chemicals (GHS), Part 3: Health and Environmental Hazards*, United Nations Economic Commission for Europe (UNECE), Geneva, Switzerland, 2004; online at: www.unece.org.

4. *Neurotoxins: At Home and in the Workplace*, US House of Representatives Committee on Science and Technology, 99th Congress, Second Session,

US Government Printing Office, Washington, DC, 1986, Report 99-827.

5. Fragrance and cosmetics – sharing strategies, with Ladd Smith, President, RIFM, *Cosmetics & Toiletries Magazine*, January 2006; 121(1): 84.

6. Bridges, B., Fragrances and health [Letter], *Environmental Health Perspectives*, July 1999; 107(7): A340.

7. Toxic substances hydrology program: frequently asked questions, US Department of the Interior, US Geological Survey (USGS), Reston, VA; accessed 13 April 2008; online at: http://toxics.usgs.gov.

8. Fisher, B.E., Scents & sensitivity, *Environmental Health Perspectives*, December 1998: 106(12).

9. Bronaugh, R.L., Maibach, H.I. (eds), *Percutaenous Absorption: Drugs, Cosmetics, Mechanisms, Methods*, 4th edn, New York: Marcel Dekker, 2005, p. 673.

10. Edman, B., The influence of shaving method on perfume allergy, *Contact Dermatitis*, November 1994; 31(5): 291–292.

11. *The Scientific Committee on Cosmetic Products and Non-food Products Intended for Consumers Opinion Concerning Fragrance Allergy in Consumers: A Review of the Problem*, European Commission, Health & Consumer Protection Directorate-General, The Scientific Committee on Cosmetic Products and Non-food Products (SCCNFP), Brussels, Belgium, adopted by the SCCNFP during the plenary session of 8 December 1999; online at http://ec.europa.eu.

12. Johansen, J.D., Fragrance contact allergy: a clinical review, *American Journal of Clinical Dermatology*, 2003; 4(11): 789–798.

13. Van Abbé, N.J., Perfume and the manufacture of consumer products, In Butler, H. (Ed), *Poucher's Perfumes, Cosmetics and Soaps*, 10th edn, Dordrecht: Kluwer Academic Publishers, 2000, p. 735.

14. Anderson, R.C., Anderson, J.H., Acute toxic effects of fragrance products, *Archives of Environmental Health*, March–April 1998; 53(2): 138–146.

15. Bridges, B., Fragrance: Emerging health and environmental concerns, *Flavour and Fragrance Journal*, 2002; 17(5): 361–371.

16. *About IFRA*, International Fragrance Association (IFRA); accessed 18 November 2007; online at: www.ifraorg.org.

17. Scheinman, P.L., Is it really fragrance-free?, *American Journal of Contact Dermatitis*, December 1997; 8(4): 239–242.

18. Lis-Balchin, M., *Aromatherapy Science: A Guide for Healthcare Professionals*, London: Pharmaceutical Press, 2006, pp. 79–85.

19. *Poisons Information Monograph 095: Camphor*, International Programme on Chemical Safety (IPCS), INCHEM, May, 1989; online at: www.inchem.org.

20. Ford, M.D., Delaney, K.A., Ling, L.J., Erickson, T., *Clinical Toxicology*,

Philadelphia: WB Saunders Company, 2001, p. 346.

21. Hagvall, L. et al., Fragrance compound geraniol forms contact allergens on air exposure. identification and quantification of oxidation products and effect on skin sensitisation, *Chemical Research in Toxicology*, May 2007; 20(5): 807–814.

22. De Groot, A.C., Weyland, J.W., Kathon CG: a review, *Journal of the American Academy of Dermatology*, February 1988; 2: 350–358.

23. Du, S. et al., In vitro neurotoxicity of methylisothiazolinone, a commonly used industrial and household biocide, proceeds via a zinc and extracellular signal-regulated kinase mitogen-activated protein kinase-dependent pathway, *The Journal of Neuroscience*, September 2002; 22(17): 7408–7416.

24. Connor, T.H. et al., Mutagenicity of cosmetic products containing Kathon, *Environmental and Molecular Mutagenesis*, 1996; 28(2): 127–132.

25. Bruckner, A.L., Weston, W.L., Morelli, J.G., Does sensitization to contact allergens begin in infancy, *Pediatrics*, January 2000; 105(1): e3.

26. Final report on the safety assessment of methylisothiazolinone and methylchloroisothiazolinone, *Journal of the American College of Toxicology*, 1992; 11(1): 75–128.

27. *What are the Main Health Hazards Associated with Breathing in Formaldehyde Solutions?* Canadian Centre for Occupational Health and Safety (CCOHS), updated 7 July 2006; online at www.ccohs.ca.

28. *Cosmetic Handbook*, Center for Food Safety and Applied Nutrition, US Department of Health and Human Services, US Food and Drug Administration (FDA), Centre for Food Safety and Applied Nutrition (CFSAN), Office of Cosmetics and Colors, FDA/IAS Booklet, College Park, MD, 1992; online at: www.cfsan.fda.gov.

29. Grant, W.M., *Toxicology of the Eye*, second edition, Springfield, IL: Charles C. Thomas, 1974, p. 964.

30. Patil, S. et al., Quantification of sodium lauryl sulphate penetration into the skin and underlying tissues after topical application – pharmacological and toxicological implications, *Journal of Pharmaceutical Sciences*, September 2006; 84(10): 1240–1244.

31. Broze, G. (ed.), *Handbook of Detergents*, Surfactant Series Volume 82, New York: Marcel Dekker, 1999, p. 456.

32. *Sodium Lauryl Sulfate*, NICNAS Existing Chemicals Information Sheet, Australian Government, Department of Health and Ageing, National Industrial Chemicals Notification and Assessment Scheme (NICNAS), Marrickville, NSW, 9 October 2007; online at: www.nicnas.gov.au.

33. Meadows, M., *Heading Off Hair-Care Disasters: Use Caution With Relaxers and Dyes*, US Department for Health and Human Services, US

Food and Drug Administration (FDA), Center for Food Safety and Applied Nutrition (CFSAN), Office of Cosmetics and Colors, FDA Consumer, College Park, MD, January/February 2001: online at www.cfsan.fda.gov.

34. Email to the author from Ton Van Lierop, Spokesman Industry and Enterprise, European Commission, 18 October 2007.

35. Meding, B., Swanbeck, G., Prevalence of hand eczema in an industrial city, *British Journal of Dermatology*, 1987; 116: 627–634.

36. Brown, N.J., *Health Hazard Manual for Cosmetologists Hairdressers Beauticians and Barbers*, Cornell University, Chemical Hazard Information Program, 1987; online at: http://digitalcommons.ilr.cornell.edu/manuals/6.

37. English, J.S.C., Current concepts in contact dermatitis, *British Journal of Dermatology*, 2001; 145: 527–529.

38. English, J.S.C., Current concepts of irritant contact dermatitis, *Occupational and Environmental Medicine*, 2004; 6: 722–726.

39. Adams, R.M., Maibach, H.I., A five-year study of cosmetic reactions, *Journal of the American Academy of Dermatology*, December 1985: 13(6): 1062–1069.

40. Maguina, P. et al., Chemical scalp burns after hair highlights, *Journal of Burn Care Research*, March–April 2007; 28(2): 361–363.

41. Warbrick, E.V. et al., Local lymph node assay responses to paraphenylenediamine: intra- and inter-laboratory evaluations, *Journal of Applied Toxicology*, July–August 1999; 19(4): 255–260.

42. *Temporary Tattoos and Henna/Mehndi*, US Department of Health and Human Services, US Food and Drug Administration (FDA), Centre for Food Safety and Applied Nutrition (CFSAN), Office of Cosmetics and Colors, College Park, MD, 18 April 2001; Updated 18 September 2006; online at: www.cfsan.fda.gov.

43. McFadden, J.P., Allergy to hair-dye, *British Medical Journal*, 2007; 334: 220.

44. Patel, S. et al., Patch test frequency to p-phenylenediamine: follow up over the last 6 years, *Contact Dermatitis*, 2007; 56: 35–37.

45. *DermNet NZ: Allergy to Paraphenylenediamine*, New Zealand Dermatological Society Incorporated; accessed 4 January 2008; online at: http://dermnetnz.org.

46. *Scientific Committee on Consumer Products (SCCP) Opinion on p-Phenylenediamine*, European Commission, Health & Consumer Protection Directorate-General, Brussels, Belgium, Adopted by the SCCP during the 9th Plenary Meeting of 10 October 2006; online at: http://ec.europa.eu/health.

47. Sosted, H. et al., 55 cases of allergic reactions to hair-dye: a descriptive, consumer complaint-based study, *Contact Dermatitis*, November

2002; 47(5): 299–303.

48. Howard, D.L., Sloughing off, *Les Nouvelles Esthetiques*, September 2003.

49. Bender, M., Don't overdo your exfoliator, *Health*, October 2004.

50. Briney, C., Asia-Pacific skin care: high margins fuel sales, *Euromonitor International*, 24 June 2002.

51. *Health and Environmental Effects Document for p-Hydroquinone*, US Environmental Protection Agency (EPA), Office of Solid Waste and Emergency Response, Office of Health and Environmental Assessment, Washington, DC, 1987; online at: http://nepis.epa.gov.

52. *NTP Technical Report on the Toxicology and Carcinogenesis Studies of Hydroquinone* (Cas No. 123–31–9 in F344/N Rats and B6C3F1 Mice (Gavage Studies), US Department of Health and Human Services, Public Health Services, National Toxicology Program (NTP), National Institutes of Health (NIH), Research Triangle Park, NC, 1989.

53. Barnett, A., Smith, Z., Toxic creams for sale as thousands seek whiter skin, *The Guardian*, 16 October 2005.

54. Edemarium, A., The cosmetic craze that's beyond the pale, *The Guardian*, 8 January 2007.

55. *Summaries and Evaluations, Kojic Acid (Group 3)*, IARC Monographs on the Evaluation of Carcinogenic Risk to Humans, World Health Organization (WHO), International Agency for Research on Cancer (IARC), Lyon, France, 2001; 79: 607; online at: http://monographs.iarc.fr.

56. Fujimoto, N. et al., Changes in thyroid function during development of thyroid hyperplasia induced by kojic acid in F344 fats, *Carcinogenesis*, August 1999; 20(8): 1567–1571.

57. *Kojic Acid*, IARC Monographs on the Evaluation of Carcinogenic Risk to Humans, World Health Organization (WHO), International Agency for Research on Cancer (IARC), Lyon, France, 2001; 79: 607–618; online at: http://monographs.iarc.fr.

58. Arndt, K., Hsu, J., *Manual of Dermatologic Therapeutics with Essentials of Diagnosis*, seventh edition, Philadelphia: Lippincott Williams and Wilkins, 2006, p. 272.

59. *House of Lords, Science and Technology – Sixth Report*, House of Lords, Science and Technology Committee Publications, 6.15, Session 2006–7; accessed 8 December 2007; online at: www.publications.parliament.uk.

60. *Which? Report: Dermatological Challenge*, Which?, 1 February 2004.

61. Reid, C., *Chemical Photosensitivity: Another Reason to be Careful in the Sun*, US Department of Health and Human Services, US Food and Drug Administration (FDA), Center for Food Safety and Applied Nutrition (CFSAN), Office of Cosmetics and Colors, FDA Consumer, College Park, MD, May 1996; online at: www.fda.gov.

62. Takeshi, H., Photoallergy, *Journal of Japanese Cosmetic Science Society*, 1999; 23(3): 154–158.

63. Hans RK et al., Assessment of the phototoxic potential of cosmetic products, *Food and Chemical Toxicology*, 2008; 46: 1653–1658.

64. Praticò, D., Lipid peroxidation and the aging process, *Science of Aging Knowledge Environment*, December 2002: 2002(50): 5.

65. Mei, N. et al., Photomutagenicity of anhydroretinol and 5,6-epoxyretinyl palmitate in mouse lymphoma cells, *Chemical Research in Toxicology*, November 2006; 19(11): 1435–1440.

66. Placzek, M. et al., Evaluation of phototoxic properties of antimicrobials used in topical preparations by a photohaemolysis test, *Acta Dermato-Venereologica*, January 2005; 85(1): 13–16.

67. Morliere, P. et al., In vitro photostability and photosensitising properties of bergamot oil: effects of a cinnamate sunscreen, *Journal of Photochemistry and Photobiology B: Biology*, November 1990: 7(2–4): 199–208.

68. NICNAS: *Priority Existing Chemical Assessment Report*, Australian Government, Department of Health and Ageing, National Industrial Chemicals Notification and Assessment Scheme (NICNAS), Marrickville, NSW, 2000; 12: 128; online at: www.nicnas.gov.au.

69. Brown, N.J., *Health Hazard Manual for Cosmetologists Hairdressers Beauticians and Barbers*, Cornell University, Chemical Hazard Information Program, 1987; online at: http://digitalcommons.ilr.cornell.edu/manuals/6.

70. *Asthma in Adults*, NHS Direct, updated 26 February 2008; online at: www.nhsdirect.nhs.uk.

71. Rumchev, K. et al., Association of domestic exposure to volatile organic compounds with asthma in young children, *Thorax*, 2004; 59: 746–751.

72. *Toxicological Profile for Toluene*, US Department of Health and Human Services, Agency for Toxic Substances and Disease Registry (ATSDR), Atlanta, GA, September 2000; online at: www.atsdr.cdc.gov.

73. *Toluene*, US Environmental Protection Agency (EPA), Technology Transfer Network Air Toxics Website, Washington, DC, updated 20 February 2008; online at: www.epa.gov.

74. Ammonium thioglyconate, Hazard Substances Databank (HSDB), TOXNET, National Library of Medicine (NLM), Bethesda, MD; accessed 20 September 2007; online at: http://toxnet.nlm.nih.gov.

75. Leino, T. et al., Occurrence of asthma and chronic bronchitis among female hairdressers, *Journal of Occupational and Environmental Medicine*, 1997; 39(6): 534–539.

76. Brisman, J. et al., The incidence of respiratory symptoms in female Swedish hairdressers, *American Journal of Industrial Medicine*, December

2003; 44(6): 673–678.

77. Akpinar-Elci, M., Cimrin, A.H., Elci, O.C., Prevalence and risk factors of occupational asthma amongst hairdressers in Turkey, *Journal of Occupational and Environmental Medicine*, June 2002; 44(6): 585–590.

78. Albin, M. et al., Incidence of asthma in female Swedish hairdressers, *Occupational and Environmental Medicine*, February 2002; 59(2): 119–123.

79. Salvaggio, J., Taylor, G., Weill, H., *Occupational Asthma and Rhinitis, Occupational Respiratory Diseases*, DHHS (NIOSH) Publication No. 86–102, US Department of Health and Human Services, Public Health Service, Centers for Disease Control and Prevention (CDC), National Institute for Occupational Health and Safety (NIOSH), Atlanta, GA, September 1986, p. 462: online at: www.cdc.gov/niosh.

Chapter 3

1. *Cancer Facts and Figures 2004: Basic Cancer Facts*, American Cancer Society (ACS); accessed 25 September 2008; online at: www.cancer.org.

2. *State of the Evidence: The Connection Between Breast Cancer and the Environment*, fifth edition, Breast Cancer Fund, 2008; online at: www.breastcancerfund.org.

3. Klatz, R., Goldman, B., *The Science of Anti-Aging Medicine*, The American Academy of Anti-Aging Medicine, January 2003, p. 10.

4. Tenenbaum, D.J., A new view of ELF-EMFs: are they linked with cancer promotion? *Environmental Health Perspectives*, October 2000: 108(10): 469.

5. *Assessment of Technologies for Determining Cancer Risks From the Environment*, OTA (Office of Technology Assessment), US Government Printing Office, Washington, DC, June 1981; online at: http://govinfo.library.unt.edu.

6. Sanio, E.L. et al., Metals and arsenic in eyeshadow, *Contact Dermatitis*, January 2000; 42(1): 5–10.

7. Rudel, R.A. et al., Chemicals causing mammary gland tumours in animals signal new directions for epidemiology, chemicals testing, and risk assessment for breast cancer prevention, *Cancer*, June 2007; 109(12): 2635–2666.

8. Kortenkamp, A., Breast cancer and exposure to hormonally active chemicals: an appraisal of the scientific evidence, A Background Briefing Paper for the Health and Environmental Alliance (HEAL) and CHEMTrust, April 2008: online at: www.chemtrust.org.

9. Kortenkamp, A., *Environmental Contaminants and Breast Cancer: The Growing Concerns about Endocrine Disrupting Chemicals*, Produced for the World Wild Fund for Nature (WWF), October, 2006: online at: www.wwf.org.uk.

10. Rajapakse, N., Silva, E., Kortenkamp, A., Combining xenoestrogens at levels below individual no-observed-effect concentrations dramatically enhances steroid hormone action, *Environmental Health Perspectives*, September 2002; 110(9): 917–921.

11. Payne, J., Scholze, M., Kortenkamp, A., Mixtures of four organochlorines enhance human breast cancer cell proliferation, *Environmental Health Perspectives*, April 2001; 109(4): 391–397.

12. Palmer, J.R. et al., Prenatal diethylstilbestrol exposure and risk of breast cancer, *Cancer Epidemiology, Biomarkers and Prevention*, August 2006; 15(8): 1509–1514.

13. Munoz-de-Toro, M. et al., Perinatal exposure to bisphenol-A alters peripubital mammary gland development in mice, *Endocrinology*, 2005; 146(9): 4138–4147.

14. Maffini, M.V., Endocrine disruptors and reproductive health: the case of bisphenol-A, *Molecular and Cellular Endocrinology*, 2006; 255–254: 179–186.

15. Campaigners urge politicians to act on chemicals-breast cancer link, *CORDIS News*, 3 April 2008; online at: http://cordis.europa.eu /news/home_en.html.

16. Batty, D., Campaigns urge ban on cancer-link chemicals, *The Guardian*, 2 April 2008; online at: www.guardian.co.uk.

17. Tomatis, L. et al., Avoided and avoidable risks of cancer, *Carcinogenesis*, 1997; 18(1): 97–105.

18. Zhang, J., Thomas, A.G., Leybovich, E., Vaginal douching and adverse health effects: a meta-analysis, *American Journal of Public Health*, July 1997; 87(7): 1207–1210.

19. Bearer, C.F., How are children different from adults?, *Environmental Health Perspectives*, 1995; 103(6): 7–12.

20. Epstein, S.S., *Unreasonable risk: How to Avoid Cancer and Other Toxic Effects, from Cosmetics and Personal Care Products: The Neway's Story*, second edition, Environmental Toxicology Inc., 2005.

21. Abamba, G., Skin Preparations, In Butler, H. (Ed), *Poucher's Perfumes, Cosmetics and Soaps*, 10th edn, Dordrecht: Kluwer Academic Publishers, 2000, p. 402.

22. *Intolerable Risk: Pesticides in our Children's Food*, Natural Resources Defense Council, 27 February 1989; online at: www.tobaccodocuments.org.

23. Czene, K., Cancer risks in hairdressers: Assessment of carcinogenicity of hair-dyes and gels, *International Journal of Cancer*, May 2003; 105(1): 108–112.

24. Skov, T., Lynge, E., Cancer risk and exposures to carcinogens in hairdressers, *Skin Pharmacology*, 1994; 7(1–2): 94–100.

25. Gago-Dominguez, M. et al., Use of permanent hair-dyes and bladder-

cancer risk, *International Journal of Cancer*, February 2001; 91(4): 903–906.

26. Skov, T. et al., Risk for cancer of the urinary bladder among hairdressers in the Nordic countries, *American Journal of Industrial Medicine*, January 2007: 17(2): 217–223.

27. Mielke, H. et al., Lead based hair products: too hazardous for household use, *Journal of the American Pharmaceutical Association*, 1997; January/February: 85–89.

28. Zhang, W. et al., Hair-colouring product use and risk of non-Hodgkin's lymphoma: a population-based case-control study in Connecticut, *American Journal of Epidemiology*, July 2003: 159(2): 148–154.

29. Thun, M., Hair-dye use and risk of fatal cancers in U.S. women, *Journal of the National Cancer Institute*, 1994; 86(3): 210–215.

30. Grodstein, F., A prospective study of permanent hair-dye use and hematopoietic cancer, *Journal of the National Cancer Institute*, 5 October 1994; 86(19): 1466–1470.

31. Takkouche, B., Etminan, M., Montes-Martínez, A., Personal use of hair-dyes and risk of cancer: A meta-analysis, *Journal of the American Medical Association*, September 2005; 294(10): 1205.

32. *Opinion of Personal Use of Hair-dyes and Cancer Risk*, Scientific Committee on Consumer Products (SCCP), European Commission, Health & Consumer Protection Directorate-General, Brussels, Belgium, adopted by the SCCP during the 5th plenary meeting of 20 September 2005; online at: http://ec.europa.eu/health.

33. Commission bans 22 hair dye substances to increase consumer safety, *EUROPA*, 20 July 2007; online at: http://europa.eu.

34. *Annual Report of the Cosmetic, Toiletry and Perfumery Association (CTPA)*, 2006; online at: www.ctpa.org.uk.

35. Email to the author from Ton Van Lierop, Spokesman Industry and Enterprise, European Commission, 18 October 2007.

36. Byrford, J.R. et al., Oestrogenic activity of parabens in MCF7 human breast cancer cells, *The Journal of Steroid Biochemistry and Molecular Biology*, January 2002; 80(1): 49–60.

37. Janjua, N.R. et al., Systemic uptake of diethyl phthalate, dibutyl phthalate, and butyl paraben following whole-body topical application and reproductive and thyroid hormone levels in humans, *Environmental Science & Technology*, June 2007; 41(15): 5564–5570.

38. Darbre, P.D., Underarm cosmetics and breast cancer, *Journal of Applied Toxicology*, March 2003: 23(2): 89–95.

39. Darbre, P.D., Environmental oestrogens, cosmetics and breast cancer, *Best Practice & Research Clinical Endocrinology & Metabolism*, 2006; 20(1): 121–143.

40. McGrath, K.G., An earlier age of breast cancer diagnosis related to

more frequent use of antiperspirants/deodorants and underarm shaving, *European Journal of Cancer Prevention*, December 2003; 12(6): 479–485.

41. NTP Toxicology and Carcinogenesis Studies of Talc (CAS No. 14807-96-6) (Non-Asbestiform) in F344/N Rats and B6CF1 Mice (Inhalation Studies), National Toxicology Program Technical Report Series, September 1993; 421: 1–287.

42. *Talc: Summary*, IARC Monographs on the Evaluation of Carcinogenic Risks to Humans No. 93, World Health Organization (WHO), International Agency for Research on Cancer (IARC), Lyon, France, 2006; online at: http://monographs.iarc.fr.

43. Heller, D.S. et al., The relationship between perineal cosmetic talc usage and ovarian talc particle burden, *American Journal of Obstetrics and Gynecology*, May 1996: 174(5): 1507–1510.

44. *Proposition 65: Chemicals Known to the State to Cause Cancer or Reproductive Toxicity*, State of California Environmental Protection Agency, Office of Environmental Health Hazard Assessment Safe Drinking Water and Toxic Enforcement Act of 1986, Sacramento, CA, 1 June 2007; online at: www.oehha.org/prop65.html.

45. Saffiotti, U., Mechanisms of carcinogenesis by crystalline silica in relation to oxygen radicals, *Environmental Heath Perspectives*, December 1994; 102(10): 159–163.

46. *Silica, Crystalline*, US National Library of Medicine (NLM), National Institutes of Health (NIH), Specialized Information Services (SIS), Haz-Map, Bethesda, MD; accessed 27 October 2007; online at: http://hazmap.nlm.nih.gov.

47. *Silica, Crystalline Silica – Inhaled in the Form of Quartz of Cristobalite from Occupational Sources*, Monographs on the Evaluation of the Carcinogenic Risk of Chemicals to Man, World Health Organization (WHO), International Agency for Research on Cancer (IARC), Lyon, France, 1997; 68: 41.

48. *Diethanolamine and Cosmetic Products*, US Department of Health and Human Services, US Food and Drug Administration (FDA), Center for Food Safety and Applied Nutrition (CFSAN), Office of Cosmetics and Colors, College Park, MD, 9 December 1999, revised 27 October 2006; online at: www.cfsan.fda.gov.

49. *Toxicology and Carcinogenesis Studies of Diethanolamine* (CAS No. 111–42–2) in F344/N Rats and B6C3F1 Mice (Dermal Studies), US Department of Health and Human Services, National Toxicology Program Technical Report Series, Research Triangle Park, NC, July 1999; 478: 1–212.

50. Gillner, M., Loeper, I., Health effects of selected chemicals 3: Diethanolamine, *Nord*, 1995; 28: 52—75.

51. Jansen, M., Letschart, H.P., Inorganic yellow-red pigments without toxic metals, *Nature*, April 2000; 404: 980–982.

52. Lauro, G.J., *Natural Food Colorants: Science and Technology*, New York: Marcel Dekker, 2000, p. 141.

53. *Hair-dye Products*, US Department of Health and Human Services, US Food and Drug Administration (FDA), Center for Food Safety and Applied Nutrition (CFSAN), Office of Cosmetics and Colors, College Park, MD, November 1997; online at: www.cfsan.fda.gov.

54. *TR-422, Toxicology and Carcinogenesis Studies of Coumarin (CAS No. 91-64-5), in F344/N Rats and B6C3F1 Mice (Gavage Studies)*, NTP Technical Report, US Department of Health and Human Services, Public Health Service, National Institutes of Health (NIH), National Toxicology Program (NTP), Research Triangle Park, NC, 1993; online at: http://ntp.niehs.nih.gov.

55. *Code of Federal Regulations, Title 21 – Food and Drugs, Chapter 1 – Food and Drug Administration, Department of Health and Human Services (Continued): Part 189 – Substances Prohibited from Use in Human Food*, National Archives and Records Administration, 189.30 (b), 42 FR 14569, Washington, DC, 15 March 1977, as amended at 49 FR 10114, 19 March 1984, 54 FRR 24899, 12 June 1989; online at: www.access.gpo.gov.

56. Wallace, L.A., Identification of polar volatile organic compounds in consumer products and common microenvironments, US Environmental Protection Agency (EPA), Paper No. A312, Washington, DC, March, 1991; online at: www.epa.gov.

57. *Title 21, Code of Federal Regulations: Cosmetic Products, Part 700 – General, Subpart B – Requirements for Specific Cosmetic Products*, US Food and Drug Administration (FDA), National Archives and Registration Administration, Electronic Code of Federal Regulations, § 700.19(a); accessed 13 April 2008; online at: http://ecfr.gpoaccess.gov.

58. *Nitrosamines in Cosmetics, Toiletries and Personal Care Products*, Australian Society of Cosmetic Chemists (ASCC) Position Papers; accessed 30 October 2007: online at: www.ascc.com.au.

59. *Prohibited Ingredients and Related Safety Issues*, US Department of Health and Human Services, US Food and Drug Administration (FDA), Center for Food Safety and Applied Nutrition (CFSAN), Office of Cosmetics and Colors, College Park, MD, 30 March 2000; online at: www.cfsan.fda.gov.

60. *ToxFAQs for 1,4-dioxane*, US Department of Health and Human Services, Public Health Service, Agency for Toxic Substances and Disease Registry (ATSDR), Atlanta, GA, September 2007: online at: www.atsdr.cdc.gov.

61. *Toxicological Profile Information Sheet: Draft Toxicological Profile for 1,4-*

dioxane, US Department of Health and Human Services, Public Health Service, Agency for Toxic Substances and Disease Registry (ATSDR), Atlanta, GA, September 2007: online at: www.atsdr.cdc.gov.

62. *1,4-Dioxane*, US Department of Health and Human Services, US Food and Drug Administration (FDA), Center for Food Safety and Applied Nutrition (CFSAN), Office of Cosmetics and Colors, College Park, MD, 3 July 2007; online at: www.cfsan.fda.gov.

63. *Notice to the Reader:Toxicological Profile for 1,4-Dioxane*, US Department of Health and Human Services, Agency for Toxic Substances and Disease Registry (ATSDR), Atlanta, GA, April 2007; online at: www.atsdr.cdc.gov.

64. *p-Dioxane Health Advisory*, US Environmental Protection Agency (EPA), Office of Drinking Water, Washington, DC, March 1987; online at: http://nepis.epa.gov.

65. *Technical Support Document for the Determination of Noncancer Chronic Reference Exposure Levels*, California Environmental Protection Agency (CalEPA), Draft for Public Comment, Office of Environmental Health Hazard Assessment, Berkeley, CA, 1997; online at: www.oehha.org.

66. *1,4-Dioxane*, US Environmental Protection Agency (EPA), National Center for Environmental Assessment, Office of Research and Development, Integrated Risk Information System (IRIS), Washington, DC, 1999; online at: www.epa.gov/iris.

67. *Government Consumer Safety Research: A Survey of Cosmetic and Certain Other Skin-contact Products for N-nitrosamines*, UK Department of Trade and Industry (DTI), May 1998.

68. *Cosmetic Handbook: Product-Related Regulatory Requirements and Health Hazard Issues*, US Department of Health and Human Services, US Food and Drug Administration (FDA) Center for Food Safety and Applied Nutrition (CFSAN), Office of Cosmetics and Colors, FDA/IAS Booklet, College Park, MD, 1992; online at: www.cfsan.fda.gov.

69. Johnson, W. Jr., Final report of the safety assessment of PEG-25 propylene glycol stearate, PEG-75 propylene glycol stearate, PEG-120 propylene glycol stearate, PEG-10 propylene glycol, PEG-8 propylene glycol cocoate and PEG-55 propylene glycol oleate, *International Journal of Toxicology*, 2001; 20(4): 13–26.

70. *Impurities of Concern in Personal Care Products*, Environmental Working Group's (EWG) Skin Deep, Cosmetic Safety Database; accessed 10 November 2008; online at: www.cosmeticsdatabase.com/research.

71. Karlberg, A.T., Bodin, A., Matura, M., Allergenic activity of an air-oxidised ethoxylated surfactant, *Contact Dermatitis*, November 2003; 49(5): 241–247.

72. *Ethylene Oxide, Hazard Summary*, US Environmental Protection

Agency (EPA), Technology Transfer Network Air Toxics Website, Research Triangle Park, NC, created in April 1992; revised in January 2000; online at: www.epa.gov.

73. *Report on Carcinogens*, eleventh edition, US Department of Health and Human Services, Public Health Service, National Toxicology Program (NTP); accessed 11 November 2007; online at: http://ntp.niehs.nih.gov.

74. *Ethylene Oxide: Some Industrial Chemicals, Summary of Data Reported and Evaluation*, IARC Monographs on the Evaluation of Carcinogenic Risks to Humans No. 60, World Health Organization (WHO), International Agency for Research on Cancer (IARC), Lyon, France, 1994.

75. *Ethylene Oxide*, US National Library of Medicine (NLM), National Institutes of Health (NIH), Specialized Information Services (SIS), Haz-Map, Bethesda, MD; accessed 13 November 2007; online at: http://hazmap.nlm.nih.gov.

76. *The Scientific Committee on Cosmetic Products and Non-food Products Intended for Consumers (SCCNFP) Opinion Concerning the Determination of Certain Formaldehyde Releasers in Cosmetic Products*, European Commission, Health & Consumer Protection Directorate-General, the Scientific Committee on Cosmetic Products and Non-food Products Intended for Consumers (SCCNFP), Brussels, Belgium, adopted by the SCCNFP during the 22nd plenary meeting of 17 December 2002; online at: http://ec.europa.eu/health.

77. *Formaldehyde (Group 1), Formaldehyde, 2-Butoxyethanol and 1-tert-Butoxypropan-2-ol*, IARC Monographs on the Evaluation of Carcinogenic Risks to Humans No. 88, World Health Organization (WHO), International Agency for Research on Cancer (IARC), Lyon, France, 2006; online at: http://monographs.iarc.fr.

78. *Polycyclic Aromatic Hydrocarbons: Substance Fact Sheet*, Australian Government, Department of the Environment and Water Resources, Parkes, ACT; accessed 15 November 2007; online at: www.npi.gov.au.

79. *Polycyclic Aromatic Hydrocarbons (PAHs)*, Illinois Department of Public Health, Springfield, IL; accessed 15 November 2007; online at: www.idph.state.il.us/envhealth/factsheets.

80. Krstev, S. et al., Occupational risk factors and prostate cancer in U.S. blacks and whites, *American Journal of Industrial Medicine*, November 1998; 34(5): 421–430.

81. *Polycyclic Aromatic Hydrocarbons*, IARC Monographs on the Evaluation of Carcinogenic Risks to Humans No. 92 (in preparation), World Health Organization (WHO), International Agency for Research on Cancer (IARC), Lyon, France; accessed 15 November 2007; online at: http://monographs.iarc.fr.

82. Rundle, A. et al., The relationship between genetic damage from

polycyclic aromatic hydrocarbons in breast tissue and breast cancer, *Carcinogenesis*, 2000: 21(7): 1281–1289.

83. Straif, K. et al., Carcinogenicity of polycyclic aromatic hydrocarbons, *Lancet Oncology*, 2005; 6: 931–932.

84. Sinha, R. et al., Dietary benzo[a]pyrene intake and risk of colorectal adenoma, *Cancer Epidemiology Biomarkers and Prevention*, 2005; 14: 2030–2034.

85. Anderson, K.E. et al., Meat intake and cooking techniques: Associations with pancreatic cancer, *Mutation Research* 2002; 506–507: 225–231.

86. *Council Directive of 27 July 1976 on the Approximation of the Laws of the Member States relating to Cosmetic Products (76/768/EEC)*, The Council of the European Communities, Brussels, Belgium, 30 December 2006, Appendix, M23, Note N.

87. Faust, H.R., Casserly E.W, *Petrolatum and Regulatory Requirements*, NPRA International Lubricants & Waxes Meeting, 13–14 November 2003, Houston, TX; accessed 16 November 2007; online at: www.penreco.com.

Chapter 4

1. Allsopp, M. et al., *Our Reproductive Health and Chemical Exposure: A Review of the Evidence for Links Between Declines in Human Reproductive Health and our Exposure to Hazardous Chemicals*, Greenpeace Report, Greenpeace Laboratories, April 2006; online at: www.greenpeace.org.

2. Jobling, S. et al., A variety of environmentally persistent chemicals, including some phthalate plasticisers, are weakly estrogenic, *Environmental Health Perspectives*, June 1995; 103(6): 582–587.

3. Kavlok, R.J. et al., Research needs for the risk assessment of health and environmental effects of endocrine disruptors: a report of the U.S. EPA-sponsored workshop, *Environmental Health Perspectives*, August 1996; 104(4): 2.

4. Soto, A.M. et al., The E–SCREEN assay as a tool to identify oestrogens: An update on oestrogenic environmental pollutants, *Environmental Health Perspectives*, October 1995; 103(7): 113–122.

5. Purdom, C.E. et al., Oestrogenic effects of effluents from sewage treatment works, *Chemistry and Ecology*, January 1994; 8(4): 275–285.

6. Brian, J.V. et al., Evidence of estrogenic mixture effects on the reproductive performance of fish, *Environmental Science & Technology*, 2007; 41: 337–344.

7. Dodds, E.C., Lawson, W., Molecular structure in relation to oestrogenic activity: Compounds without a phenanthrene nucleus, *Proceedings of the Royal Society of London*, 1938; 125: 222–232.

8. Burlington, H., Lindeman, V.F., Effect of DDT on testes and secondary sex characters of white leghorn cockerels, *Proceedings of the Society for Experimental Biology and Medicine*, 1950; 74: 48–51.

9. Colton, T., Greenberg, E.R., Epidemiologic evidence for adverse effects of DES exposure during pregnancy, *The American Statistician*, August 1982; 36(3)2: 268–272.

10. Gill, W.B. et al., Association of diethylstilbestrol exposure in utero with cryptorchidism, testicular hypoplasia and semen abnormalities, *Journal of Urology*, July 1979; 122(1): 36–39.

11. Sumpter, J.P., Jobling, S., Vitellogenesis as a biomarker for estrogenic contamination of the aquatic environment, *Environmental Health Perspectives*, October 1995; 103(7): 173–178.

12. Ikezuki, Y., Determination of bisphenol A concentrations in human biological fluids reveals significant early prenatal exposure, *Human Reproduction*, 2002; 17(11): 2839–2841.

13. Darbre, P.D., Environmental contaminants in milk: the problem of organochlorine xenobiotics, *Biochemical Society Transactions*, 1998; 26: 106–112.

14. Bigsby, R. et al., Evaluating the effects of endocrine disruptors on endocrine function during development, *Environmental Health Perspectives*, August 1999; 107(4): 613–618.

15. The Prague Declaration on Endocrine Disruptors, *Environmental Health Perspectives*; accessed 6 April 2008; online at: www.ehponline.org.

16. Solomon, G.M., Schettler, T., Environment and Health: 6, Endocrine disruption and potential human health implications, *Journal of the American Medical Association*, November 2000; 163(11): 1471–1476.

17. Soto, A.M. et al., p-Nonyl-phenol: an oestrogenic xenobiotic released from 'modified' polystyrene, *Environmental Health Perspectives*, 1991; 92: 167–173.

18. Darbre, P.D., Environmental oestrogens, cosmetics and breast cancer, *Best Practice & Research Clinical Endocrinology & Metabolism*, 2006; 20(1): 121–143.

19. Dunford, R. et al., Chemical oxidation and DNA damage catalysed by inorganic sunscreen ingredients, *FEBS Letters*, November 1997; 418(1–2): 87–90.

20. Donaldson, K., Beswick, P.H., Gilmour, P.S., Free radical activity associated with the surface of particles: A unifying factor in determining biological activity? *Toxicology Letters*, November 1996; 88(1–3): 293–298.

21. Kumazawa, R. et al., Effects of Ti Ions and Particles on Neutrophil Function and Morphology, *Biomaterials*, September 2002; 23(17): 3757–3764.

22. Danovaro, R. et al., Sunscreens cause coral bleaching by promoting

viral infections, *Environmental Health Perspectives*, April 2008: 116(4): 441–447.

23. Bigby, M., The sunscreen and melanoma controversy, *Archives of Dermatology*, 1999; 1135: 1526–1527.

24. Autier, P., Sunscreen and melanoma revisited [letter], *Archives of Dermatology*, 2000; 1136: 423.

25. Schlumpf, M. et al., In vitro and in vivo estrogenicity of UV screens, *Environmental Health Perspectives*, March 2001: 109(3): 239–244.

26. Schlumpf, M. et al., Developmental toxicity and estrogenicity of UV screens, *Frontiers in Fetal Health*, November–December 2001; 3(11–12): 287.

27. Lichtensteiger, W. et al., New arising endocrine disruptors: UV screens and PBDE, *Reproductive Toxicology*, July–August 2002; 16(4): 397–398.

28. Janjua, N.R. et al., Systemic absorption of the sunscreens benzophenone-3, octyl-methoxycinnamate, and 3-(4-methyl-benzylidene) camphor after whole-body topical application and reproductive hormone levels in humans, *Journal of Investigative Dermatology*, 2004; 123(1): 57–61.

29. Jiang, R. et al. Absorption of sunscreens across human skin: An evaluation of commercial products for children and adults. *British Journal of Clinical Pharmacology*, October 1999; 48(4): 635–637.

30. Calafat, A.M. et al. Concentration of the sunscreen agent, benzophenone-3, in residents of the United States: National Health and Nutrition Examination Survey 2003–2004, *Environmental Health Perspectives* No. 116, 21 March 2008; online at: www.ehponline.org.

31. Buser, H.R. et al., Occurrence of UV filters 4-methylbenzylidene camphor and octocrylene in fish from various Swiss rivers with inputs from wastewater treatment plants, *Environmental Science and Technology*, January 2006; 40(5): 1427–1431.

32. Serpone, N. et al., An in vitro systematic spectroscopic examination of the photostabilities of a random set of commercial sunscreen lotions and their chemical UVB/UVA Active Agents, *Photochemical & Photobiological Sciences*, 2002; 1: 970–981.

33. Pont, A.R., Charron, A.R., Brand, R.M., Active ingredients in sunscreens act as topical penetration enhancers for the herbicide 2,4-dichlorophenoxyacetic acid, *Toxicology and Applied Pharmacology*, 2004; 195(3): 348–354.

34. Jeong, S.H., Effects of butylated hydroxyanisole on the development and functions of the reproductive system in rats, *Toxicology*, March 2005; 208(1): 49–62.

35. Jeong, S., Steroid and thyroid hormonal receptor gene transcription assay and one-generation reproduction study of butylated hydroxyanisole, *Toxicologist*, March 2003; 72(S-1): 284.

36. Pederson, K.L., The preservatives ethyl-, propyl- and butylparaben are oestrogenic in an in vivo fish assay, *Pharmacology and Toxicology*, March 2000; 86(3): 110–113.

37. Prusakiewicz, J.J. et al., Parabens inhibit human skin estrogen sulfotransferase activity: Possible link to paraben estrogenic effects, *Toxicology*, April 2007; 232(3): 248–256.

38. Miller, D. et al., Estrogenic activity of phenolic additives determined by an in vitro yeast bioassay. *Environmental Health Perspectives*, 2001; 109: 133–138.

39. Nishihara, T. et al., Estrogenic activities of 517 chemicals by yeast two-hybrid assay, *Journal of Health Sciences*, 2000; 46: 282–298.

40. Routledge, E.J. et al., Some alkyl hydroxy benzoate preservatives (parabens) are estrogenic, *Toxicology and Applied Pharmacology*, 1998; 153: 12–19.

41. Vinggaard, A.M. et al., Identification and quantification of estrogenic compounds in recycled and virgin paper for household use as determined by an in vitro yeast estrogen screen and chemical analysis, *Chemical Research in Toxicology*, 2000; 13: 1214–1222.

42. Darbre, P.D. et al., Concentrations of parabens in human breast tumours, *Journal of Applied Toxicology*, 2004; 24: 5–13.

43. Makino, T., Female reproductive tract and mammary disorders caused by endocrine disruptor, *Japanese Medical Association Journal*, 2003; 46: 93–96.

44. Harvey, P.W., Everett, D.J., Regulation of endocrine-disrupting chemicals: Critical overview and deficiencies in toxicology and risk assessment for human health, *Best Practice and Research Clinical Endocrinology and Metabolism*, 2006; 20(1): 145–165.

45. Blount, B.C. et al., Levels of seven urinary phthalate metabolites in a human reference population, *Environmental Health Perspectives*, October 2000; 108(10): 979–982.

46. *The Determination of Additives in Food Products*, Greenpeace UK, 11 December 2003; online at: www.greenpeace.org.uk.

47. *State of the Evidence: The Connection Between Breast Cancer and the Environment*, fifth edition, Breast Cancer Fund, 2008; online at: www.breastcancerfund.org/evidence.

48. *Third National Report on Human Exposure to Environmental Chemicals*, US Department of Health and Human Services, Centers for Disease Control and Prevention (CDC), Atlanta, GA, July 2005; online at: www.cdc.gov.

49. Permanent phthalates ban in toys approved, *EurActiv.com*, 5 July 2005; online at: www.euractiv.com.

50. *The Rules Governing Cosmetic Products in the European Union*: Volume 1,

Cosmetics Legislation, European Commission, 1999 edition with February 2003 update (Directive 2003/15/EC); Directive 76/768/EEC, also see 'Annex XVII of REACH,' which will replace Directive 76/769/EEC on 1 June 2009, European Commission, Brussels, Belgium; online at: http://ec.europa.eu/enterprise/chemicals.

51. Council Directive of 27 July 1976 on the Approximation of the Laws of the Member States relating to Cosmetic Products (76/768/EEC), The Council of the European Communities, Brussels, Belgium, 30 December 2006, Appendix, M37 and M45.

52. *Pretty Nasty – Phthalates in European Cosmetic Products*, Health Care Without Harm, Women's Environmental Network (WEN) and Swedish Society for Nature Conservation, 2002; online at: www.wen.org.uk.

53. Houlihan, J., Brody, C., Schwan, B., *Not Too Pretty: Phthalates, Beauty Products and the FDA*, Environmetal Working Group (EWG), Health Care Without Harm, 8 July 2002; online at: www.safecosmetics.org.

54. Kim, I.Y., Han, S.Y., Moon, A., Phthalates inhibit tamoxifen-induced apoptosis in MCF-7 human breast cancer cells, *Journal of Toxicology and Environmental Health: Part A*, December 2004; 67(23–24): 2025–2035.

55. Main, M.K. et al., Human breast milk contamination with phthalates and alterations of endogenous reproductive hormones in infants three months of age, *Environmental Health Perspectives*, February 2006; 114(2): 270–276.

56. Parks, L.G., The plasticiser diethylhexyl phthalate induces malformations by decreasing fetal testosterone synthesis during sexual differentiation in the male rat, *Toxicological Sciences*, 2000; 58: 339–349.

57. Stahlhut, R.W. et al., Concentrations of urinary phthalate metabolites are associated with increased waist circumference and insulin resistance in adult U.S. males, *Environmental Health Perspectives*, June 2007: 115(6): 876–883.

58. Colón, I. et al., Identification of phthalate esters in the serum of young Puerto Rican girls with premature breast development, *Environmental Health Perspectives*, September 2000; 108(9): 895–900.

59. Email to author from Professor Richard M Sharpe, MRC Human Reproductive Sciences Unit, Centre for Reproductive Biology, Queen's Medical Research Institute, Edinburgh, 20 November 2007.

60. Swan, S.H. et al., Decrease in anogenital distance among male infants with prenatal phthalate exposure, *Environmental Health Perspectives*, August 2005; 113(8): 1056–1061.

61. Daughton, C.G., Ternes, T.A., Pharmaceuticals and personal care products in the environment: agents of subtle change? *Environmental Health Perspectives*, December 1999; 107(6): 907–938.

62. *ENDS Report 345*, Haymarket Media, October 2003, p. 35.

63. *Scientific Committee on Consumer Products (SCCP) Opinion on Triclosan*, European Commission, Health & Consumer Protection Directorate-General, Scientific Committee on Consumer Products (SCCP), Brussels, Belgium, adopted by the SCCP during the 9th plenary meeting of 10 October 2006; online at: http://ec.europa.eu/health.

64. Tatarazako, N. et al., Effects of triclosan on various aquatic organisms, *Environmental Science*, 2004; 11(2): 133–140.

65. Allmyr, M. et al., Triclosan in plasma and milk from Swedish nursing mothers and their exposure via personal care products, *Science and the Total Environment*, December 2006: 372(1): 87–93.

66. Veldhoen, N., The bactericidal agent triclosan modulates thyroid hormone-associated gene expression and disrupts postembryonic anuran development, *Aquatic Toxicology*, December 2006; 80(3): 217–227.

67. Latch, D.E. et al., Photochemical conversion of triclosan to 2,8-dichlorodibenzo-p-dioxin in aqueous solution, *Journal of Photochemistry and Photobiology A: Chemistry*, 2003; 158: 63–66.

68. ESKHA5 Eisei Shikenjo Hokoku, *Bulletin of the Institute of Hygienic Sciences V.1-1886*, 1987; 105: 28.

69. *ENDS Report 352*, Haymarket Media, May 2004, p. 50.

70. Mueller, G.C., Kim, U.H., Displacement of estradiol from estrogen receptors by simple alkyl phenols, *Endocrinology*, 1978; 102: 1429–1435.

71. Werner, K., Lutz, I., Einspanier, R., Amphibians as a model to study endocrine disruptors: II. Estrogenic activity on environmental chemicals in vitro and in vivo, *The Science of the Total Environment*, January 1999; 1–2(225): 59–68.

72. Sharpe, R.M. et al., Gestational exposure of rats to xenoestrogens results in reduced testicular size and sperm production, *Environmental Health Perspectives*, December 1995; 103(12): 1136.

73. *Risky Chemicals: A Guide for Retailers and Other Downstream Users*, Friends of the Earth (FOE) Briefing, July 2002; online at: www.foeeurope.org.

74. Darbre, P.D., Environmental oestrogens, cosmetics and breast cancer, *Best Practice & Research Clinical Endocrinology & Metabolism*, 2006; 20(1): 121–143.

75. Darbre, P.D., Metalloestrogens: An emerging class of inorganic xenoestrogens with potential to add to the oestrogenic burden of the human breast, *Journal of Applied Toxicology*, May–June 2006; 26(3): 191–197.

76. McGrath, K.G., An earlier age of breast cancer diagnosis related to more frequent use of antiperspirants/deodorants and underarm shaving, *European Journal of Cancer Prevention*, December 2003; 12(6): 479–485.

77. Email to the author from Kris G McGrath, M.D., Associate Professor of Clinical Medicine, Northwestern University, Feinberg School of

Medicine/Lecturer, Department of Medicine, Section of General Internal Medicine, The University of Illinois at Chicago/Section Chief of Allergy-Immunology, Saint Joseph Hospital, Resurrection Health Care, Chicago Illinois, 26 October 2007.

78. *Draft Toxicological Profile for Aluminium*, US Department of Health and Human Services, Public Health Service, Agency for Toxic Substances and Disease Registry (ATSDR), Atlanta, GA, September 2006: online at: www.atsdr.cdc.gov.

79. *Title 21, Code of Federal Regulations: Cosmetic Products, Part 700 – General, Subpart B – Requirements for Specific Cosmetic Products*, US Food and Drug Administration (FDA), National Archives and Registration Administration, Electronic Code of Federal Regulations, § 700.16(a); accessed 13 April 2008; online at: http://ecfr.gpoaccess.gov.

80. Kannan, K. et al., Polycyclic musk compounds in higher trophic level aquatic organisms and humans from the United States, *Chemosphere*, November 2005; 61(5): 693–700.

81. Rimkus, G.G., Wolf, M., Polycyclic musk fragrances in human adipose tissue and human milk, *Chemosphere*, November 1996: 33(10): 2033–2043.

82. Hutter, P. et al., Blood concentrations of polycyclic musks in healthy young adults, *Chemosphere*, April 2005; 59(4): 487–492.

83. Schreurs, R. et al., In vitro and in vivo antiestrogenic effects of polycyclic musks in zebrafish, *Environmental Science & Technology*, December 2003; 38(4): 997–1002.

84. Bitsch, N. et al., Estrogenic activity of musk fragrances detected by the E-screen assay using human MCF-7 cells, *Archives of Environmental Contamination and Toxicology*, October 2002; 43(3): 257–264.

85. Eisenhardt, S. et al., Nitromusk compounds in women with gynecological and endocrine dysfunction, *Environmental Research*, December 2001; 87(3): 123–130.

86. Peters, R.J.B., *Phthalates and Artifical Musks in Perfumes*, TNO-Report, R&I-A R2005/011, TNO Environment and Geosciences, Netherlands Organization for Applied Scientific Research, intended for Mr B Van Opzeeland, Greenpeace, The Netherlands, January 2005; online at: www.greenpeace.org.

87. *Dioxins*, National Institute of Environmental Health Sciences (NIEHS), National Institutes of Health (NIH), Research Triangle Park, NC; accessed 25 November 2007; online at: www.niehs.nih.gov.

Chapter 5

1. *Nanoscience and Nanotechnologies: Opportunities and Uncertainties*, The Royal Society and the Royal Academy of Engineering, July 2004; online at: www.nanotec.org.uk.

2. Oberdörster, G., Oberdörster, E., Oberdörster, J., Nanotoxicology: An emerging discipline evolving from studies of ultrafine particles, *Environmental Health Perspectives*, July 2005; 113(7): 823–839.

3. *Scientific Committee on Consumer Products Preliminary Opinion on Safety of Nanomaterials in Cosmetic Products*, European Commission, Health & Consumer Protection Directorate-General, Scientific Committee on Consumer Products (SCCP), Brussels, Belgium, Approved by the SCCP for Public Consultation 12th Plenary of 19 June 2007; online at: http://ec.europa.eu/health.

4. *Preliminary Opinion on Safety of Nanomaterials in Cosmetic Products*, European Commission, Health & Consumer Protection Directorate-General, Scientific Committee on Consumer Products (SCCP), Brussels, Belgium, Approved by the SCCP for Public Consultation 12th Plenary of 19 June 2007; online at: http://ec.europa.eu/health.

5. *Nanosciences and Nanotechnologies: A Review of Government's Progress on Its Policy Commitments*, Council for Science and Technology, London, March 2007; online at: www.cst.gov.uk.

6. Miller, G. et al., *Nanomaterials, Sunscreens and Cosmetics: Small Ingredients, Big Risks: Friends of the Earth Report*, Friends of the Earth (FOE), May 2006; online at: www.foe.org.

7. Davies, J.C., *Managing the Effects of Nanotechnology*, Woodrow Wilson International Center for Scholars: Project on Emerging Nanotechnologies, Washington, DC, 2006; online at: www.wilsoncenter.org.

8. *Nanotechnology's Invisible Threat: Small Science, Big Consequences*, National Resources Defense Council (NRDC), December 2006, online at: www.nrdc.org.

9. Li, N., Ultrafine particulate pollutants induce oxidative stress and mitochondrial damage, *Environmental Health Perspectives*, April 2003; 111(4): 455–460.

10. Donaldson, K. et al., Combustion-derived nanoparticles: A review of their toxicology following inhalation exposure, *Particle and Fibre Toxicology*, October 2005; 2(10).

11. Frampton, M.W. et al., Inhalation of ultrafine particles alters blood leukocyte expression of adhesion molecules in humans, *Environmental Health Perspectives*, January 2006; 114(1): 51–58.

12. Pope, C.A, III et al., Cardiovascular mortality and long-term exposure to particulate air pollution: epidemiological evidence of general pathophysiological pathways of disease, *Circulation*, January 2004; 109(1): 71–77.

13. Tran, C.L. et al., A scoping study to identify hazard data needs for addressing the risks presented by nanoparticles and nanotubes, Institute of Occupational Medicine (ICM), December 2005; online at: www.defra.gov.uk.

14. Oberdörster, E., Manufactured nanomaterials (fullerenes, C60) induce oxidative stress in the brain of juvenile largemouth bass, *Environmental Health Perspectives*, July 2004; 112(10): 1058–1062.

15. Hoet P HM, Brüske-Hohlfield I, Salata OV, Nanoparticles – known and unknown health risks, *Journal of Nanobiotechnology,* December 2004; 2(12).

16. Long, T.C. et al., Titanium dioxide (P25) produces reactive oxygen species in immortalized brain microglia (BV2): implications for nanoparticle neurotoxicity, *Environmental Science & Technology*, 2006; 40(14): 4346–4352.

17. Wang, B. et al., Acute toxicity of nano- and micro-scale zinc powder in healthy adult mice, *Toxicology Letters*, February 2006; 161(2): 115–123.

18. Miller, G., *Cosmetics, Nanotoxicity and Skin Penetration – A Brief Summary of the Toxicological and Skin Penetration Literature*, Friends of the Earth (FOE) Australia, October 2006; online at: http://nano.foe.org.au.

19. Sheu, H.M. et al., Depletion of stratum corneum intercellular lipid lamellae and barrier function abnormalities after long-term topical corticosteroids, *British Journal of Dermatology*, 1997; 136(6): 884–890.

20. Fartasch, M., Bassukas, I.D., Diepgkn, T.L., Structural relationship between epidermal lipid lamellae, lamellar bodies and desmosomes in human epidermis: an ultrastructural study, *British Journal of Dermatology*, January 1993; 128(1): 1–9.

21. Babynin, E.V. et al., Study of mutagenic activity of fullerene and some of its derivatives using His+ reversions of Salmonella typhimurium as an example, *Russian Journal of Genetics*, April 2002; 38(4): 359–363.

22. Nano's troubled waters: latest toxic warning shows nanoparticles cause brain damage in aquatic species and highlights need for a moratorium on the release of new nanomaterials, ETC Group (Action Group on Erosion, Technology and Concentration), 1 April 2004; online at: www.etcgroup.org.

23. Holmes, B., Buckyballs cause brain damage in fish, *New Scientist*, 29 March 2004.

24. Zua S, Oberdörster E, Haasch M, Toxicity of an engineered nanoparticle (fullerene, C60) in two aquatic species, daphnia and fathead minnow, *Marine Environmental Research*, 2006; 62(1): S5–S9.

25. Miyata, N., Yamakoshi, Y., Nakanishi, I., Reactive species responsible for biological actions of photoexcited fullerenes, *Yakagaku Zasshi*, October 2000; 120(10): 1007–1016.

26. El Amin, A., Global nanotech code up for consultation, Cosmeticsdesign-europe.com, 12 October 2007; online at: www.cosmeticsdesign-europe.com.

27. *ENDS Report 387*, Haymarket Business Media, April 2007, p. 29.

28. Towards a code of conduct for responsible nanosciences and nanotechnologies research, Consultation Paper, the European Commission, Brussels, Belgium, 2007; online at: http://ec.europa.eu.

29. Nanotechnology, *EurActiv*, 17 August 2004, updated 14 March 2008; online at: www.euractiv.com.

30. *Research on Environmental and Safety Impacts of Nanotechnology: Current Status of Planning and Implementation under the National Nanotechnology Initiative*, Hearing, United States House of Representatives Committee on Science and Technology, Subcommittee on Research and Science Education, Washington, DC, 31 October 2007; online at: http://science.house.gov/publications.

31. *Nanotechnology: A Report of the U.S. Food and Drug Administration Nanotechnology Task Force*, US Department of Health and Human Services, US Food and Drug Administration (FDA), Rockville, MD, 25 July 2007; online at: www.fda.gov/nanotechnology.

32. Schierow, L.J., *Engineered Nanoscale Materials and Derivative Products: Regulatory Challenges*, Congressional Research Service (CRS) Report for Congress, Washington, DC, 22 January 2008; online at: http://fas.org.

33. US FDA lacks resources to regulate nanotechnology, MTB Europe, Technology for Healthcare, 21 August 2007; online at: www.mtbeurope.info.

34. Taylor, M.R., Regulating the products of nanotechnology: does the FDA have the Tools it Needs?, Woodrow Wilson International Center for Scholars, Project on Emerging Nanotechnologies, PEN 5, Washington, DC, October 2006; online at: http://nanotechproject.org.

Chapter 6

1. *Title 7: Agriculture: Part 205 – National Organic Program – Subpart A – Definitions*, US Department of Agriculture, National Organic Program (NOP) Regulations, Electronic Code of Federal Regulations; accessed 18 April 2008, section 205.2; online at: http://ecfr.gpoaccess.gov.

2. Dodson, D., Benefits predicted under a more regulated natural cosmetics category, *Euromonitor Archive*, Euromonitor International, 28 September 2007.

3. Cosgrave, J., Cracking the mystery of brand loyalty, *Household and Personal Products Industry*, October 2007.

4. Email to the author from Diana Kaye and James Kahn of Terressentials, 27 December 2007.

5. Exposure: bursting the bubble: the myth of the 'natural' surfactant, Terressentials, 7 April 2008; online at: www.terressentials.com.

6. Stalmans, M. et al., European life-cycle inventory for detergent surfactants production, *Tenside Surfactants Detergents*, 1995; 32(2): 84–109.

7. Van Gelder, J., *Greasy Palms: European Buyers of Indonesian Palm Oil*, Friends of the Earth, March 2004; online at: www.foe.co.uk/resource/reports.

8. Webster, R., Rimmer, L., Bennett, C., *Greasy Palms – Palm Oil, the Environment and Big Business*, Friends of the Earth, March 2004; online at: www.foe.co.uk/resource/reports.

9. Email to the author from Hector Bolanos, Joint Managing Director of Raw Gaia, 19 April 2008.

10. *Fatty Acid Monoesters with Glycerol or Propanediol Fact Sheet (011288)*, US Environmental Protection Agency (EPA), Office of Pesticide Programs, Washington, DC; accessed 21 April 2008; online at: www.epa.gov/pesticides.

11. Takeoka, G. et al., Identification of benzethonium chloride in commercial grapefruit seed extracts, *Journal of Agriculture and Food Chemistry*, 2001; 49: 3316–3320.

12. Benzethonium chloride in extracts of grapefruit seeds, Swiss Toxicological Information Centre, 7 November 2005; online at: www.toxi.ch.

13. *Opinion of the Scientific Committee on Cosmetic Products and Non-food Products (SCCNFP) Intended for Consumers, Concerning Benzethonium Chloride*, European Commission, Health & Consumer Protection Directorate-General, Scientific Committee On Cosmetic Products and Non-food Products, Brussels, Belgium, adopted by the SCCNFP during the 19th plenary meeting of 27 February 2002; online at: http://ec.europa.eu/health.

14. Henley, D.V. et al., Prepubertal gynecomastia linked to lavender and tea tree oil, *New England Journal of Medicine*, February 2007; 356(5): 479–485.

15. Howes, M.J., Assessment of estrogenic activity in some common essential oil constituents, *Journal of Pharmacy and Pharmacology*, November 2002; 54(11): 1521–1528.

16. *Material Safety Data Sheet: Dehydroacetic Acid*, Sciencelab.com; accessed 16 April 2008; online at: www.sciencelab.com.

17. *What are Natural Ingredients?* Natural Ingredient Resource Center; accessed 23 December 2007; online at: www.naturalingredient.org.

18. *OCA Holds Press Conference at Natural Products Expo East*, Organic Consumers Association (OCA), 6 September 2003; online at: www.organicconsumers.org.

19. Email to the author from Dr Philippa Darbre, senior lecturer in oncology, Biomolecular Sciences Section, School of Biological Sciences, the University of Reading, 30 November 2007.

20. Anctzak, G., Anctzak, S., *Cosmetics Unmasked: Your Family Guide to Safe*

Cosmetics and Allergy-free Toiletries, London: Thorsons, 2001, pp. 15–16.

21. *Survey Indicates Consumers Are Confused About Organic Personal Care Product Labelling: Survey Summary,* Organic Consumers Association (OCA), 2007; online at: www.organicconsumers.org/bodycare.

22. Loden, M., Maibach, H.I. (eds), *Dry Skin and Moisturisers: Chemistry and Function,* Florida: CRC Press, 2000, p. 408.

23. *3-Dimethylaminopropylamine (109–55–7): Executive Summary,* prepared for the National Cancer Institute (NCI) for consideration by the Chemical Selection Working Group (CSWG) by Technical Resources International, Inc., under Contract No. N02-07007, US Department of Health and Human Services, National Toxicology Program (NTP), Research Triangle Park, NC; accessed 21 April 2008; online at: http://ntp.niehs.nih.gov.

Chapter 7

1. OCA holds press conference at Natural Products Expo East, Organic Consumers Association (OCA), 6 September 2003; online at: www.organicconsumers.org.

2. *Title 7: Agriculture: Part 205 – National Organic Program,* US Department of Agriculture, National Organic Program (NOP) Regulations, Electronic Code of Federal Regulations; accessed 22 May 2008; online at: http://ecfr.gpoaccess.gov.

3. Generic cease and desist letter sent to certain companies engaged in organic misbranding from OCA and Dr. Bronner's, Organic Consumers Association (OCA), 14 March 2008; online at: www.organic consumers.org/bodycare.

4. Coming clean: campaigning for organic integrity in bodycare products, Organic Consumers Association (OCA); accessed 14 April 2008; online at: www.organicconsumers.org/bodycare.

5. OCA and Dr. Bronner's challenge weak Ecocert and OASIS standards, Organic Consumers Association (OCA), 17 March 2008; online at: www.organicconsumers.org/bodycare.

6. OCA and Dr. Bronner's offer companies a contract to address organic misbranding and labelling in personal care, Organic Consumers Association (OCA), 26 March 2008; online at: www.organic consumers.org/bodycare.

7. *OASIS Organic and Sustainable Industry Standards: Health and Beauty Products,* OASIS (Organic and Sustainable Industry Standards), 11 March 2008, Beta version No. 3, OASIS Standard no. 100; online at: www.oasisseal.org.

8. *OASIS Materials List: List of Approved Materials,* OASIS (Organic and Sustainable Industry Standards), 12 March 2008; online at:

www.oasisseal.org.

9. Industry creates new bogus 'OASIS' organic standard for personal care products, Organic Consumers Association (OCA), 14 March 2008; online at: www.organicconsumers.org/bodycare.

10. *NaTrue Label: Requirements to be Met by Natural and Organic Cosmetics*, NaTrue, Version 1.0 − 7 May 2008; online at: www.natrue.de.

11. *Soil Association Organic Standards*, Soil Association, Revision 15, April 2005, 50.6.

12. *The OF&G Certification Scheme for Cosmetics and Bodycare Products: OF&G Technical Leaflet TL221*, Organic Farmers & Growers, 26 September 2007; online at: www.organicfarmers.org.uk.

13. *OF&G Inspection and Certification Control Manual: Cosmetics and Bodycare Standards*, Organic Farmers & Growers (OF&G), Section 16, Annex 2.3.1, 11 January 2007.

14. *Standards for Ecological and Organic Cosmetics*, Ecocert Inspection and Certification, January 2003, 3:15.

15. *BDIH Guideline 'Certified Natural Cosmetics': Preamble*, BDIH Certified Natural Cosmetics; accessed 21 April 2008; online at: www.kontrollierte-naturkosmetik.de.

16. *The Australian Organic Industry: A Summary*, Australian Government, Department of Agriculture, Fisheries and Forestry (DAFF), Canberra, ACT, 2004; online at: www.daff.gov.au.

17. May, R., Monk, A., *Organic and Biodynamic Produce: Comparing Australian and Overseas Standards*, Australian Government, Rural Industries Research and Development Corporation (RIRDC), Publication No. 01/05, RIRDC Project No. RAM-1A, Kingston, ACT, March 2001; online at: www.rirdc.gov.au.

18. *Raising the Standards Up*, Standards Australia, 2007, Volume 06, p. 8; online at: www.standards.org.au.

19. *Biological Farmers of Australia: Australian Organic Standard 2006*, Biological Farmers of Australia (BFA), Australian Certified Organic (ACO), March 2006, 3.5.

20. *NASAA Organic Standard*, National Association for Sustainable Agriculture, Australia (NASAA), Second revision, August 2007, 12.1.

21. *National Standard for Organic and Bio-dynamic Produce*, Organic Industry Export Consultative Committee, Australian Quarantine and Inspection Service (AQIS), Canberra, ACT, edition 3.3, July 2007, 7.

Index

A
abrasive substances 55
acetaldehyde 42, 176
acetamide MEA 177
acetic acid 52, 177
acetone 42, 177–8
acne 57
acrylates 52, 178
aerosol products, nanoparticles in 121
aftershave 38–9
ageing, lipid peroxidation and 60
agonistic effect, endocrine disrupters 93
agriculture, biodynamic 158
air pollution, nanoparticles 121
alcohol 178–9
alcohol denat 179
alkylphenol ethoxylates (APEs) 95, 109–10
alkylphenols (APs) 179
  and contact dermatitis 52
  endocrine disruption, 94, 109–10
  environmental damage 28
  in umbilical cord blood, 96
allergic contact dermatitis 52
allergies 37–8
  asthma 61–3
  and hair dyes 54–5
  hypoallergenic products 57–8
  perfume 40–2
  photoallergy 59–60

potential allergens 49–51
aloe barbadensis leaf juice 147
alpha hydroxy acids (AHAs) 49, 60, 179–80
alpha-pinene 42
alpha-terpineol 43, 180
alternative beauty brands 169–75
alum 180–1
alumina 181
aluminium 52, 84, 112–13, 181–2
Alzheimer's disease 112, 124
4-amino-2-nitrophenol 183
aminomethyl propanol 182–3
aminophenols 52, 183–4
ammonia 79, 184
ammonium laureth sulphate (ALES) 184–5
ammonium lauryl sulphate (ALS) 185
ammonium thioglycolate 49, 53, 62, 185
amyl acetate 185
androgens 94
animal colourants 80
animal fats, oleochemicals 133
antagonistic effect, endocrine disrupters 93
anthranilates 99
anti-ageing products 60
anti-microbials 46–7
antibiotic resistance 108
antibodies 37–8, 59
antigens 37, 59

antiperspirants 18, 77, 91, 111,
    112–13
apocrine sweat glands 111
aqua *see* water
armpit odours 111
aromatic hydrocarbons 186
asbestiform fibres, in talc 78
asthma 61–3
astringents 57
Australia 161–5, 169–71
avobenzone 101, 186
azo dyes 49, 82, 186–7
azulene 187

B
babies 18–19, 78
bacteria: antibiotic resistance 108
    and underarm odour 111
bath products 47
BDIH 160–1
benzaldehyde 43, 53, 187
benzalkonium chloride 49,
    187–8
benzene 62, 67, 188–9
benzethonium chloride 136–7
benzo(a)pyrene 90
benzoates 189
benzoic acid 137, 189
benzophenones 49, 98, 99–100,
    189–90
benzoyl peroxide 53, 190
benzyl acetate 190
benzyl alcohol 21, 43, 53, 138,
    148, 191
benzyl butyl phthalate (BBP)
    105
bergamot oil 42
bergapten 60

berloque dermatitis 60
beta-carotene 80
beta hydroxy acids (BHAs)
    191–2
bioaccumulation 9, 24–8, 31
Biodynamic Agricultural
    Association (BDAA) 165
biodynamic agriculture 158
Biological Farmers of Australia
    (BFA) 162–4
biomagnification 24–5
birds 24
bisabolol 192
bismuth oxychloride 84
bisphenol A 23
    in amniotic fluid 95–6
    and breast cancer 67
    endocrine disruption 69, 95
    low-dose testing 23
bisulphites 192
bladder cancer, hair dyes and 74
bleaching agents, skin lighteners
    56
blood-brain barrier 40
boric acid 192–3
brain: blood-brain barrier 40
    fullerene damage 123–4
    nanoparticles in 121
    neurotoxicity 47
Brazil, alternative beauty brands
    171
breast cancer 64, 66–70, 76–7,
    91, 112
breastfeeding 96, 115
breasts, premature development
    106
brominated flame retardants 96
bronopol 53, 60, 193
bubble baths 47

buckyballs 123–4
1, 3-butadiene 67, 193–4
butane 53, 194
butterfly bush extract 148
butylated hydroxyanisole (BHA)
    50, 53, 102–3, 194–5
butylated hydroxytoluene (BHT)
    50, 53, 195
butylene glycol 53, 195
butylphenyl methylpropional 195

C
calcium thioglycolate 196
California Certified Organic
    Farmers (CCOF) 165
camphor 43, 100, 196
Canada, alternative beauty brands
    171
cancer 64–91
    breast cancer 64, 66–70, 76–7,
        91, 112
    carcinogenic chemicals 72–80
    colourants and 80–3
    contaminated products and
        84–91
    endocrine disrupters and 93,
        102
    identifying risks 70–1
    melanoma 99
    skin lighteners and 56–7
carbon, fullerenes 123–4
carcinogens 17
carmine 80
carrageenan 196–7
certification schemes, organic
    products 145, 146–7, 150–1,
    155–65, 175
ceteareth compounds 197

cetearyl alcohol 197–8
cetrimonium bromide 50
cetrimonium chloride 50, 198
cetyl alcohol 198
'chemical free' labelling 142
children 18–19, 47, 73
chlorhexidine 53, 198
chlorine 108–9
chlorobenzene 199
chlorofluorocarbons (CFCs)
    199
chloroxylenol 53
cinnamal 43, 53
cinnamates 50, 98, 100–1, 200
cinnamyl alcohol 53, 200
citral 53, 137, 147–8, 200–1
citric acid 148, 201
citronellol 53, 201
cleansing products: pseudo-
        natural brands 150–1
    surfactants 88
coal tar 201–2
coal tar dyes 80, 81–3
cobalt 66
cocamide DEA 50, 53, 79, 202
cocamide MEA 21, 53, 79, 86–7
cocamide MIPA 21
cocamidopropyl betaine 50, 53,
    143, 148, 151, 202
cocktail effect 22
coco glucoside 147
coconut oil 133, 143
cocoyl sarcosine 203
cold-pressed oils 135–6
Colour Index (CI) numbers 81
colourants 50, 80–3
    see also dyes
consumer power 28
contact dermatitis 40, 46, 51–5

contamination: and cancer risk
    84–91
  organic products 136
coral bleaching 98–9
Cosmebio 165
Cosmetic Ingredient Review
    (CIR) 33–4
coumarin 43, 50, 83, 203

D
DDT 94, 95
DEA-cetyl phosphate 79
DEA-oleth-3 phosphate 80
dehydroacetic acid 138, 149
Denmark, alternative beauty
    brands 171
deodorants 111
  aluminium salts in 112–13
  and breast cancer 76, 77, 91
  nanoparticles in 121
  paraben-free 104
  triclosan in 109
  vaginal deodorants 71
dermatitis: berloque dermatitis
    60
  contact dermatitis 40, 46,
    51–5
'dermatologist tested' products
    57–8
detergents 20
developmental toxicants 17
diabetes 106
2, 4-diaminoanisole sulphate 67
diaminobenzenes 203–4
diaminotoluenes 204
diazolidinyl urea 21–2, 50, 53,
    138, 204
dibenzoylmethanes 101

dibutyl phthalate (DBP) 104,
    105–6
dichlorodibenzo-p-dioxin 108–9
diethanolamine (DEA) 53,
    79–80, 86–7, 204–5
diethyl phthalate (DEP) 104,
    105–6
diethylhexyl adipate 205
diethylhexyl phthalate (DEHP)
    105, 106
diethylstilboestrol (DES) 69, 95
dihydroxyacetone (DHA) 50,
    205–6
dimethyl ether 206
dimethyl phthalate (DMP) 104
dimethylaminopropylamine
    143
1, 4-dioxane 67, 85, 149–51,
    206
dioxins: endocrine disruption
    94, 115
  triclosan conversion to 108–9
disodium cocoamphodipropi-
    onate 50, 207
disodium EDTA 21, 207
DMDM hydantoin 50, 53, 138,
    207
DNA: and cancer 65
  chemical damage 17
  nanoparticle damage 120, 121,
    122
  titanium dioxide damage 98
douches, vaginal 71
drugs, and photosensitivity 60
dyes: coal tar dyes 80, 81–3
  and contact dermatitis 54–5,
    63
  hair 49, 54–5, 63, 73–6, 81
  and photosensitivity 60

E
eccrine sweat glands 111
Ecocert 151, 152, 159–60
Ecogarantie 165
eczema 51
emollients 36–7
emulsifiers 88
emulsifying waxes 134
emulsions, nano-emulsions 118, 128
endocrine disrupting chemicals (EDCs) 17, 66, 68–70, 92–116, 137
environment: cancer and 65–6
    nanoparticles in 118, 119, 121
    persistent chemicals 23–8, 31
essential fatty acids 73
essential oils: adverse effects 42
    endocrine disruption 137
    floral water 140–1
    natural beauty products 137
    and photosensitivity 42, 60
ethanol 44, 57
ethanolamine 53, 207–8
ethoxylated surfactants 208
ethoxylation 150
ethyl acetate 44, 209
ethyl acrylate 209
ethylbenzene 62
ethylene glycol 87
ethylene oxide 210
    and breast cancer 67
    contamination by 87–8
    diethanolamine production 79
    labelling of organic products 150, 151
ethylenediamine 62
ethynyloestradiol 95
eugenol 44, 53, 148, 210–11

Europe: EU Cosmetics Directive 9, 29, 30
    organic labelling 153–4
    regulation 29–32
exfoliants 55
eye irritation 48
eyeshadows 66

F
farnesol 211
fetus, endocrine disrupters and 95–6, 97, 106
Fiji, alternative beauty brands 171
fish: endocrine disrupters and 94–5
    fullerene damage 123–4
flame retardants 96
floral water 140–1, 151
fluoride 211
foaming agents 88
food chains 24–5
formaldehyde 47, 211–12
    allergic reactions 51
    cancer risk 89
    and contact dermatitis 53
    uses 88–9
fragrance free products 42
fragrances 39–45, 225
    adverse effects 40–5
    allergies 40–2
    and asthma 61
    cancer risk 83
    labelling 41, 114–15
    musk fragrances 113–14
    in organic products 147
    in shampoo 22
France, organic certification 159–60

free radicals 81, 98
fruit acids 60
fullerenes 123–4
furfural 44

G
genetic damage 17, 65–6
genital malformation 96
geraniol 44, 53, 137, 148, 212
Germany: alternative beauty
    brands 171
  organic certification 160–1
glycerides 212–13
glycerin 148, 213
glyceryl caprylate 136
glycine 21
glycol ethers 213–14
glycolic acid 60
glycols 214
grapefruit seed extract 136–7
Greece, alternative beauty brands
    171
Guaranteed Organic
    Certification Agency (GOCA)
    165

H
hair: dyes 49, 54–5, 63, 73–6, 81
    shaving 38–9, 40
hairdressers 62, 73–6, 143
hairspray 61
henna 74
herbal infusions, in natural
    beauty products 140
herbicides, endocrine disrupters
    94
hexyl cinnamal 53

hexylene glycol 53, 214
hormones, endocrine disrupters
    17, 66, 68–70, 92–116, 137
humectants 23
hydrochlorofluorocarbons
    (HCFCs) 215
hydrofluorocarbons (HFCs) 215
hydrogen peroxide 215–16
hydrogenation, vegetable oils
    133–4
hydroquinone 53, 56, 216
hydrosols 140–1, 151
hydroxycitronellal 53
hypersensitivity 39
hypoallergenic products 57–8

I
imidazolidinyl urea 53, 217
immune system, allergies 37–8,
    52
immunoglobulin E (IgE) anti-
    bodies 37–8
impurities, cancer risk 84–91
infertility 92, 94
inflammation, hypersensitivity
    39
inorganic colours 80, 83–4
insulin resistance 106
International Federation of
    Organic Agriculture
    Movements (IFOAM) 155
International Fragrance
    Association (IFRA) 41
iodopropynyl butylcarbamate 21,
    51, 217
irritant contact dermatitis 51–2
irritants 38–9
isobutane 53, 217

isoeugenol 53
isopropanol 57
isopropyl alcohol 218
isopropyl palmitate 218
isothiazolinone 46–7

K
Kathon CG 46–7, 53, 218–19
kojic acid 56–7
Körperpflege- und Waschmittel
    e.V. (IKW) 153

L
labelling: nanoparticle-containing
    products 128
    natural beauty products 140,
    142
    organic products 142, 145–65
    perfumes 41, 114–15
lactic acid 60
lakes, colourants 80
lanolin 51, 53, 73, 219
lauramide DEA 80
laureth compounds 20, 219
lavender oil 137
lead acetate 75, 219–20
legislation see regulation
light, photosensitivity 59–60
limonene 44, 53, 147, 220
linalool 53, 147, 220
lindane 94
linoleamide MEA 80
lipid peroxidation 60
lipophilic molecules 24
lipstick 7
low-dose phenomenon
    22–3

lungs: nanoparticles in 120–1,
    122
    zirconium compounds in
    112–13

M
malic acid 20, 60
marketing, natural beauty
    products 131–2
melanin 56
melanoma 99
men's toiletries 15
menthyl anthranilate 99
mercury 56, 220–1
metals: in dyes 80, 81
    impurities in cosmetics 66
methyl salicylate 141
methylchloroisothiazolinone
    46–7
methylene chloride 44–5,
    83
methylisothiazolinone 46–7
methylparaben 53
mica 83
microdermabrasion 55
mineral make-up 83–4
mineral oil 53
miscarriages 114
moisturizers 23, 46
MRSA 108
musk fragrances 26
    and asthma 62
    and breast cancer 67
    endocrine disruption 113–14
    environmental damage 26
    in umbilical cord blood 96
mutagenic chemicals 67
myristamide DEA 80

N
nanomaterials 118
nanoparticles 118
    fullerenes 123–4
    health risks 120–3
    product labelling 128
    in sunscreens 98, 118–19, 129
nanotechnology 20, 84, 117–29
National Association for
    Sustainable Agriculture,
    Australia (NASAA) 164–5
NaTrue (European Natural and
    Organic Cosmetics Interest
    Group) 153
natural beauty products 130–44
    certification standards 132
    definitions 130, 131, 139, 141
    essential oils 137
    grapefruit seed extract 136–7
    labelling 140, 142, 145–65
    marketing 131–2
    oleochemicals 133–6
    preservatives 137–9
    pseudo-natural brands 149–51
    surfactants 142–3
    versus synthetic 141
    water content 140–1, 151
'natural' colours 80
Naturland 165
'nearly natural' substances 153
neurotoxicity 47
nickel 66
nitrates 72
nitro musks 113–14
N-nitrosodiethanolamine
    (NDELA) 72, 79, 86
nitrosamines 67, 84–5, 85–7, 222
nonylphenol (NP) 67, 97, 110
NSF International 152

O
obesity, abdominal 106
ochronosis, exogenous 56
octocrylene 101
octyl dimethyl PABA 101–2
octylphenol (OP) 110
odours, underarm 111
oestradiol 69
oestrogen 93–4
    and breast cancer 66, 68–70,
        76–7
    endocrine disrupters 17, 93,
        94–5, 102, 103–5, 107, 110,
        112
    essential oils and 137
'oil disease' 72
oils see essential oils; vegetable
    oils
oily skin, astringents 57
oleamide DEA 80
olefin sulphonate 142–3, 151
oleic acid 222
oleochemicals 133–6
oleth compounds 222–3
oleyl betaine 143
Oregon Tilth 165
Organic and Sustainable Industry
    Standards (OASIS) 151, 152
organic colours 80
Organic Consumers Association
    (OCA) 149–51, 152
Organic Crop Improvement
    Association (OCIA) 165
Organic Farmers & Growers
    (OF&G) 157–8
Organic Food Chain (OFC)
    165
Organic Growers of Australia
    (OGA) 165

Organic Guarantee System
  (OGS) 155
organic products: certification
  132, 145, 146–7, 150–1,
  155–65, 169, 175
  contamination 136
  definition 131
  essential oils 137
  labelling 142, 145–65
  limited availability of raw
  materials 139
  oleochemicals 133
  preservatives 137–9
  pseudo-natural brands 149–51
  water content 140–1, 151
organochlorines 69, 96, 108–9
ovarian cancer 78
oxidation, nanoparticles and
  120–1
ozone 16

P
packaging 15
  dioxins in 115
  nanopackaging 124
  phthalates in 104
palm oil 133, 135, 143
palmitic acid 223–4
para-aminobenzoic acid (PABA)
  51, 59, 101, 223
parabens 46, 224
  allergic reactions 51
  and breast cancer 67
  cancer risk 76–8
  endocrine disruption 69,
  103–4, 107–8
  in natural beauty products 138
paraffinum liquidum 224

paraphenylenediamine 62, 224–5
parfum 225
  see also fragrances
particles, nanoparticles 118
PEG-12 dimethicone 21
penetration enhancers 19, 72–3,
  122–3
pentasodium triphosphate 225–6
perfluorinated compounds
  (PFCs) 27, 96
perfluorooctanoic acid (PFOA)
  27
perfumes see fragrances
persulphate salts 62
pesticides: endocrine disrupters
  69, 94, 95
  environmental damage 24
  in umbilical cord blood 96
petrochemicals 133, 134, 143,
  150–1
petrolatum (petroleum jelly) 90,
  226
petroleum distillates 226–7
phenol 227
phenoxyethanol 138, 227–8
phenoxyisopropanol 228
phenyl mercuric acetate 228
phenylenediamines 53, 228
Philippinnes, alternative beauty
  brands 171
photoallergy 59–60
photosensitivity 59–60
phototoxicity 42, 59
phthalates 229
  allergic reactions 51
  cancer risk 67, 73
  endocrine disruption 17, 69,
  104–7
  in environment 26–7

in perfumes 114
'phthalate syndrome' 106
pigments 80, 83–4
placental extract, and breast
    cancer 67
plasticizers 104, 106
pollution: endocrine disrupters
    94
    nanoparticles 121
    persistent chemicals 23–8, 31
    by sunscreens 98
polychlorinated biphenyls
    (PCBs) 69, 72, 94
polycyclic aromatic hydrocarbons
    (PAHs) 67, 89–91, 229
polycyclic musks 113–14
polyethylene 230
polyethylene glycol (PEG)
    compounds 51, 53, 87, 230–1
polysorbates 231
polystyrene 231
polyvinylpyrrolidone (PVP) 62,
    232
potassium hydroxide 232
potassium sorbate 149
PPG-9 21
PPG-14 butyl ether 232–3
pregnancy, endocrine disrupters
    and 95–6, 97, 106
preservatives: allergies and 46–7
    'natural' 137–9
    parabens 76–8
propane 53, 233
propylene glycol (PG) 21, 51, 53,
    233
1, 2-propylene oxide 67
prostaglandins 134
2-pyrrolidone-5-carboxylic acid
    (PCA) 87

Q
Quality Assurance Institute
    (QAI) 165
quaternary ammonium
    compounds 234

R
rainforest destruction 135
REACH 30–2, 126
reactive oxygen species (ROS)
    molecules, nanoparticles 120,
    121, 124
regulation 29–34
    nanotechnology 125–8
    organic products 145, 146–7
reproductive toxicants 17
Research Institute of Fragrance
    Materials (RIFM) 41
resorcinol 45, 234–5
respiratory system, asthma 61–3
retinoic acid 235
retinyl palmitate 60

S
salicylates 51, 102, 235
salicylic acid 57, 60, 235–6
sarcosines 236
selenium sulphide 236
sensitive skin 57–8
sensitizers 39
sewage: dioxin formed by
    triclosan in 109
    endocrine disrupters in
    94–5
shampoo 20–2, 48
shaving 38–9, 40, 77, 112
shea butter 136

silica 78–9, 237
silicates 237
silicones 237–8
skin: ageing 60
  astringents 57
  contact dermatitis 51–5
  emollients 36–7
  exfoliants 55
  hypersensitivity 39
  irritants 38–9
  keeping healthy 133
  lighteners 55–7
  nanoparticle penetration 119, 122–3
  penetration enhancers 19, 72–3
  photosensitivity 59–60
  sensitive skin 57–8
  sodium lauryl sulphate and 48–9
  sweat glands 111
soaps 47
sodium benzoate 138, 149
sodium bisulphite 238
sodium borate 238
sodium dodecylbenzene-sulphonate 239
sodium hydroxide 54, 239
sodium hydroxymethylglycinate 138–9, 239
sodium laureth sulphate (SLES) 20, 49, 240
sodium lauryl sulphate (SLS) 20, 48–9, 54, 240
sodium metabisulphite 240–1
sodium myreth sulphate 151
sodium PCA 87
Soil Association 154, 155–6
solubilizers 88

solvents 67
sorbitol 241
Spain, alternative beauty brands 171
sperm count, decline in 92, 94
stearalkonium chloride 241
stearamide MEA 80
steareth compounds 241–2
stearic acid 242
stearyl alcohol 242
Steiner, Rudolf 158
strontium compounds 242–3
styrene oxide 45
sulisobenzone 54
sunburn 59, 60
sunlight, photosensitivity 59–60
sunscreens: endocrine disrupters 98–102
  nanoparticles 118–19, 122, 129
  photoallergy 59
suntan accelerators 60
surfactants 88
  contamination 87
  ethoxylated surfactants 109–10, 208
  in natural beauty products 142–3
  oleochemicals 133, 134–5
  skin irritation 48
sweat glands 111
synergism, and cancer 65, 69
synthetic, definition 130
synthetic musks see musk fragrances
synthetically produced natural ingredients 141

T
talc 78, 84, 243
tallow 133
tartrazine 82
TEA lauryl sulphate 80
tea tree oil 137
Teflon 27, 244
teratogens 17
testicular dysgenesis syndrome 106
testing chemicals 29–30, 32–4
testosterone 94, 106
tetrasodium EDTA 244
thimerosal 51, 54, 244–5
thioglycolic acid 54
titanium dioxide 245
  and breast cancer 67
  nanoparticles in sunscreens 98,
    118, 119, 121–2, 129
toluene 45, 54, 61, 245–6
toluene sulphonamide 246
2, 4–toluenediamine 246–7
toothpastes 48, 109
toxic body burden 16–17
trans fats 134
triclosan: and breast cancer 68
  and contact dermatitis 54
  conversion to dioxin 108–9
  environmental damage 26
  in umbilical cord blood 96
triethanolamine (TEA) 80, 86–7,
  247–8
turpentine 51, 248

U
UK, alternative beauty brands
  172–3
ultraviolet (UV) filters: cancer
  risk 73

endocrine disrupters 69,
  98–102
  nanoparticles 119, 122
ultraviolet (UV) radiation:
  photosensitivity 59–60
  skin lighteners and 56
underarm odour 111
United States of America:
  alternative beauty brands
    173–5
  Department of Agriculture
    (USDA) organic certification
    145, 146–7, 150–2
  Food and Drug Administration
    (FDA) 8, 32–3, 38
  Nanotechnology Task Force
    127–8
  regulation 32–4
urea 248–9
urethrane 68
urinary tract infections 47
urticaria, contact 52

V
vaginal deodorants 71
vanillin 45, 141
vegetable dyes 74, 76
vegetable oils 133–6
vinyl acetate 249
vinyl polymers 249–50
vitamin A derivatives 60
volatile organic compounds
  (VOCs) 16, 61

W
water: in natural beauty products
  140–1, 151

in organic products 147
sunscreen pollution 98
waxes, emulsifying 134
West Indies, alternative beauty
    brands 175
wetting agents 88
wildlife 24
wintergreen, oil of 141

X
xenoestrogens 94–5
xylene 54, 250

Z
zinc acetate 250
zinc oxide 98, 118–19, 122,
    250–1
zinc pyridinethione 251
zirconium compounds 112–13

Acknowledgements

Researching and writing this book has been a phenomenal feat and one I would not have been able to achieve without the love and support of my family and partner, Andy Chrysostomou. I dearly love you all and am eternally grateful for your faith in me. Thank you Andy for helping me to decipher complex scientific papers, researching various issues and lending a hand when and wherever you could. I am blessed with a perfect soulmate. Thank you to my mother Irene Mellowship and my brothers Peter and Brian Brotherston for consistently being such caring, loving, humble, humorous and grounded people. Thank you to all the individuals who allowed me to interview them for this book and share their valuable contributions. Thank you to my commissioning editor at Gaia Thinking Books, Sandra Rigby, who asked me to pen this piece of work and finally, thank you to the readers who have the collective power to move mountains. As Mahatma Gandhi once said, 'Be the change you want to see in the world.'

Executive Editor: Sandra Rigby
Managing Editor: Clare Churly
Executive Art Editor: Penny Stock
Page make-up: Dorchester Typesetting Group Ltd
Production Manager: David Hearn